best practices in
psychiatric
rehabilitation

Second Edition

Edited by
Patricia B. Nemec & Kathleen Furlong-Norman

**Psychiatric
Rehabilitation
Association**

Growing and Training the Recovery Workforce

McLean, Virginia

Published by
Psychiatric Rehabilitation Association
1760 Old Meadow Road, Suite 500
McLean, VA 22102
www.psychrehabassociation.org
Phone: 703-442-2078

Printed in the United States of America.

Library of Congress Control Number: 2014933187
ISBN 978-0-615-96265-8

CONTENTS

PREFACE

BEST PRACTICES ARE THOSE PRINCIPLES, TECHNIQUES, INTERVENTIONS, AND SERVICE MODELS THAT experts acknowledge as the most effective in a particular field. In psychiatric rehabilitation, a human services field, best practices also must be valued by the service users. Effectiveness has to do with achieving specific desired outcomes, and in psychiatric rehabilitation, we define the desired outcome as recovery—a life of meaning and purpose for people who live with mental health conditions. To know whether a practice is effective, research and evaluation must demonstrate that the practice does, in fact, achieve the outcomes desired. When a certain threshold of research evidence is reached, showing that one practice has better outcomes than alternatives, the practice is evidence-based.

This book includes both evidence-based practices (specific interventions and service models that have been shown effective through multiple high-quality research studies by different research teams) and best practices (those approaches, tools, and techniques that are recognized as desirable and effective, but that have not yet been studied adequately, and so lack hard evidence). The chapter authors for this book are well-respected experts in psychiatric rehabilitation, and some have been in the field from its early days in the mid-1970s when the Psychiatric Rehabilitation Association (PRA) was founded as the International Association of Psychosocial Rehabilitation Services. Our confidence in their ability to describe the very best practices was born out in the emergence of clear themes across chapters.

Themes

The principles of psychiatric rehabilitation (see Chapter 1) are evident throughout the book as are the principles, standards, and guidelines in the 2012 *Code of Ethics for Certified Psychiatric Rehabilitation Practitioners* (see www.psychrehabassociation.org). To summarize more broadly, we see four over-arching themes: psychiatric rehabilitation requires (1) services that are person-centered, (2) services focused on full integration and participation in a person's community of choice, (3) vigilance and activism to combat prejudice and discrimination, and (4) effective and ongoing training that is relevant to the field and targeted towards developing the attitudes, knowledge, and skill needed to be an effective psychiatric rehabilitation practitioner.

Person-centered services are built on self-determination and choice and promote individual responsibility. Service plans in psychiatric rehabilitation (Chapter 5) are designed to define and achieve goals that are personally relevant and valuable. Assessments (Chapter 6) and interventions (Chapter 7) target the skills and supports needed to achieve those personal goals. Psychiatric rehabilitation services focus on the whole person and what is needed to promote overall wellness in all life domains (Chapter 13).

Community is a comprehensive concept encompassing a physical location as well as a sense of belonging. As social beings, most people require an interdependent and supportive social network in order to thrive. Psychiatric rehabilitation programs historically have done well with creating such a community within their own walls, but have done less well in helping people using their services to build a larger network of natural supports who are not connected to the mental health system. A focus on community integration (Chapter 14) requires attending to social relationships, recreational activities, and spiritual or religious communities for those who seek them as well as helping people access ordinary non-segregated housing (Chapter 10), supporting employment in real jobs for real pay (Chapter 11), and providing the support and opportunity for further education (Chapter 12).

Activism is needed on a small scale and on a daily basis—it is not only represented in large and organized protests or advocacy campaigns although such larger efforts are often critical to improving services, increasing opportunity, and influencing policy (Chapter 15). Psychiatric rehabilitation practitioners need to work on community acceptance and understanding in local neighborhoods, but also on improving the attitudes of service provider colleagues who dwell on symptoms, believe in an overly pessimistic prognosis, and fail to see the person behind the disability (Chapter 2).

Training requires identifying and addressing the knowledge, skills, and attitudes needed for a particular job as well as a focus on the foundational competencies of psychiatric rehabilitation (Chapter 3). Specific competencies are needed for unique roles, such as peer specialists (Chapter 8) and organization leaders (Chapter 17), and there are competencies that transcend roles and require a lifetime of development, such as cultural competence (Chapter 9). Research (Chapter 4) provides new knowledge, which then must be disseminated to the field through training initiatives, often requiring shifts in how services are delivered. Transforming services (Chapter 16) is not an easy process, but psychiatric rehabilitation practitioners who value ongoing quality improvement will recognize that change is a constant—the field will continue to evolve.

An Overview of the Second Edition

The first edition of *Best Practices in Psychiatric Rehabilitation* was published in 2000 after developing a concept map of the field but prior to the first role delineation study for the Certified Psychiatric Rehabilitation Practitioner exam (see Chapter 3). The many changes in the field since that time have included the development and dissemination of evidence-based practices in the form of toolkits for implementation, the acceptance of recovery as a guiding vision for mental health services at the national level, and the now widespread recognition that many people taking psychiatric medications are in poor health (Chapter 13)—in part due to their treatment.

The concept map of competencies presented in the first edition structured the book's chapters and chapter content. In this edition, the original chapters were used as a guide, and new chapters were added, updating the book's outline to reflect changes in the field. The chapter on multiple disabilities in the first edition was not carried over due to space considerations and the now widely available information on co-occurring mental health and substance use disorders. Perhaps, the third edition will revisit reincorporating this chapter, or perhaps an enterprising author or editor will compile best practices information on psychiatric rehabilitation for people who have co-occurring developmental disabilities or HIV/AIDS and on effectively serving people who are Deaf or hard of hearing and also require mental health services.

We were fortunate to have some authors from the first edition update their chapters— Laurene Finley, who has worked to keep cultural issues in the forefront (Chapter 9), and Rick Baron, whose credentials in employment services are extensive (Chapter 11). The remaining authors are not only experts in the field, but have contributed much time and energy to PRA through Board membership, service on the CPRP Commission, active support of their local chapters, and work on many PRA committees. Opportunities for participation in PRA at the local and national level are many, and we hope this book inspires readers to step up and get involved.

This book is organized into four sections: (1) an introduction, (2) psychiatric rehabilitation practices, (3) the various areas or domains where psychiatric rehabilitation focuses its efforts, and (4) administration and management issues. Based on the organization of the first edition, these sections are designed to guide the reader.

The first section introduces and defines psychiatric rehabilitation (Chapter 1) and the concept of psychiatric disability (Chapter 2). These provide an overview of who we are (the "we" being psychiatric rehabilitation practitioners, our primary audience) and who we serve. Those of us who came to psychiatric rehabilitation in the early days, and many who have come after, recognize that the vision, philosophy, and principles of psychiatric rehabilitation are its life force. There's a sense that someone either gets it or doesn't, that it's almost a way of life as much as it is a profession. However, the philosophical foundation is not enough. A practitioner must have both general and specialty competencies, introduced in Chapter 3, and presented in somewhat more detail in the CPRP certification exam blueprint, which is available on the PRA website. What we do should not be based on instinct or tradition, but should be grounded in what we know for sure about what works as described in the chapter on research (Chapter 4).

The second section, *Psychiatric Rehabilitation in Practice*, looks at what practitioners do in the process of their day-to-day work. Service planning (Chapter 5), assessment (Chapter 6), and interventions (Chapter 7) are the primary components of the person-centered process of psychiatric rehabilitation services. Peer support and peer-run services (Chapter 8) enrich that process by providing concrete evidence that recovery is real by offering role models and relationships of mutuality, and through the deep understanding that comes only from shared experience. Service providers and service users alike are shaped by their cultures of origin, cultures of affinity, and the cultures that surround them, making multicultural competence (Chapter 9) a key area for life-long education and improvement.

The third section, *Psychiatric Rehabilitation Service Focus*, covers the traditional psychiatric rehabilitation domains of housing (Chapter 10) and employment (Chapter 11). Since the first edition, the field has expanded its interest in education (Chapter 12), based not only on the expressed interests of the people we serve, but on the recognition that educational achievement is an important pathway to advancement in employment. Increases in work income contribute to increased opportunities and choices, including choices about where to live. To work successfully, live independently, and enjoy the life you have requires maintaining good physical health. The relatively new focus on wellness in psychiatric rehabilitation (Chapter 13) recognizes this and highlights the importance of preventing premature death and developing a balanced and meaningful life that feels worth living. Part of wellness, for most people, is connectedness and belonging. The idea of community integration (Chapter 14), while always a central concept in psychiatric rehabilitation, is finally getting the increased attention it deserves as the field comes to recognize that a place to live and a job do not, by themselves, make a full life.

The final section, *Administration and Management*, goes beyond the day-to-day practice of psychiatric rehabilitation. Practitioners do not operate in a vacuum, but are affected by policies, regulations, and legislation and are, too often, limited by lack of funds. Addressing these systems deficits requires advocacy (Chapter 15), and practitioners need advocacy skills to be part of the change effort as well as to teach people using services to advocate for the changes that they would like to see. Not only is systems change needed, but many programs and organizations have internal barriers to implementing rehabilitative and recovery-oriented services. Transforming program culture (Chapter 16) can be difficult but often is essential to make psychiatric rehabilitation possible. Any transformation effort requires a leader, or more often, many leaders. Organizational efforts to enhance and develop leadership (Chapter 17) contribute to the local operation of programs and agencies, and over time, enhance the field.

Each chapter concludes with a list of Best Practice Guidelines focused on the chapter content. These serve as a chapter summary and can provide guidance for practitioners, supervisors, managers, and administrators in designing, delivering, and evaluating services. People who use services and their families can use these guidelines as a platform while advocating for service quality in their area. Students, interns, and job seekers new to the field can use these guidelines when making choices about where to work. Service teams and work groups can use these guidelines to form goals and plans for quality improvement.

A Word about Language

Editorial choices for the language used in this book were deliberate. We made a concerted effort to follow the PRA *Language Guidelines* and to include people with lived experience as authors throughout the volume to ensure that the terminology as well as the message remained person-centered and person-first. Like the knowledge in our field and the services we deliver, language use guidelines evolve over time. Meanings alter, opinions change, and customs and current events influence what messages we hear. Should you, the reader, take issue with the terms, structure, or concepts used here, we invite you to speak up, take action, and be part of the next cycle of PRA's continuing development. First and foremost, in everything, including what we say, must be recognition that the people using psychiatric rehabilitation services are just that—people, with all of the complexities and uniqueness that make each individual and one of a kind with hopes, dreams, and possibilities that are there to discover.

Acknowledgements

Our greatest thanks go to our colleagues who were gracious enough to give their time to write the chapters that make up the book and who were patient throughout the process of putting the book together. To our friends and families, who encouraged and supported us in so many ways, we can only offer, in return, our gratitude and love. Two visionaries deserve a special mention. Isaiah Uliss, a Boston-based mental health advocate after whom the PRA Advocacy Award is named, was a powerful presence early in our careers. His tireless efforts, including his successful campaign to include people in recovery in IAPSRS conferences, and his vision of a better service system, shaped our work and our image of this book. Bill Anthony, founder and former director of the Boston University Center for Psychiatric Rehabilitation, taught us so much that we can no longer distinguish the line where his ideas and ours separate. His influence can be found in nearly every paragraph in every chapter in this book. Finally, our deep appreciation goes to our colleague and dear friend, Art Dell Orto, who thinks we are much better people than we really are, and who, therefore, has made us much better people than we could have been.

    – Patricia B. Nemec
      Kathleen Furlong-Norman

CHAPTER 1

WHAT IS PSYCHIATRIC REHABILITATION?

Lisa A. Razzano
Phil Floyd
Patricia A. Shipley
Jean M. Kelser

ABSTRACT

This chapter defines psychiatric rehabilitation and delineates the core principles that are fundamental to the best practice of psychiatric rehabilitation. A brief history of psychiatric rehabilitation highlights its relevance and importance in meeting the needs of individuals living with serious psychiatric disabilities in both community and institutional settings. The growth of psychiatric rehabilitation as an evidence-based practice is presented in conjunction with data regarding service models and approaches. The concept of recovery and its interface with psychiatric rehabilitation is described and explored to provide readers with both an understanding and a vision that promotes growth and the opportunity for individuals served within our mental health systems. Workforce issues and certification in psychiatric rehabilitation services are addressed.

FOR MORE THAN 60 YEARS, MENTAL HEALTH SERVICES HAVE FOCUSED ON WAYS TO SUPPORT individuals with psychiatric disabilities. During this time, a myriad of strategies have emerged, and while some have demonstrated minimal or inconsistent success, others have supported better mental health and facilitated community reintegration for individuals in recovery. Overwhelmingly, psychiatric rehabilitation (PsyR) has been established as one approach with demonstrated success in supporting individual recovery. What distinguishes this process is its continued ability to expand, develop, and diversify within the context of ever-changing funding streams, the evolution of the science of evidence-based practices (EBPs), and the growth of advocacy by individuals in recovery, their families, and other stakeholders.

A Brief History

Psychiatric rehabilitation (PsyR) was born out of the need to restore health and well-being among individuals with psychiatric disabilities. Burdened by stigma, isolation, and poverty, individuals with mental illnesses generally languished within institutional treatment settings for decades with little or no hope of ever returning to their homes and communities. As a result of the lack of any restorative treatment within institutions, a small group of individuals with psychiatric disabilities began meeting informally in New York City in the late 1940s and later focused their efforts to organize into a collective. Their efforts focused on helping people in recovery make their way back to live within their home communities, return to meaningful work, and re-establish valuable family and social relationships they had lost while hospitalized. Ultimately, the group formed what is now considered the first PsyR program, Fountain House (Propst, 1992). With Fountain House as a launching point, PsyR grew and diversified into other programs with unique, nuanced models: Philadelphia's Horizon House (1952), Boston's Center Club (1958), Chicago's Thresholds (1959), Miami's Fellowship House (1973), Fairweather Lodge programs (1960s), and a myriad of others throughout the United States. Although each brought its own identity to the services offered to individuals in recovery, all of these programs coalesced around similar themes: services within community-based settings, work and meaningful vocational activity, development of social and recreational networks, skills training, and personal growth and empowerment (Stroul, 1986; Weinstein & Hughes, 2000).

What Is Psychiatric Rehabilitation?

Psychiatric rehabilitation (PsyR) has been defined in many ways. For more than 35 years, community organizations and service providers, national and state mental health systems, individuals in recovery, and countless other stakeholders have supported PsyR, studied it, improved it, and diversified its workforce. Based on a definition from the Psychiatric Rehabilitation Association (PRA), psychiatric rehabilitation:

> … promotes recovery, full community integration and improved quality of life for persons who have been diagnosed with any mental health condition that seriously impairs their ability to lead meaningful lives. Psychiatric rehabilitation services are collaborative, person-directed and individualized. These services are an essential element of the health care and human services spectrum, and should be evidence-based. They focus on helping individuals develop skills and access resources needed to increase their capacity to be successful and satisfied in the living, working, learning, and social environments of their choice. (PRA, 2011)

This definition is only one way to characterize the complex nature of PsyR. In practice, these services also are shaped by core principles, delivered within ethical guidelines, and support a process based on multicultural diversity and competence.

Principles of Psychiatric Rehabilitation

In an effort to define the fundamental aspects of PsyR, 12 core principles have been identified. Several focus on the role of practitioners (Principles 1-3), while others focus on best practices in the field (Principles 4-10) and PsyR service delivery (Principles 11-12). The complete list of the 12 PsyR principles is provided at the end of the chapter.

First, psychiatric rehabilitation practitioners convey hope and respect and believe that all individuals have the capacity for learning and growth. Next, all practitioners must recognize that culture is central to recovery and strive to ensure that all services are culturally relevant to individuals receiving services. As described in Principle 3, practitioners engage in the processes of informed and shared decision making and facilitate partnerships with other people the individual receiving services identified.

Practitioners and other PsyR service providers strive to promote both recovery and inclusion using evidence-based and best practice (EBP) service models. Based on this overarching philosophy, Principle 4 suggests that PsyR practices build on the strengths and capabilities of individuals. Furthermore, these EBPs are person-centered; they are designed to address the unique needs of individuals, consistent with their values, hopes, and aspirations. Psychiatric rehabilitation practices also support and seek to facilitate the full integration of people in recovery into their communities. Community integration not only focuses on the physical location of individuals and the places they reside, but also supports people in recovery exercising their rights of citizenship, while accepting the responsibilities and exploring the opportunities that come with being a member of a community and a larger society. As stated in Principle 7, PsyR practices also support and promote self-determination and empowerment, such that all individuals have the right to make their own decisions about the types of services and supports they receive. PsyR best practices also must support the development of personal support networks by using natural supports within communities, including peer support initiatives and self- and mutual-help groups. In doing so, it is expected that individuals will experience improved quality in multiple life domains, such as social, occupational, educational, residential, intellectual, spiritual, and financial. Based on Principle 10, PsyR practices promote health and wellness by encouraging individuals to develop and use individualized wellness plans, such as those developed as part of Wellness Recovery Action Planning (WRAP).

Psychiatric rehabilitation services range from intensive, integrated models, such as Assertive Community Treatment (ACT) and supported employment (SE) to services focusing on the unique needs and goals for persons in recovery at an individual level, such as collaborative psychopharmacology and shared decision making (SDM). A core aspect of all of these services is that they emphasize evidence-based, promising, and emerging best practices that produce outcomes congruent with personal recovery (Principle 11). Given growing evidence of physical health needs among individuals in recovery, PsyR services must be integrated with other medical, behavioral, and holistic treatments and practices. Programs also must include structured forms of program evaluation as well as mechanisms to ensure ongoing quality improvement, all of which actively involves persons receiving services. Finally, and perhaps most importantly, PsyR services also must be readily accessible to all individuals whenever they need them for as long as they need them.

Growth of Psychiatric Rehabilitation as an Evidence-based Practice

The Institute of Medicine (IOM) and the Agency for Healthcare Research & Quality (AHRQ) both focus on the need for the highest quality mental health services possible. Psychiatric rehabilitation is cited by the IOM as one area that has substantial evidence of success in promoting recovery. In addition, the IOM has focused on core components of PsyR models as "best practices" to be used across diverse professional disciplines, such as better communication among stakeholders, combining knowledge and EBP with individual choice and treatment preferences, and working collaboratively across multiple disciplines (IOM, 2001; 2006). Similar to the IOM's identification of PsyR as a successful model, the AHRQ also recognizes PsyR using a six-level structure for rating scientific evidence.

The AHRQ "evidence grades" include: Level 1a (meta-analysis of multiple randomized controlled trials [RCTs]); Level 1b (at least one RCT); Level 2a (at least one well-designed controlled study without randomization); Level 2b (at least one other type of non-controlled, quasi-experimental study); Level 3 (non-experimental descriptive studies, comparative, correlational, & case studies); and Level 4 (expert committee reports, opinions, and/or clinical experiences of recognized authorities). Based on a review of the literature using established criteria for EBPs, six models within the overarching structure for PsyR are recognized using AHRQ standards: (1) collaborative psychopharmacology, (2) supported employment (SE), (3) assertive community treatment (ACT), (4) family psychoeducation, (5) integrated treatment for dual diagnosis, and (6) skills training (Mueser et al., 2004). Using the AHRQ grading system, PsyR models demonstrate evidence at the highest levels, including Level 1a and Level 1b (Campbell et al., 2011; Mueser et al., 2003).

Recently, Campbell et al. (2011) established evidence for supported employment at the highest grade using meta-analysis. To accomplish this, data from four separate randomized control trial studies of supported employment (SE) were pooled and analyzed to determine the overall effect across multiple sites. Meta-analytic results demonstrated large, positive effects for SE compared to other vocational models for several key outcomes, including getting work (job acquisition) and keeping jobs (total time worked).

In addition to more traditional PsyR services, the body of evidence for PsyR services delivered by people in recovery continues to grow. For close to 30 years, studies have demonstrated the positive effects of psychiatric rehabilitation services provided by people in recovery, such as consumer-operated post-hospital social network enhancement programs (Edmunson et al., 1982), supported employment services (Kaufmann et al., 1995), consumer-operated intensive case management services (Solomon & Draine, 1995), and assertive community treatment (ACT) services provided by peers (Paulson et al., 1999). Other services that characterize PsyR have moderate support (Level 2a or 2b) and have led to major policy shifts in the use of these techniques within the field. These studies include: reductions in rates of seclusion and/or restraint (Jonikas et al., 2004; McCue et al., 2004), use and support of psychiatric advance directives (Backlar, 2000; Srebnik et al., 2004; 2005), self-directed care services (Cook & Russell, 2008; Cook et al., 2008; Teague & Boaz, 2003), and shared decision making (Deegan, 2007; Deegan & Drake, 2006; Deegan et al., 2008).

Most recently, the foundations of high-level evidence supporting PsyR service models designed and delivered by individuals in recovery led to the inclusion of Wellness Recovery

Action Planning (WRAP®), developed by Dr. Mary Ellen Copeland, in the National Registry of Evidence-Based Programs and Practices (http://nrepp.samhsa.gov). Studies of WRAP® have established this peer-designed model at AHRQ Level 1b evidence with at least one RCT (Cook et al., 2009; 2010). Thus, despite some lingering conflict between more traditional goals and outcomes in EBPs and those reflecting more recovery and peer-oriented perspectives, PsyR models and services continue to lead the way in person-driven care, shared decision-making, and other recovery strategies within a context of EBPs. However, as noted by Cook et al. (2004), behavioral health care services, including PsyR, continue to need improvement and refinement at the personal, provider, and organizational levels.

Psychiatric Rehabilitation and Recovery

Several major federal policy initiatives have had a substantial impact on psychiatric rehabilitation, including those noted in mental health reports from the U.S. Surgeon General (1999), the Institute of Medicine (2001; 2006), the President's New Freedom Commission on Mental Health (PNFC; 2003), and the Annapolis Coalition on Behavioral Health Workforce (2005; 2007; 2009). Increasingly, these bodies have endorsed concepts of recovery, self-determination, and personal choice in their policy initiatives—concepts that have long been incorporated into PsyR services and continue to be infused into new PsyR models and practices (Anthony, 2000; Deegan, 1988; Jacobson & Curtis, 2000). Regardless of the support and endorsement of recovery-oriented services and practices, the field of PsyR continues to examine and refine the concept of recovery itself. However, a singular definition of the concept of recovery has been elusive.

Defining recovery in psychiatric rehabilitation

For decades, the concept of recovery has been central in the literature of physical disability and the management of chronic, life-long illnesses that do not fit into curative paradigms (e.g., diabetes, spinal injury; see e.g., Wright, 1983). A core goal of PsyR services has been to support individuals with psychiatric disabilities in restoring their lives within community settings, broadly referring to this practice as "promoting recovery." Within the PsyR field, however, discussion continues to focus on developing a more detailed definition of recovery, often concentrating on a standardized operational definition.

Despite ongoing efforts to define recovery, one general definition remains widely cited in the literature, which was offered first by Anthony:

> [Recovery is] … a deeply personal unique process of changing one's attitudes, values, feelings, goals, skills, and/or roles. It is a way of living a satisfying, hopeful, and contributing life even with limitations caused by illness. Recovery involves the development of new meaning and purpose in one's life as one grows beyond the catastrophic effects of mental illness. (Anthony, 1993, p. 21)

Further, as recovery relates to specifically to principles of PsyR:

> Recovery from mental illness involves much more than recovery from the illness itself. People with mental illness [es] may have to recover from the stigma that they incorporated into their very being; from the iatrogenic effects of treatment settings; from the lack of recent opportunities for self-determination; from the negative side effects of unemployment; and from crushed dreams. Recovery is a complex, time-consuming process. (Anthony, 1993, p. 21).

Others have offered definitions as well as conceptual models of recovery and its relevance to PsyR. For example, Jacobsen and Greenley (2001) suggest that recovery incorporates internal factors for individuals, such as hope and empowerment, as well as external or social factors, such as recovery-focused service systems and general human rights. Similarly, based on a review of evaluation tools in the field, Noordsy et al. (2002) offered a definition of recovery as centered around three core concepts: (1) hope, (2) taking personal responsibility, and (3) getting on with life.

Andresen (2003) notes that person-centered concepts of recovery reflect a strong focus on sustaining "a fulfilling, meaningful life and positive sense of identity founded on hopefulness and self-determination" (p. 588). Andresen and colleagues also propose a set of key components to the process of recovery that reflect the principles of PsyR. First, recovery focuses on developing and sustaining hope. Next, individuals in recovery must work to re-establish a positive personal identity free of a stigmatizing view of illness. Third, recovery supports finding meaning in life as defined by the individual (self-determination). Finally, and perhaps most importantly, recovery includes taking responsibility for one's own life.

One common characteristic among all, however, is that these definitions and models extend beyond aspects from a singular, medical model of mental health (i.e., symptoms, hospitalizations) to include features of the lived experience of individuals in recovery. Debate continues, however, with more recent theories examining recovery as a process compared to recovery as a static outcome (Anthony, 2000; Resnick et al., 2005; Tepper, 2007). In a review of 30 years of published literature regarding recovery, Davidson and Roe (2007) discuss a "broad 'heterogeneity' in outcomes" for people with psychiatric disabilities (p. 462). Examining terms related to clinical compared to rehabilitative factors, the authors posit two distinct and complementary meanings. First, recovery is characterized by clinical features (e.g., improvements in symptoms) of a mental illness. Second, recovery is evidenced through community inclusion, empowerment, and self-determination despite any ongoing aspects or experience of a clinical illness or disability.

Recovery-oriented psychiatric rehabilitation services

Regardless of how recovery is defined, it is essential that people with psychiatric disabilities have the opportunity to participate in services that promote mental and physical health and community integration. Anthony (1993) described eight essential features (or assumptions, p. 530) of recovery-oriented mental health services (including PsyR):

1. Recovery can occur without professional intervention.

2. A common denominator of recovery is the presence of individuals who believe in the person in recovery and will stand by him or her.

3. Recovery as a vision does function as a part of a person's ideas or theories about "mental illnesses."

4. Recovery occurs despite that mental health symptoms may reoccur.

5. Recovery changes the frequency and duration of mental health symptoms.

6. Recovery is not necessarily a linear process.

7. The consequences of the "illness" (e.g., stigma) often can be harder to overcome than any of its symptoms.

8. Recovery does not suggest that a person never had a mental illness or never experienced mental health symptoms.

In response to federal initiatives from the President's New Freedom Commission on Mental Health (2001) and the Institute of Medicine (2006), systems must broaden their focus to provide supports that are effective at assisting individuals in achieving recovery and returning to full participation in life in the community (Farkas, Gagne, Anthony, & Chamberlin, 2005). In one framework, key recovery values drive the development and implementation of PsyR services. In particular, values of recovery-oriented services focus on person orientation, person involvement, self-determination and choice, and growth potential. A person orientation ensures that individuals are treated as a person first with a focus on strengths rather than limitations. Person involvement promotes individuals' rights for full partnership and involvement in the planning of PsyR services and how they are received. Self-determination and choice are evident in the right to make individual decisions about services and choices about treatment. Finally, potential for growth suggests that all individuals have the ability to recover, regardless of times of crisis or other experiences of disability (Farkas, Anthony, & Cohen, 1989; Farkas et al., 2005).

These more conceptual values have been translated to characterize the actual structure of PsyR services themselves. First, organizations must address their mission, policies, procedures, information management, quality assurance, program setting, and program networks to ensure that they reflect the core values of recovery. For example, an organization's recovery mission can be characterized by improvements that allow individuals to live and function in the environments they choose rather than a singular focus on treatment with lack of attention to choice and self-determination. Similarly, PsyR programs use quality assurance to examine outcomes and milestones of interest to service users, not only those measures required by funders or regulators. Recovery-oriented PsyR services also must incorporate measures to select, train, and supervise staff. For example, staff training must include opportunities for PsyR providers to have regular interaction with people in recovery who are "living beyond their disability" (Farkas et al., 2005, p. 150). Given that staffing, including peer providers, is fundamental to establishing and maintaining recovery-oriented PsyR programs, the field continues to examine the quality and needs of the PsyR workforce as well as the evolving services needs of people in recovery.

The psychiatric rehabilitation workforce

The increased focus on workforce quality, exposure, and training in PsyR reflects similar challenges in evidence-based medicine (EBM) overall for medical doctors and other clinical health providers. However, translation of concepts of recovery into practical applications for PsyR models continues to challenge the field (Agrawal, 2008; Coverdale et al., 2008; Hoge et al., 2005). Despite this challenge, the IOM as well as the Annapolis Coalition have recognized PsyR as one model that fills identified gaps in behavioral workforce competencies (Hoge et al., 2005). In spite of this recognition, programs focusing on mental health education and training, whether for students or practicing professionals, are lacking in their focus on PsyR overall as well as on factors related to recovery (Buckley et al., 2007; Hoge, 2002; Mascola, 2008; U.S. DHHS, 2003). This includes an identified lack of exposure to PsyR service models and concepts in major academic programs and professional organizations. Groups, including the IOM and both the American Psychological Association (APA) and the American Psychiatric Association, endorse and promote the idea that PsyR concepts are central to the success of clinicians and other professionals within rapidly changing health care systems (APA, 2005).

Some academic centers have embarked on projects to reconfigure training opportunities that include more exposure to PsyR, its principles, values, and concepts of recovery within behavioral science programs, such as the Recovery Education in the Academy Program (REAP) project at the University of Illinois at Chicago National Research and Training Center. There are other projects aimed at transforming education and training of the workforce with regard to PsyR and recovery, such as the residency training programs at the University of Massachusetts (Fisher and colleagues), the Medical University of South Carolina (Buckley and colleagues), and multidisciplinary training initiatives at the University of Kansas (Rapp and colleagues), among others. A federal grant initiative called "Recovery to Practice" (http://www2.dsgonline.com/rtp/resources.html) is funding the development of curricula on recovery for several professional mental health disciplines.

Barriers remain, however, to implementing the recommendations for PsyR education and training supported by the IOM, PNFC, the Annapolis Coalition, the National Association of State Mental Health Program Directors, and other stakeholders. For example, accredited academic programs for psychiatrists, psychologists, and social workers have curricula with little or no standardized focus on PsyR models, even though these providers play an active role in PsyR services and recovery. Few degree-granting programs focus specifically on PsyR; at the time of this writing, the University of Medicine and Dentistry of New Jersey supports the only degree-granting program specifically in PsyR (K. Gill, personal communication). San Diego State University and other schools support a certificate program as part of a larger department (M. Olney; personal communication). Thus, growth, expansion, and translation of PsyR services continues to be limited by the lack of academic programs that educate and train the next generation to provide these services.

Certification in Psychiatric Rehabilitation Services

Given the fundamental role of PsyR in promoting recovery, it is essential that its multidisciplinary workforce meets the challenges outlined in recommendations made by the Institute of Medicine, the Annapolis Coalition, and other groups calling for an increase in relevant knowledge and skills. One program that addresses this need in the workforce is the credentialing program for certification of psychiatric rehabilitation practitioners (CPRP) developed and operated by the Psychiatric Rehabilitation Association's (PRA). The CPRP credential mandates requirements for continuing education and periodic recertification based on a standardized curriculum in psychiatric rehabilitation. Thus, the CPRP fills a valuable education and training gap within a multidisciplinary workforce. In addition, the CPRP focuses on core competencies of PsyR services and values, affording consistency of workforce knowledge and skills across diverse environments.

The credential also represents a strategy to offer PsyR within the context of its principles with attention to ethical conduct and multicultural diversity. It also supports standards for ethical behavior in professional relationships and directs PsyR practitioners to adopt the person-first methods that support and promote self-determination. Unquestionably, these standards demonstrate that the nature of practitioners' and individuals' relationships is central to PsyR, promoting recovery, and the continued evolution of the field.

Future Directions for Psychiatric Rehabilitation

Ongoing advances in PsyR bring new challenges and new stakeholders. As such, the field of PsyR must grow and adapt to the need of individuals affected by psychiatric disabilities and their families. For example, PsyR services are being adapted to focus on the recovery needs of children and adolescents with emotional and behavioral conditions, their families, and caregivers. PsyR services for children not only promote recovery and assist in developing resiliency among young people, but they do so within developmental contexts so that services are relevant to children's world views and are responsive to their interests and needs (Jonikas, Laris, & Cook, 2003). PsyR services for children also identify and emphasize the vital skills and needs, teaching skills relevant to those needs and engaging both children and their families/caregivers in teaching and practice of skills along with other interventions. Other new PsyR EBP services for children also include an adaptation of WRAP® specifically designed for children (Copeland, 2011).

Another rapidly growing area in PsyR relates to the needs of veterans. As noted by Goldberg and Resnick (2010), the U.S. Department of Veterans Affairs has responded to the PNFC's recommendations and has become a leader in the use of PsyR services and EBPs. Goldberg and Resnick highlight several services for returning veterans that focus on PsyR and recovery, such as local recovery care coordinators. LCCs focus on providing and expanding services as well as managing activities related to systems transformation. Another component is peer-delivered services supported by trained individuals who serve as mentors and share their personal experiences of recovery. Family services also are critical to community integration and quality of life for returning veterans. Other services offered to veterans range from formation of veterans' mental health councils, psychosocial rehabilitation and recovery centers, and models of assertive community treatment (ACT) and supported employment (SE) specifically adapted to address the needs of veterans (Goldberg & Resnick, 2010).

In the last decade, the area that may have affected PsyR services the most dramatically is the recognition of the physical health needs among people in recovery. In 2006, National Association of State Mental Health Program Directors (NASMHPD) reported that throughout the world, physical health disparities continue to widen between individuals in recovery and individuals in the general population. Individuals in recovery not only demonstrate disparities in rates of physical illnesses, such as diabetes and heart disease, but also experience more symptoms of those illnesses (morbidity) and a shortened lifespan (mortality; NASMHPD, 2006). By some estimates, people in recovery have approximately 25 years of life lost, primarily from largely preventable and treatable medical conditions, such as hypertension, high blood pressure, and diabetes. As a result, major initiatives to address the physical health and wellness among individuals in recovery have become common within PsyR. As a result, PsyR programs have acted quickly to identify ways to identify and treat physical health illnesses as well as promote whole health recovery. However, there remains a substantial amount to work to be accomplished before PsyR services will have a significant impact on the longevity of people in recovery.

SUMMARY

From the birth of the first public gathering of mental health consumers and the formation of the clubhouse program at Fountain House to state-reimbursable certified peer specialist programs, PsyR has consistently been a model that grows and evolves alongside the individuals for whom it was envisioned. What most distinguishes PsyR from many other service models is its history of promoting recovery, empowerment, and self-determination. In many ways, PsyR services have come full circle. Although initial efforts focused on seeing individuals beyond the cluster of the medicalized psychiatric symptoms they experienced or the barriers they encountered in day-to-day life, new efforts have identified the alarming disparities in co-occurring physical health conditions among people in recovery, reminding the field that mental illness is not a singular concern. Moving away from the medical model of illness ironically resulted in more holistic and person-centered mental health care. By refocusing attention toward empowerment and self-determination, PsyR services have not only transformed mental health systems, they have transformed lost lives into recovered lives.

PRINCIPLES GUIDING BEST PRACTICES IN PSYCHIATRIC REHABILITATION
(www.psychrehabassociation.org)

- Psychiatric rehabilitation practitioners convey hope and respect and believe that all individuals have the capacity for learning and growth.

- Psychiatric rehabilitation practitioners recognize that culture is central to recovery and strive to ensure that all services are culturally relevant to individuals receiving services.

- Psychiatric rehabilitation practitioners engage in the processes of informed and shared decision-making and facilitate partnerships with other people the individual receiving services has identified.

- Psychiatric rehabilitation practices build on the strengths and capabilities of individuals.

- Psychiatric rehabilitation practices are person-centered; they are designed to address the unique needs of individuals, consistent with their values, hopes and aspirations.

- Psychiatric rehabilitation practices support full integration of people in recovery into their communities where they can exercise their rights of citizenship as well as to accept the responsibilities and explore the opportunities that come with being a member of a community and a larger society.

- Psychiatric rehabilitation practices promote self-determination and empowerment. All individuals have the right to make their own decisions, including decisions about the types of services and supports they receive.

- Psychiatric rehabilitation practices facilitate the development of personal support networks by utilizing natural supports within communities, peer support initiatives, and self- and mutual-help groups.

- Psychiatric rehabilitation practices strive to help individuals improve the quality of all aspects of their lives, including social, occupational, educational, residential, intellectual, spiritual and financial.

- Psychiatric rehabilitation practices promote health and wellness, encouraging individuals to develop and use individualized wellness plans.

- Psychiatric rehabilitation services emphasize evidence-based, promising, and emerging best practices that produce outcomes congruent with personal recovery. Programs include structured program evaluation and quality improvement mechanisms that actively involve persons receiving services.

- Psychiatric rehabilitation services must be readily accessible to all individuals whenever they need them. These services also should be well coordinated and integrated with other psychiatric, medical, and holistic treatments and practices.

ABOUT THE AUTHORS

Lisa Razzano, PhD, CPRP is a tenured associate professor of psychiatry at the University of Illinois at Chicago and deputy director of the UIC Center on Mental Health Services Research and Policy. She has worked in mental health services research and training for more than two decades. She has recognized expertise in mental health services research, psychiatric rehabilitation, and program evaluation, including vocational rehabilitation and employment, the mental health aspects of HIV/AIDS and treatment adherence, and physical health co-morbidities. She is the current chair of the PRA Board of Directors.

Phil Floyd, QMHP, CPRP is manager of adult clinical support at Rockbridge Area Community Services Board in Lexington, Virginia where he has worked since 1983. In 2002 Phil was elected by the IAPSRS Membership to be vice president of IAPSRS. He held this position until 2004 when he was elected chair-elect of PRA and assumed the position of PRA chair from 2006 to 2008. In 2012 Phil was the recipient of PRA's John Beard Award, presented annually to an individual who has made outstanding contributions to the field of psychiatric rehabilitation. Phil is a 1983 graduate of Ferrum College with a bachelor's degree in psychology. He has taken graduate courses at James Madison University in counseling and psychology.

Patricia A. Shipley was born and raised in Chicago, where she still resides. She earned a Bachelor of Arts degree from Butler University. She subsequently graduated from the University of Houston with a Bachelor of Accountancy, while maintaining Dean's list status as well as a Golden Key and Beta Alpha Psi (national accounting honorary fraternity) membership. She passed the CPA exam on her first attempt. She is currently working towards a Peer Specialist Certification.

Jean M. Kelser, Chair, Rockbridge Human Rights Committee, was born in Washington, DC in 1966. She recovered from long-term use of drugs & alcohol and has been sober since November 11, 2000. She attended college for three years of college while enlisted in the U.S. Army and ROTC. She left the Army and college in 1993 due to Post Traumatic Stress Disorder and Bipolar Disorder. She has been a member of Eagle's Nest Clubhouse in Buena Vista, Virginia since April, 2002. She became a WRAP trainer in 2008 and currently works with the Rockbridge Human Rights Committee in Lexington, Virginia. She has served as the chair of the committee since 2011.

REFERENCES

Agrawal, S. (2008). Teaching evidence-based psychiatry: Integrating and aligning the formal and hidden curricula. *Academy of Psychiatry, 32*(6), 470-474.

American College of Psychiatrists (2009). *The Psychiatry Resident in Training Examination* (PRITE). Retrieved from http://www.acpsych.org/prite

American College of Psychiatrists. (n.d.). *Psychiatry Resident in Training Exam.* Retrieved August 1, 2005 from http://www.acpsych.org/prite

American Psychiatric Association. (n.d.). *Use of the concept of recovery.* Retrieved August 10, 2005 from http://www.mhrecovery.org/var/library/file/26-APA%20position%20on%20the%20concept%20of%20recovery.pdf

Andresen, R., Oades, L., & Caputi, P. (2003). The experience of recovery from schizophrenia: Towards an empirically validated stage model. *Australian and New Zealand Journal of Psychiatry, 37,* 586-594.

Anthony, W. A. (1993). Recovery from mental illness: The guiding vision of the mental health service system in the 1990s. *Psychiatric Rehabilitation Journal, 16*(4), 11-23.

Anthony, W. A. (2000). A recovery oriented service system: Setting some service level standards. *Psychiatric Rehabilitation Journal 24*(2), 159-169.

Bates, D. W., Kuperman, G. J., Wang, S., et al. (2003). Ten commandments for effective clinical decision support: Making the practice of evidence-based medicine a reality. *Journal of the American Medical Informatics Association, 10*(6), 523-530.

Buckley, P., Bahmiller, D., Kenna, C. A., Shevitz, S., Powell, I., & Fricks, L. (2007). Resident education and perceptions of recovery in serious mental illness: Observations and commentary. *Academic Psychiatry, 31*(6), 435-438.

Campbell, K. Bond, G. R., & Drake, R. E. (2011). Who benefits from supported employment: A meta-analytic study. *Schizophrenia Bulletin, 37*(2), 370-380.

Chew-Graham, C. A., Rogers, A., & Yassin, N. (2003). I wouldn't want it on my CV or their records: Medical students' experiences of help-seeking for mental health problems. *Medical Education, 37*(10), 873-880.

Cook, J. A., Toprac, M., & Shore, S. E. (2004). Combining evidence-based practice with stakeholder consensus to enhance psychosocial rehabilitation services in the Texas benefit design initiative. *Psychiatric Rehabilitation Journal, 27*(4), 307-318.

Cook, J. A., Russell, C., Grey, D. D., & Jonikas, J. A. (2008). A self-directed care model for mental health recovery. *Psychiatric Services, 59,* 600-602.

Cook, J. A., Copeland, M. E., Hamilton, M. M., Jonikas, J. A., Razzano, L. A., Floyd, C. B., Hudson, W., Macfarlane, R., & Grey, D. D. (2009). Outcomes of mental illness self-management using Wellness Recovery Action Planning. *Psychiatric Services, 60*(2), 246-249.

Cook, J. A., Copeland, M. E., Corey, L., Bufflington, E., Jonikas, J. A., Curtis, L. C., Gray, D. D., & Nichols, W. H. (2010). Developing the evidence base for peer-led services: Changes among participants following Wellness Recovery Action Plan education in two statewide initiatives. *Psychiatric Rehabilitation Journal, 34*(2), 113-120.

Coomarasamy, A., & Khan, K. S. (2004). What is the evidence that post-graduate teaching in evidence-based medicine changes anything? A systematic review. *British Journal of Medicine, 329,* 1017-1021.

Copeland, M. E. (2011). The Wellness Recovery Action Planning Project for Children. Retrieved from http://www.mentalhealthrecovery.com/wrap/wv_children.php

Coverdale, J. H., Roberts, L. W., & Louie, A. K. (2008). Teaching evidence-based psychiatry to residents and fellows: Developing the curriculum. *Academic Psychiatry, 32*(6), 453-457.

Davidson, L., & Roe, D. (2007). Recovery from versus recovery in serious mental illness: One strategy for lessening confusion plaguing recovery. *Journal of Mental Health, 16*(4), 459-470.

Deegan, P. E. (1988). Recovery: The lived experience of rehabilitation. *Psychosocial Rehabilitation Journal, 11*(4), 11-19.

Druss, B. G. (2002). The mental health/primary care interface in the United States: History, structure, and context. *General Hospital Psychiatry, 24*(4), 197-202.

Farkas, M., Anthony, W. A., & Cohen, M. R. (1989) An overview of psychiatric rehabilitation programs. In M. Farkas & W. A. Anthony (Eds.). *Psychiatric rehabilitation programs: Putting theory into practice* (pp. 2-27). Baltimore, MD: Johns Hopkins University.

Farkas, M., Gagne, D., Anthony, W. A., & Chamberlin, J. (2005). Implementing recovery-oriented evidence-based programs: Identifying critical dimensions. *Community Mental Health Journal, 41*(2), 141-157.

Feinstein, R. E., Rothberg, B., Weiner, N., & Savin, D. M. (2008). University of Colorado Department of Psychiatry evidence-based medicine educational project. *Academic Psychiatry, 32*(6), 525-530.

Folstein, M. F., Folstein, S. E., & McHigh, P. R. (1975). Mini-mental state: A practical method for grading the cognitive state of patients for the clinician. *Journal of Psychiatry Research, 12,* 189-198.

Harrison, V. (1984). A biologists' view of pain, suffering, and marginal life. In F. Doherty, (Ed). *The depraved, the disabled, and the fullness of life.* Delaware: Michael Glazier.

Hoge, M. A., Morris, J. A., Daniels, A. S., Stuart, G. W., et al. (2007). *An action plan on behavioral health workforce development.* Cincinnati, OH: Annapolis Coalition Conference on Behavioral Health Workforce.

Hoge, M. A., Morris, J. A., Daniels, A. S., et al. (2005). Report of recommendations: The Annapolis Coalition Conference on Behavioral Health Workforce Competencies. *Administration and Policy in Mental Health, 32*(5), 651-663.

Hoge, M. A. (2002). The training gap: An acute crisis in behavioral health education. *Administration and Policy in Mental Health, 29*(4/5), 305-317.

Institute of Medicine. (2001). *Crossing the quality chasm: A new health system for the 21st century.* Washington, DC: National Academy Press.

Jacobson, N., & Curtis, L. (2000). Recovery as policy in mental health services: Strategies emerging from the states. *Psychiatric Rehabilitation Journal, 23*(4), 333-341.

Jonikas, J. A., Laris, A., & Cook, J. A.(2003). The passage to adulthood: Psychiatric rehabilitation service and transition-related needs of young adult women with emotional and psychiatric disorders. *Psychiatric Rehabilitation Journal, 27*(2), 114-121.

Kaufmann, C. L. (1995). The self-help employment center: Some outcomes from the first year. *Psychosocial Rehabilitation Journal, 18*(4), 145-162.

Mascola, A. J. (2008). Guided mentorship in evidence-based medicine for psychiatry: A pilot cohort study supporting a promising method of real-time clinical instruction. *Academic Psychiatry, 32*(6), 475-483.

McCue, R. E., Urcuyo, L., & Tobias, T. (2004). Reducing restraint use in a public psychiatric inpatient service. *The Journal of Behavioral Health Services & Research, 31*(2), 217-224.

Mueser, K. T., Torrey, W. C., Lynde, D., Singer, P., & Drake, R. E. (2003). Implementing evidence-based practices for people with severe mental illness. *Behavior Modification, 27*(3), 387-411.

Noordsy, D., Torrey, W., Mueser, K., Mead, S., O'Keefe, C., & Fox, L. (2002). Recovery from severe mental illness: An intrapersonal and functional outcome definition. *International Review of Psychiatry, 14*(4), 318-326.

Paulson, R., Herinckx, H., Demmler, J., Clarke, G., Cutler, D., & Birecree, E. (1999). Comparing practice patterns of consumer and non-consumer mental health service providers. *Community Mental Health Journal, 35*(3), 251-269.

President's New Freedom Commission on Mental Health. (2003). *Achieving the promise: Transforming mental health care in America, final report.* No. Pub. No. SMA-03-3832. Rockville, MD: U.S. Department of Health and Human Services.

Propst, R. (1992). Standards for clubhouse programs: Why and how they were developed. *Psychosocial Rehabilitation Journal, 12*(2), 25-30.

Sackett, D. L., & Rosenberg, W. M. C. (1995). On the need for evidence-based medicine. *Journal of Public Health, 17*(3), 330-334.

Singh, S. P., Baxter, H., Standen, P., & Duggan, C. (1998). Changing the attitudes of "tomorrow's doctors" towards mental illness and psychiatry: A comparison of two teaching methods. *Medical Education, 32,* 115-120.

Smith, J. (1998). Organic brain syndrome. In P. Rosen, R. M. Barkin, G. R. Braen, et al. (Eds). *Emergency medicine: Concepts and clinical practice* (3rd ed., pp. 1771-1772). St. Louis, MO: Mosby.

Solomon, P., & Draine, J. (1995). The efficacy of a consumer case management team: Two-year outcomes of a randomized trial. *The Journal of Mental Health Administration, 22*(2), 135-146.

Srihari, V. (2008). Evidence-based medicine, clinical expertise and the tasks of psychiatry. *Academic Psychiatry, 32*(6), 463-469.

Stroul, B. A. (1986). *Models of community support services: Approaches to helping persons with long-term mental illness.* Boston, MA: Center for Psychiatric Rehabilitation, Sargent College of Allied Health Professions, Boston University.

Stuart, G. W., Hoge, M. A., Morris, J. A., Adams, N., & Daniels, A. S. (2009). The Annapolis Coalition Report on the behavioral health workforce needs of the United States: International implications. *International Journal of Mental Health, 38*(1), 46-60.

Tepper, M. C. (2007). Psychosocial rehabilitation: A newcomer's eye. *Psychiatric Services, 58*(8), 1116-1118.

U.S. Department of Health and Human Services. (2001). *Mental health: Culture, race, and ethnicity—A supplement of mental health: A report of the Surgeon General.* Rockville, MD: U.S. Department of Health and Human Services, Substance Abuse and Mental Health Services Administration, Center for Mental Health Services.

U.S. Department of Health and Human Services. (1999). *Mental health: A report of the Surgeon General.* Rockville, MD: U.S. Department of Health and Human Services, Substance Abuse and Mental Health Services Administration, Center for Mental Health Services.

Weinstein, D., & Hughes, R. (2000). What is psychosocial rehabilitation? In R. C. Baron, R. A. Hughes, & D. Weinstein (Eds.). *Best practices in psychosocial rehabilitation* (pp. 35-62). Columbia, MD: International Association of Psychosocial Rehabilitation Services.

Wood, D. F. (2003). ABC of learning and teaching in medicine: Problem-based learning. *British Medical Journal, 326,* 328-330.

Wright, B. (1983). *Physical disability: A psychosocial approach.* New York: Harper and Row.

UNDERSTANDING PSYCHIATRIC DISABILITY

Kim L. MacDonald-Wilson
Debbie S. Andersen

A B S T R A C T

This chapter examines the impact of mental health conditions and social/
environmental factors on functioning in various life roles. Distinctions
between mental illness and psychiatric disability are drawn. After defining
disability, health, and functioning, the chapter compares and contrasts the
medical model or biological approach with the rehabilitation and recovery
approach to psychiatric disability and examines the implications of this
approach for how we view individuals, design programs, and implement
service systems. While a medical model emphasizes psychiatric diagnosis
and treatment of symptoms, the rehabilitation and recovery approach
emphasizes maximizing functioning and examining the environmental and
personal factors that play a role in functioning, disability, and recovery. The
designation of disability is described in reference to public benefits, personal
experience, civil rights, and implications for staff development.

THERE ARE MULTIPLE WAYS TO REFER TO PEOPLE WHO RECEIVE MENTAL HEALTH AND REHABILITATION services who have been given a diagnostic label from the *Diagnostic and Statistical Manual* (APA, 2000): People with lived experience, person in recovery, individuals with psychiatric disabilities, a person who has a psychiatric diagnosis (or mental health condition or emotional illness), a schizophrenic (or a manic-depressive or a borderline).

The language we use communicates so much. In our attempts to be respectful, we change terms that have been accepted in the past. However, what is acceptable changes with the times and with an individual's perspective, making it difficult to communicate with each other clearly and to know what the other person means by the terms s/he uses. Over the past 30 years or so, the mental health field has been slowly moving away from a primary focus on the illness, on reducing symptoms, on providing treatment (known as the medical model), and towards focusing on recovery—from a mental health condition, from the negative effects of treatment and involvement in public service systems, and from discrimination and exclusion perpetrated by individuals, programs, systems, and society.

Recovery has become our buzzword in mental health, but it is also a primary aim guiding the development and delivery of mental health services in the United States (U.S. Department of Health and Human Services, 1999; President's New Freedom Commission on Mental Health, 2003). In fact, the Substance Abuse and Mental Health Services Administration (SAMHSA), a federal agency within the U.S. Department of Health and Human Services, has incorporated *Supporting Recovery* as one of its strategic initiatives (2011-2014), defining it as "partnering with people in recovery from mental and substance use disorders to guide the behavioral health system and promote individual, program, and system level approaches that foster health and resilience; increase permanent housing, employment, education, and other necessary supports; and reduce barriers to social inclusion" (SAMHSA, 2011a). The Center for Mental Health Services within SAMHSA has also funded an initiative called *Recovery to Practice,* which intends to advance a recovery-oriented approach to behavioral health care by developing, promoting, and delivering training curricula in the major disciplines on how to translate the concept of recovery into service delivery.

Defining Recovery

One challenge to focusing on recovery in the mental health field is that the term recovery can mean many things; there is, as yet, no one definition that has been agreed upon. It can refer to a process or outcomes of intervention or both. Anthony (2006) suggests that as a process, recovery is long-term and multidimensional with dimensions that should be viewed along a continuum (p. xvi). Recovery can involve adjustment to a disability, achievement of subjective well-being, some degree of symptom remission, and/or improvement in instrumental role functioning and community integration. Recovery outcomes can include improvements in role functioning in work, social, and living situations. Today, "recovery is increasingly being used to denote a ... person's potential for growth, healing, and community integration" (Anthony, 2006, p. xvi). "Recovery also refers to a person's right and ability to live a safe, dignified, and meaningful life in the community of his or her choice despite continuing disability associated with the illness ... learning how to live fully in the presence of a disabling condition" (Davidson, Harding, & Spaniol, 2006, p. xxi). A new working definition of recovery developed with the involvement of stakeholders' comments solicited by SAMHSA (2011b) is: "Recovery from Mental Disorders and Substance Use Disorders: A process of change through which individuals improve their health and wellness, live a self-directed life, and strive to reach their full potential."

Through the Recovery Support Strategic Initiative, SAMHSA has delineated four major dimensions that support a life in recovery:

1. *Health:* Overcoming or managing one's disease(s) as well as living in a physically and emotionally healthy way;

2. *Home:* A stable and safe place to live;

3. *Purpose:* Meaningful daily activities, such as a job, school, volunteerism, family caretaking, or creative endeavors, and the independence, income, and resources to participate in society; and

4. *Community:* Relationships and social networks that provide support, friendship, love, and hope.

Within this vision of behavioral health services, there is a role for treatment, rehabilitation, and recovery interventions to assist people with lived experience in living self-directed lives and achieving their full potential. To be effective, service providers must know about the medical aspects of mental health conditions, the rehabilitation aspects of building strengths and overcoming limitations to function in chosen life roles, and the recovery aspects of living a life with meaning for a person who has a diagnostic label. The medical model still dominates our public mental health and rehabilitation service systems and is the language of insurance reimbursement and eligibility for many services. However, knowing about the medical aspects of mental health conditions and treatments alone does not prepare psychiatric rehabilitation practitioners to improve role functioning or assist individuals who have mental health conditions in developing lives of meaning and purpose. There is a need for a framework providing a common understanding of psychiatric disability in relation to treatment, rehabilitation, and recovery. This chapter draws distinctions between the concepts of mental illness, psychiatric disability, and recovery; presents an overview of best practices in understanding psychiatric disability, examines the challenges and concerns of people in recovery and practitioners in understanding psychiatric disability, and explores implications for using a rehabilitation and recovery framework in our work with individuals, in programs, and in policy for systems providing services and supports.

PERSPECTIVES ON PSYCHIATRIC DISABILITY

Four perspectives are described here: medical, disability, bio-psycho-social, and social. Like any categorization, this one has its flaws, and there are certainly areas of intersection among the categories. It is also important to remember that the use of any one framework does not preclude the use of another.

The Medical Perspective

Traditionally, most mental health professionals have been trained in a medical model focused on treating the mental health condition, that is, the symptoms of the psychiatric illness. Other terms that have been used to refer to the mental health condition include mental illness, mental impairment, psychiatric disorder, emotional disturbance (the term used most often with children), or psychiatric diagnosis. In general, the American Psychiatric Association's

Diagnostic and Statistical Manual (DSM IV-TR; APA, 2000) considers a mental health condition to be a disorder if it is:

- Clinically significant (essentially meaning that it is noticeable)
- Causing (or at risk of causing) distress or difficulties in role functioning
- Not a "normal" or expected reaction to an event and not a "culturally sanctioned" (Stein et al., 2010) behavior or response to circumstances or events
- A manifestation of a behavioral, psychological, or biological dysfunction—implying deviance from normal or typical behavior, a faulty way of perceiving or reacting to the world, or an underlying biological cause (a criterion that could be considered somewhat redundant to other criteria; Stein et al., 2010).
- Not primarily the result of (or a demonstration of) conflict with society.

In the United States, in any given year, approximately one in four adults meet the criteria for a diagnosable mental health condition; in a lifetime, the chance of developing a diagnosable mental health condition is nearly one in two (Kessler, Chiu, Demler, & Walters, 2005). As a result, having experience with a mental health condition is fairly common. In this chapter, the term mental health condition is used to distinguish it from medical illnesses, to account for the possibility of social and experiential aspects of the condition, and to focus on the positive health and wellness aspects.

Descriptions of mental health conditions were formulated to categorize or classify them based upon particular patterns of symptoms and signs, resulting in a diagnostic label. In technical jargon, symptoms are the subjective experience of the person, what the person reports as the problem, such as difficulty sleeping or feeling anxious. Signs are the observable behaviors, such as awaking at 4 a.m., pacing, jiggling legs, or drumming fingers; or test results, such as meeting or exceeding a certain score on a standardized assessment. In practice, most people use the term symptoms to refer to both symptoms and signs. Some common types of symptoms can be classified as positive or negative. Positive symptoms, which can be thought of as being in addition to typical behavior (positive or present), include such things as delusions (unreal beliefs maintained despite evidence, not accepted in one's culture), hallucinations (perceptions of the senses without external stimuli), bizarre behavior, gestures (motions of the body to express thoughts or emotions), and posturing. Negative symptoms, which can be thought of as reflecting a lack of something (negative or absent), include social withdrawal, poverty of thought or speech (difficulty producing thoughts or speech), blunted or flat affect, and anhedonia (loss of or lack of pleasure). Another way to understand symptoms is in the nature of symptoms; that is whether they are by nature affective (emotions or how we feel), behavioral (actions or how we behave), or cognitive (thoughts or how we think).

In the United States, this medical model of mental health conditions has dominated the mental health field represented by the prominence of the *Diagnostic and Statistical Manual of Mental Disorders,* currently in its fourth edition with a text revision (APA, 2000), which was developed by psychiatrists and other experts in the American Psychiatric Association (APA). This classification system of mental and emotional disorders, along with its international counterpart, the *International Classification of Diseases* (WHO, 2004) is based on a medical model perspective of health and disease (WHO, 2001). A medical approach focuses on the injury, illness, disease, or disorder; examines the pathology or impairments in the body that are affected by the illness, and prescribes treatment interventions to reduce or eliminate the symptoms, signs, and discomfort or distress of an illness to improve psychological functioning. In mental health treatment, the most common interventions are psychotropic medications and psychotherapy.

The psychiatric diagnoses that are considered the most severe, incurring high treatment costs and cited most often as those contributing to psychiatric disability, include schizophrenia and schizoaffective disorder, bipolar disorder, major depression, some anxiety disorders, and borderline personality disorder (Goldman, Gattozzi, & Taube, 1981). The prevalence rate of severe mental health conditions that result in functional impairment that substantially limit one or more major life activities (i.e., one definition of psychiatric disability) is close to 6% (Kessler et al., 2005). Long-term, episodic, and unpredictable fluctuations in symptoms of these conditions may contribute to variability in functioning in work, school, and other community roles (Baron & Salzer, 2000; Cook & Razzano, 2000; Strauss, Hafez, Lieberman, & Harding, 1985). However, while treatments may be effective in reducing symptoms and distress, they typically have not resulted in improvements in work functioning, educational achievement, or community integration (Anthony et al., 2002; MacDonald-Wilson & Nemec, 2005).

The Disability Perspective

Psychiatric disabilities occur when a mental health condition interferes with a person's functioning in living, learning, working, and/or managing social environments and roles (Anthony, Cohen, Farkas, & Gagne, 2002). How disability is defined varies by the services and systems organized to support people with disabilities. For example, the Americans with Disabilities Act (ADA), a federal law that prohibits discrimination against people with disabilities, defines disability as "a physical or mental impairment that substantially limits one or more major life activities of such individual," "a record of such an impairment," or "being regarded as having such an impairment." Recent amendments to the ADA have resulted in a broadening of the definition so that certain medical conditions are now presumed to be disabling along with a number of psychiatric diagnoses (ADA, 1990; ADA Amendments Act, 2008). The Social Security Administration, a U.S. federal agency that provides retirement and disability income benefits, defines disability strictly under the Social Security Act as "the inability to engage in any substantial gainful activity by reason of any medically determinable physical or mental impairment which can be expected to result in death or which has lasted or can be expected to last for a continuous period of no less than 12 months." (Social Security Act, Section 223d1).

The Social Security Administration definition focuses specifically on the inability to work (substantial gainful activity) while the ADA definition focuses on difficulties in performing tasks and activities and in some cases, focuses specifically on the medical impairment. People disabled by a mental health condition account for more than 35% of working-age adults receiving SSI (Danziger, Frank, & Meara, 2009) and for 28% receiving SSDI (Social Security Administration, 2011). Psychiatric disability is the primary disabling condition for 20% of the people who receive services from the State-Federal vocational rehabilitation (VR) program (Hayward & Schmidt-Davis, 2003).

In psychiatric rehabilitation, the term psychiatric disability is used in preference to the term mental illness, as recommended by the *Language Guidelines* of the Psychiatric Rehabilitation Association (PRA, 2003). The concept of disability is seen as more relevant to rehabilitation than is the concept of illness and implies the hope of reacquiring abilities and valued roles and the "regeneration of ability through rehabilitation. Terms focusing on illness, disorder, and diagnosis reflect a medical model rather than a rehabilitation perspective" (USPRA, 2003, p. 2) and emphasize symptoms and pathology over functioning and role achievement.

The Bio-Psycho-Social Perspective

The World Health Organization (WHO, 2001) has described a framework for understanding health, functioning, and disability that considers the interaction of the health condition, the environment, and personal characteristics and their impact on functioning. The *International Classification of Functioning, Disability and Health* (ICF) is a bio-psycho-social model that emphasizes functioning and participation in community and society (WHO, 2001). The health condition is seen as interacting with environmental and personal factors to affect an individual's functioning at the level of body functions and structures, in performance of daily activities, and in participation in valued roles and life domains. The ICF model moves beyond a focus on impairments and symptomatology and allows for a description of performance of activities and participation in life situations. The ICF provides a way of conceptualizing the major areas of functioning that may be affected by a mental health condition.

Body Structure and Functions: This component of the ICF model details a number of functions related to systems of the body. A complete list is available on the ICF website (http://www.who.int/classifications/icf/en). Some of the affective, behavioral, and cognitive functions that research indicates are affected by mental health conditions (MacDonald-Wilson & Nemec, 2005; Peterson, 2011) are:

- Affective functions: wxperience, expression, range, and regulation of affect
- Behavioral functions: energy and drive (energy level, motivation, and impulse control), sleep and appetites (sexual, food, drink, and substances), psychomotor functions
- Cognitive functions: experience of self and time, attention/concentration, memory, perception, and executive functions (abstracting, organizing and planning, managing time, solving problems, shifting mental set judgment, and ability to process information quickly, accurately, and consistently)

Activities and Participation: Specific behaviors, tasks, and skills that build on these mental functions, especially interpersonal and cognitive skills, are found under the *Activities and Participation* section of the ICF. Some examples of activities that may be affected by a mental health condition include:

- Learning and applying knowledge, such as listening, acquiring skills, solving problems
- General tasks and demands, such as undertaking multiple tasks, carrying out a daily routine
- Communication, including speaking, producing nonverbal messages, and conversation
- Interpersonal interactions and relationships, such as showing warmth, responding to basic cues, initiating and terminating relationships, maintaining social space, and other relationships such as social, family, or intimate relationships
- Self-care, mobility, and domestic life, including caring for body parts, using transportation, preparation of meals, doing housework, assisting others

Mental health conditions may also have an impact on participation in various life domains and in valued social roles such as student/trainee, worker, resident/tenant/homeowner, parent, spouse/partner, friend, and citizen—all of which can be a particular focus of psychiatric rehabilitation. Some of these domains and roles are more fully described in the ICF, along with

- Major life areas, such as education, employment, economic self-sufficiency
- Community, social, and civic life, including recreation and leisure, religion and spirituality, citizenship

In any of these areas of function, the rehabilitation questions of particular interest are what the person can do, what the person does do, and what skills and supports are required to enable the person to do what s/he needs and wants to do (MacDonald-Wilson & Nemec, 2005). A focus on the strengths of the person relative to her chosen environments and roles can be accomplished by asking the first two questions. To answer the third question, interventions can be selected that emphasize things that can be changed in the person to improve performance (skills), and things that can be changed in the environment to improve performance (supports). Assessment in rehabilitation does not emphasize pathology, symptoms, or what is wrong with the individual, but emphasizes the capabilities and capacities of the person. In psychiatric rehabilitation, assessment also includes a look at the environment or context, and not just the individual. The ICF model details some of the environmental factors that are important to consider.

Environmental factors clearly play a role as facilitators and barriers of functioning of the person. Some examples of environmental factors that are particularly important for people with mental health conditions include the following:

- Services, Systems, and Policies, including housing, legal, health, social security, education, and medical policies, regulations, and funding streams
- Products and Technology, such as food, medicines, transportation, communication
- Natural and Built Environments, including climate, light, sound
- Support and Relationships, such as family, friends, neighbors, and professionals
- Attitudes, including those of family, friends, professionals, employers, and society

Supports and relationships are often cited as key facilitators of recovery by people writing about their experience with psychiatric disabilities (see, e.g., Deegan, 1998; Kramer & Gagne, 1997). Poverty can present a barrier to success in education, employment, and independent living (Cook, 2006). Negative societal attitudes towards people with psychiatric disabilities also create barriers to participation in community life (Burt & Aron, 2003; Corrigan & Kleinlein, 2005; Reidy, 1993; Wahl, 1999), contribute to the internalized stigma that lowers self-esteem (Corrigan & Kleinlein, 2005; Link, Struening, Neese-Todd, Asmussen, & Phelan, 2001), reduce self-efficacy, and reduce willingness to seek help (Corrigan & Kleinlein, 2005; Sirey, Bruce, Alexopoulos, Perlick, Friedman, & Meyers, 2001).

Lack of adequate services, limited integration between mental health and vocational rehabilitation systems, and policies that create disincentives for independence all create significant barriers to successful community integration for people with psychiatric disabilities (Cook, 2003; Salzer & Baron, 2006).

Certain aspects of the physical environment can create difficulties for people with psychiatric disabilities. For example, the high noise levels and bright lights often experienced when working in an office cubicle can cause problems with concentration for a worker (MacDonald-Wilson, 1997). Clearly, environmental factors play a significant role as facilitators or barriers to functioning for people with psychiatric disabilities. Interventions that focus on changing the environment, such as strengthening family support, ensuring collaboration between mental health and vocational rehabilitation providers, and providing academic accommodations can all support the person's ability to thrive in various life domains.

The current version of the ICF includes personal context, but does not describe these factors in detail. Personal context factors not only have a potential impact on functioning, but may help in developing an understanding of the person and the psychiatric disability. In facilitating recovery and rehabilitation, it is essential to understand the personal context of culture, personal beliefs, personal history and experiences, interests, and preferences. One's worldview may have a significant impact on functioning. For example, how one's culture values work or past negative experiences with authority figures may affect the person's interest in setting rehabilitation goals, identifying personal strengths, interacting with supervisors, or accepting supports.

In summary, the ICF (WHO, 2001) is a bio-psycho-social framework for understanding psychiatric disability that considers the whole person in the context of their environment.

The Social Perspective

This perspective sees psychiatric disability as the product of social and interpersonal factors rather than as a brain disorder or functional impairment. This social issue perspective encompasses a variety of ideas: that there is no such thing as a mental illness (Szasz, 1967), that psychiatric symptoms can be healthy responses to a dysfunctional world (Laing, 1967), or that what looks like illness often represents a method of surviving difficult times or coping with trauma (Giller, 1999). Some advocates believe that disability (and, to some extent, illness) is a socially defined construct; without the social context and definition, there would not be disability. For example, if you live in a society that does not use the written word, can you really have a reading disability such as dyslexia? What is disabling in one environment may not be disabling in another. For example, if I cannot hear spoken words, but everyone in my community uses sign language to communicate, I am not disabled by my lack of ability to hear spoken words (Sacks, 1989). If I live in a culture where hearing voices is considered a spiritual experience and people who hear voices are spiritual leaders, I am not prevented from achieving social status or an important role in my society because I hear voices. Since environment helps define disability, disability is a socially constructed concept.

Contrasting the Medical and Rehabilitation Perspectives

Psychiatric rehabilitation uses an approach that focuses on functioning and integrates the person, the health condition, and the environment to understand the psychiatric disability and to design interventions that will promote rehabilitation and recovery. One way of understanding the difference between the medical perspective and the rehabilitation/recovery perspective is to consider how differently services might assess and treat symptoms in contrast to assessing and improving function.

For example, the common signs and symptoms of schizophrenia emphasized in the medical perspective include delusions, hallucinations, disorganized speech, loss of drive, and social withdrawal or isolation. From a rehabilitation perspective, functional limitations and skill building become important, so assessment and interventions would focus on difficulties with processing information and sustaining attention; problems with decoding subtle social cues and/or social communication (Corrigan & Penn, 2001); and challenges with organizing, planning, and impulse control. Of course, these functional limitations are not exclusively evident in people diagnosed with schizophrenia; some may be relevant to some people diagnosed with depression, bipolar disorder, borderline personality disorder, or attention-deficit disorder. Psychiatric diagnosis alone does not provide the information needed for providing psychiatric rehabilitation services.

Perspective of a Person in Recovery

It's not a universal response to diagnosis, but many of us who have experienced life challenges felt a sense of relief when we were given a diagnosis. Somehow our difficulties seemed more acceptable when viewed as a consequence of disability. When presented in a non-stigmatizing way, a diagnosis can even feel validating and lead to a sense of hopefulness: "This mess I'm in makes sense to somebody, and there is something I can do about the future" is a very empowering belief. A diagnostic label can play a role in the development of a sense of affiliation with peers and can provide some comfort in discovering that "there are others like me."

On the other hand, many of us have not found diagnostic labels to be helpful in understanding our experience and have rejected them, even if we understood the need for a diagnosis to obtain necessary services or support. When a label is reinforced and becomes a permanent part of identity, it can be limiting and create long-term disadvantages. A system that is focused on the labels, rather than on the people it serves, is not prepared to provide services that expect recovery, such as early and assertive short-term support. The concept of chronic illness, and even of psychiatric disability, implies the need for life-long services—yet a belief in such a need can stand in the way of service providers recognizing and respecting the rights of people in recovery to drive their own care, communicate their priorities and needs, and work towards increased independence.

Whether accepting or rejecting the label of ill or disabled, an individual can be supported in gaining skills, making healthful life choices, and increasing a sense of self direction and independence. The way the individual is perceived by the service provider and the language used to communicate that perception are critical to the success of the service provider-service user relationship. Person-first and person-centered language, along with terms that are experiential and more temporary-sounding (less permanent), demonstrate recognition of the personhood of the service user, can contribute to a positive identity, and convey acceptance, respect, and hopefulness. The language of the service provider is critical in that it may be where someone using services learns to speak about his/her experience, shaping his/her perceptions of what is possible.

The experience of receiving a diagnosis of a disabling condition can also be devastating. An illness perspective can lead to an additional barrier to recovery when diagnosis becomes a blueprint for understanding self and experience. Seeing myself as a diagnosis, or even as an individual with a diagnosis, can influence what I expect of myself and limit my sense of possibility. This potential barrier is increased by service providers who interpret my everyday experience through the lens of my disability, but is decreased through a more normalized response to me as an individual. A strengths perspective requires the system not to just shift from seeing me as my diagnosis to seeing me as a person with a diagnosis, but to actually seeing me as a person of value—whole and entire.

Unlike a medical model, where there may be a perceived need to push for the diagnosed person to accept the label, conversations about increased wellness, improved skills, and moving toward what a person wants in life are not dependent on an individual's self-perception as disabled or diseased. A focus on skills and supports can lead service providers to acknowledge the person's understanding of his/her own experience and choice of language and to use experiential terms that imply a temporary condition, conveying hope and belief in recovery while communicating respect.

One value of a disability framework that goes beyond diagnosis is that it can lead to an understanding of the mental health condition and its signs and symptoms as barriers to leading the life the person wants. A focus on barriers leads to an exploration of the skills and supports needed to overcome those barriers. Recovery-focused conversations begin by developing an understanding of who the person is, of what is important to him or her, what s/he values, and what a better life would look like—these set the context for understanding barriers, but also move away from disability and toward using strengths to grow and develop. A focus on skill-building and other strategies to overcome barriers can even change an individual's perception of the disability diagnosis.

My perception of my diagnosis will be influenced by having professional supports who can imagine a positive future for me and who believe that I have the necessary strengths to build skills and supports to overcome the barriers created by my condition and my history. Similarly, my perception will be influenced by professionals who see my future as hopeless and my abilities as permanently restricted by my illness. Belief in and support for my recovery could provide a context that honors the discovery of my condition as a facet of myself and not as my core.

Entitlement systems and mental health services have been designed with a view of psychiatric disability as permanent. Accepting that a diagnosis will mean long-term or permanent disability has been integral to receiving support for many people who receive benefits and use psychiatric support services. Understandably, some family members and other advocates fight for the life-long services that they assume will be necessary. An expectation of increased well-being, self-direction, and improved skills can be seriously hampered by a belief that recovery and independence are not possible. While many people may need some sort of life-long support, either continuous or recurrent, the argument for long-term care options needs to include ways to make continuing progress towards increasing self-determination and independence.

Seeing an individual rather than a condition or disability broadens the definition of wellness. While diagnostic labels can lead to specialty services that treat conditions separately or consecutively, an integrated process or system is focused on the whole person. Well-being will be supported through offering services for recovery from substance use, mental health challenges, physical health and wellness, and the too-common experience of trauma. A single provider or a well-coordinated provider team not only coordinates care for different conditions, but needs to equip people in recovery with the skills necessary to drive their own care and to communicate their priorities and needs. The person using services needs to be seen as an active member of the team, needs to be included in collaborative treatment planning, and needs to be taught the skills of effective self-advocacy.

IMPLICATIONS FOR STAFF DEVELOPMENT

Like some people in recovery, many service providers find comfort in having a label that offers an explanation for a person's behavior and experience. Agencies, programs, and service systems find diagnostic categories a helpful way to define eligibility and to organize assessments, plans, and interventions. Shifting from a medical model to a disability-rehabilitation-recovery perspective requires a new way of viewing services and service users. The complexity of making that shift (often combined with a lack of local expertise) means that many service providers continue to employ a medical framework, even if a service system is driving change towards rehabilitation and recovery.

Service providers benefit from learning about a person's experience of a mental health condition and an understanding of how that condition creates a barrier to achieving valued social roles—that is, what is disabling for the person. Staff members need to develop the skills for creating a relationship that is close enough to allow for recovery conversations as well as the skills needed to explore the meaning of the diagnostic label for that person.

Practitioners who are responsible for assessments must learn to view disability and rehabilitation as identifying skills, knowledge, strengths, and needs for a person in recovery to move on in life, manage the condition, and be successful. Service providers working within a medically oriented system or program will need skills in communicating and balancing the illness framework with a focus on strengths and needs, functional limitations, and rehabilitation interventions.

Training is essential for creating the perspective shift (and practice shift) needed to provide rehabilitation- and recovery-oriented services, but training programs often duplicate the treatment mistake of not meeting people where they are. If a practitioner is in pre-contemplation (Prochaska, DiClemente, & Norcross, 1992) and does not recognize a need to change, then an action-oriented training program focused on techniques is likely to fall flat. Instead, training and other staff development activities may need to focus on gradually introducing the possibility of other frameworks, such as having people in recovery describe their own experiences and demonstrate that recovery can and does occur. Opportunities are needed for ongoing training, dialogue, implementation tools, technical assistance, and outcomes evaluation. Learning collaboratives (*Institute for Healthcare Improvement*, 2003) and communities of practice (Wenger, McDermott, & Snyder, 2003) offer a methodology for supporting needed systems change.

SUMMARY

The framework shift from mental illness to psychiatric disability and from treatment to rehabilitation creates a broader view of a person's hopes, goals, abilities, and needs, and a way to understand what skills and support the person needs to achieve valued social roles. Recently, the field of psychiatric rehabilitation is considering another framework shift—from disability and rehabilitation to a focus on achieving and maintaining wellness. We celebrate this shift with its positive and optimistic message. There is a question, then, about the value of understanding and operating through a disability framework.

The advantages of a disability framework include the guidance it provides for a detailed and integrated assessment of the whole person—the mental health condition, functional strengths and limitations, abilities and interests related to various life activities, and hopes and dreams for participating as a full member of a larger community and society. In addition, considerations of an individual's environmental and personal context give a deep understanding of what motivates, concerns, or limits an individual. Careful and detailed assessments can lead to specific objectives and relevant interventions.

The disadvantages of a disability framework (especially when compared with a wellness framework) is that it can be interpreted as pessimistic—too similar to the discouraging medical idea of permanent mental illness. Many people with a psychiatric diagnosis do not want to be considered as disabled, and in fact, many are not. The disability framework does not apply to all people with a psychiatric diagnosis, but rather to those people who are unable to fulfill their desired roles (worker, student, spouse/partner, friend, family member, or home owner) because their mental health conditions interact with their personal characteristics and the environment to create barriers to success.

As we see it, the idea of disability still has merit. It acknowledges ongoing challenges while recognizing that those challenges do not necessarily have to prevent a person from living, learning, and working in his/her community of choice. In addition, the disability framework opens the door for cross-disability advocacy where people with various conditions work together to create systems change, such as extending medical benefits to people with disabilities who are gainfully employed.

One framework does not need to fully replace another. For other populations, such as people with a spinal cord injury or Parkinson's Disease, medically focused treatment, rehabilitation, and whole-health wellness are addressed in a collaborative fashion. Service providers work together to refer people for medical interventions, physical rehabilitation, and education on self-care and wellness management. Psychiatric rehabilitation can be, but is not always, considered in a similar way—as a valuable approach to helping a person define and achieve his/her personal goals. That said, we also envision systems, services, and civil rights that do not focus on illness or disability, but on recovery and personhood—putting the person first and seeing the disability as part of the background.

BEST PRACTICE GUIDELINES

- Use person-first language whenever referring to people in recovery.
- Refer to the mental health condition or psychiatric disability only when relevant to the situation or context; otherwise, do not mention it.
- View the whole person (e.g., hopes and dreams of the person; roles, function, strengths, and needs; and environment, culture, and context) and how those different aspects may affect the person, especially when systems and program pressures focus on one aspect (health condition).
- Envision a positive future when working with the individual and significant others and share this hope regularly.
- Engage the individual in becoming the driver of the rehabilitation and recovery process, including assisting the person in developing the skills to direct their recovery journey and advocate for themselves.
- Focus on strengths when assessing needs and designing interventions, identifying skills, knowledge, resources, and characteristics that the person can use to manage their health, develop a direction, and build a life of meaning and purpose.

- Include the environment as an essential component of any assessment; the systems, physical environment, products and technology, family and social supports, internal and external stigma, culture and other context that may impact the person in their recovery

- Consider the contributions of treatment, rehabilitation, and recovery interventions in assisting a person in developing the domains of health, home, purpose, and community.

- Emphasize wellness and well-being by coordinating services for recovery from substance use, mental health challenges, physical health concerns, and trauma.

ABOUT THE AUTHORS

Kim MacDonald-Wilson, ScD, CRC, CPRP is the director of recovery and transformation for Community Care Behavioral Health. Her experience in providing and directing psychiatric rehabilitation services, teaching, training, and conducting research is informed by her personal and family experiences in recovery from and thriving with behavioral health conditions. With these experiences, Kim has developed expertise in partnering with people in recovery to develop the skills and supports needed to be successful and satisfied in chosen life roles.

Debbie Andersen lives in Frederick, Maryland. She is the executive director of On Our Own of Howard County Wellness and Recovery Center. Her experience of community support for her personal recovery created a passion for the development of programs based in peer relationships. She has professional experience working with youth, families, and adults in a variety of settings. In recent years she has consulted for the Centers of Excellence in Recovery Project of On Our Own Maryland and traveled extensively for the Copeland Center as a facilitator and trainer.

The authors would like to acknowledge the contributions of Anne Rea of Waystation in Frederick, Maryland, to an earlier version of this chapter.

REFERENCES

EDITORS' NOTE: References to *Diagnostic and Statistical Manual of Mental Disorders* in this chapter are based on the 4th edition of this publication. A revised 5th edition is now available. No substantive content changes are required in this chapter based on the new edition.

American Psychiatric Association. (2000). *Diagnostic and statistical manual of mental disorders* (4th ed., text revision). Washington, DC: Author.

American Psychiatric Association. (2013). *Diagnostic and statistical manual of mental disorders* (5th ed.) Arlington, VA: Author.

Americans with Disabilities Act of 1990, 42 U.S.C. § 12101 et seq.

Americans with Disabilities Amendments Act of 2008, 42 USCA § 12101 et seq.

Anthony, W. A. (2006). Foreword. In L. Davidson, C. Harding, & L. Spaniol. (Eds.). *Recovery from severe mental illnesses: Research evidence and implications for practice* (Volume 2, pp. xv-xvii). Boston, MA: Boston University Center for Psychiatric Rehabilitation.

Anthony, W. A., Cohen, M. R., Farkas, M., & Gagne, C. (2002). *Psychiatric rehabilitation* (2nd ed.). Boston, MA: Boston University Center for Psychiatric Rehabilitation.

Anthony, W. A., Cohen, M. R., & Nemec, P. B. (1987). Assessment in psychiatric rehabilitation. In B. Bolton (Ed.), *Handbook of measurement and evaluation in rehabilitation* (2nd ed., pp. 299-312). Baltimore, MD: Paul H. Brookes.

Baron, R., & Salzer, M. C. (2000). The career patterns of persons with serious mental illness: Generating a new vision of lifetime careers for those in recovery. *Psychiatric Rehabilitation Skills, 4*(1), 136-156.

Burt, M. R., & Aron, L. Y. (2003). Promoting Work among SSI/DI Beneficiaries with Serious Mental Illness. Retrieved January 22, 2005 from: http://www.socialsecurity.gov/work/panel/panel_documents/pdf_versions/Burt-Aron%20TTW-MI%20paper%20%20III%2010-03.pdf

Cook, J. A. (2006). Employment barriers for persons with psychiatric disabilities: A report for the President's New Freedom Commission. *Psychiatric Services, 57,* 1391-1405.

Cook, J. A., & Razzano, L. (2000). Vocational rehabilitation for persons with schizophrenia: Recent research and implications for practice. *Schizophrenia Bulletin, 26*(1), 87-203.

Corrigan, P. W., & Kleinlein, P. (2005). The impact of mental illness stigma. In P. W. Corrigan (Ed.), *On the stigma of mental illness: Practical strategies for research and social change* (pp. 11-44). Washington, DC: American Psychological Association.

Corrigan, P. W., & Penn, D. (2001). *Social cognition and schizophrenia.* Washington, DC: American Psychological Association.

Danziger, S., Frank, R. G., & Meara, E. (2009). Mental illness, work, and income support programs. *American Journal of Psychiatry, 166*(4), 398-404.

Davidson, L., Harding, C., & Spaniol, L. (2006). Preface. In L. Davidson, C. Harding, & L. Spaniol (Eds.), *Recovery from severe mental illnesses: Research evidence and implications for practice* (Volume 2, pp. xix-xxiii). Boston, MA: Boston University Center for Psychiatric Rehabilitation.

Deegan, P. (1988). Recovery: The lived experience of rehabilitation. *Psychosocial Rehabilitation Journal, 11*(4), 11-19.

Giller, E. (1999). *What is Psychological Trauma?* Retrieved from http://sidran.org/sub.cfm?contentid=88&sectionid=4

Goldman, H. H., Gattozzi, A. A., & Taube, C. A. (1981). Defining and counting the chronically mentally ill. *Hospital & Community Psychiatry, 32*(1), 21-27.

Hayward, B., & Schmidt-Davis, H. (2003). *Longitudinal Study of the Vocational Rehabilitation Services Program.* Retrieved February 2, 2004 from http://www.ed.gov/rschstat/eval/rehab/vr-final-report-2.pdf

IAPSRS. (2003). *Language Guidelines.* McLean, VA: Psychiatric Rehabilitation Association. Retrieved October 16, 2013 from http://www.psychrehabassociation.org/sites/default/files/images/PRA%20Language%20Guidelines.pdf

Institute for Healthcare Improvement. (2003). *The breakthrough series: IHI's collaborative model for achieving breakthrough improvement.* IHI Innovation Series white paper. Boston: Institute for Healthcare Improvement.

Kessler, R. C., Chiu, W. T., Demler, O., & Walters, E. E. (2005). Prevalence, Severity, and Comorbidity of Twelve-month DSM-IV Disorders in the National Comorbidity Survey Replication (NCS-R). *Archives of General Psychiatry, 62*(6), 593-602. Statistics retrieved January 18, 2012 from www.nimh.nih.gov/statistics/1ANYDIS_ADULT.shtml

Kramer, P. J., & Gagne, C. (1997). Barriers to recovery and empowerment for people with psychiatric disabilities. In L. Spaniol, C. Gagne, & M. Koehler (Eds.), *Psychological and social aspects of psychiatric disability* (pp. 467-476). Boston, MA: Boston University Center for Psychiatric Rehabilitation.

Laing, R. D. (1967). *The politics of experience and the bird of paradise.* Harmondsworth: Penguin.

Link, B. G., Struening, E. L., Neese-Todd, S., Asmussen, S., & Phelan, J. C. (2001). Stigma as a barrier to recovery: The consequences of stigma for the self-esteem of people with mental illnesses. *Psychiatric Services, 52,* 1621-1626.

MacDonald-Wilson, K. L. (1997). *Frequently asked questions about employees with psychiatric disabilities: Tips and resources on the ADA, job accommodations, and supervision.* Boston University Center for Psychiatric Rehabilitation, Boston, MA.

MacDonald-Wilson, K. L., & Nemec, P. B. (2005). The ICF in psychiatric rehabilitation. *Rehabilitation Education, 19*(2 & 3), 159-176.

MacDonald-Wilson, K., & Nemec, P. B. (2008). Assessment in psychiatric rehabilitation. In B. Bolton (Ed.). *Handbook of measurement and evaluation in rehabilitation* (4th ed., pp. 527-568). Baltimore, MD: Paul H. Brookes.

MacDonald-Wilson, K. L., Nemec, P. B., Anthony, W. A., & Cohen, M. R. (2001). Assessment in psychiatric rehabilitation. In B. Bolton (Ed.), *Handbook of measurement and evaluation in rehabilitation* (3rd ed., pp. 423-448). Baltimore, MD: Paul H. Brookes.

Peterson, D. (2011). *Psychological aspects of functioning, disability, and health.* New York: Springer Publishing Company.

President's New Freedom Commission on Mental Health. (2003). *Achieving the promise: Transforming mental health care in America, final report.* No. Pub. No. SMA-03-3832. Rockville, MD: U.S. Department of Health and Human Services.

Prochaska, J. O., DiClemente, C. C., & Norcross, J. C. (1992). In search of how people change: Applications to addictive behaviors. *The American Psychologist, 47*(9), 1102-14.

Reidy, D. (1993). *"Stigma is social death": Mental health consumer/survivors talk about stigma in their lives.* Unpublished manuscript, Holyoke, MA: Education for Community Initiatives.

Sacks, O. (1989). *Seeing voices.* New York: Vintage Books.

Salzer, M. S., & Baron, R. C. (2006). *Promoting community integration: Increasing the presence and participation of people with psychiatric and developmental disabilities in community life.* Philadelphia: University of Pennsylvania Collaborative on Community Integration. Retrieved from http:// tucollaborative.org/pdfs/Toolkits_Monographs_Guidebooks/community_inclusion/Increasing_the_ Presence_and_Participation_of_People_with_Psychiatric_Disabilities.pdf

Sirey, J. A., Bruce, M. L., Alexopoulos, G. S., Perlick, D. A., Friedman, S. J., & Meyers, B. S. (2001). Stigma as a barrier to recovery: Perceived stigma and patient-rated severity of illness as predictors of antidepressant drug adherence. *Psychiatric Services, 52,* 1615-1620.

Social Security Act, Section 223 (d) (1).

Social Security Administration. (2011). *Annual statistical report on the Social Security Disability Insurance Program.* Retrieved from http://www.ssa.gov/policy/docs/statcomps/di_asr/2011/charts-text. html#chart6

Stein, D. J., Phillips, D., Bolton, K. W., Fulford, M., Sadler, J. Z., & Kendler, K. S. (2010). What is a mental/psychiatric disorder? From DSM-IV to DSM-V. *Psychological Medicine, 40*(11), 1759-1765.

Strauss, J., Hafez, H., Liberman, R., & Harding, C. (1985). The course of psychiatric disorder: III. Longitudinal principles. *American Journal of Psychiatry, 142*(3), 289-296.

Substance Abuse and Mental Health Services Administration (SAMHSA). (2011a). *SAMHSA's definition and guiding principles of recovery: Answering the call for feedback.* Retrieved January 4, 2012 from http://blog.samhsa.gov/2011/12/22/ samhsas-definition-and-guiding-principles-of-recovery-answering-the-call-for-feedback

Substance Abuse and Mental Health Services Administration (SAMHSA). (2011b). *Recovery support.* Retrieved January 4, 2012 from http://www.samhsa.gov/recovery

Szasz, T. (1967). *The myth of mental illness.* New York: Harper & Row.

U.S. Department of Health and Human Services. (1999). *Mental health: A report of the Surgeon General.* Rockville, MD: USDHHS. Retrieved from http://www.surgeongeneral.gov/library/reports

Wahl, O. F. (1999). Mental health consumers' experience of stigma. *Schizophrenia Bulletin, 25,* 3, 467-78.

Wenger, E., McDermott, R., & Snyder, W. M. (2003). *Cultivating communities of practice: A guide to managing knowledge.* Cambridge, MA: Harvard Business School Press.

World Health Organization (WHO). (2001). *International Classification of Functioning, Disability and Health.* Geneva: Author.

World Health Organization (WHO). (2004). *International Statistical Classification of Diseases and Health-Related Problems: ICD-10* (2nd ed.). Geneva: Author.

CHAPTER 3

PSYCHIATRIC REHABILITATION PRACTITIONER COMPETENCIES

Beth C. Stoneking
Aaron Dion Foster

ABSTRACT

This chapter describes the rationale behind the need for the Certified Psychiatric Rehabilitation Practitioner credential (CPRP) and certification in psychiatric rehabilitation (PsyR), the psychometric process used to construct the CPRP credentialing exam, and a cursory review of the CPRP practice domains that form the basis for the exam. While a certification program is an important step in professionalizing the psychiatric rehabilitation workforce, it is not enough. The chapter presents best practice guidelines for workforce development, including pre-service academic preparation, on-the-job training, and supervision. Examples of state-of-the-art implementation of the CPRP credential are also provided.

HOW WELL WE, AS HUMAN BEINGS, FUNCTION HAS EVERYTHING TO DO WITH HOW WELL WE MANAGE and how effective we are when we approach the multiple tasks that life demands. Psychiatric rehabilitation (PsyR) is about enhancing function and supporting individuals with psychiatric and co-occurring substance use disorders in living, learning, working, and being social members of their communities. When practitioners do this, in partnership with the people they serve, then the likelihood of achieving each individual's desired outcomes is greatly increased. The connection we make with each individual and the skills we use in assisting people as psychiatric rehabilitation practitioners *is* our work, and the relationship we form is our best tool. Practitioners vary in their ability to provide support and build effective relationships. Quality services require a quality workforce. "Less competent providers are less likely to provide quality services, and healthcare providers must have the competencies necessary to perform their jobs according to standards in order to provide quality services" (Kak, Burkhalter, & Cooper, 2001, p. 3). People with psychiatric disabilities deserve service providers who have the knowledge, skills, personal qualities, and attitudes that allow them to competently deliver psychiatric rehabilitation services.

COMPETENCIES DEFINED AND DESCRIBED

"A competency is the ability to apply or use knowledge, skills, attitudes, and personal characteristics to successfully perform critical work tasks, specific functions, or operate in a given role or position" (Ennis, 2008, p. 4). Competence, in professional terms, refers to an acceptable level of performance of various competencies, often labeled as KSAs—the knowledge, skills, and attitudes required to do a job well. Personal characteristics (e.g., beliefs, values, and traits), communication, mutual respect, and ethnically or culturally learned habits and assumptions may have a positive and/or negative impact on a practitioner's service delivery. Many of these personal characteristics are familial, cultural, economic, and/or socio-political in origin; others develop through lived experience. Some can be considered more of an inherent trait or ability that is difficult to develop or change; others can be learned or unlearned.

Defining work success in terms of competencies began in the early 1970s when McClelland (1973) posited that traditional intelligence testing was inadequate and espoused, instead, a multi-method, multi-trait, criterion-based method that assesses and groups competencies related to personal and vocational roles (p. 9). For the purposes of this chapter, we will use the words competency (singular) and competencies (plural) to denote those behavioral, attitudinal, and performance-based components of knowledge, skills, and attitudes (KSA) as they relate to the practice and ethos of psychiatric rehabilitation.

One competency model, developed by the U.S. Department of Labor (2011), groups nine tiers of work KSAs into three competency blocks: foundational, industry-related, and occupation-related. Foundational competencies can be generalized to a wide variety of industries and are considered to be core competencies. The three tiers within this competency block are basic workplace skills, basic academic skills, and the personal effectiveness skills often called soft skills, such as interpersonal communication. The next block up in the model is comprised of industry-specific and industry-wide technical competencies, and the top block contains the technical, theoretical, and managerial KSAs needed for a particular occupation or job. This tiered model can be beneficial in differentiating competencies that apply to all workers (foundational), those that apply to workers in behavioral health (industry-specific), and those that apply to the PsyR workforce in general (occupation-specific) or to a particular job role within PsyR.

In 2007, the Annapolis Coalition generated the *Action Plan for Behavioral Health Workforce Development* report (Stuart, Hoge, Morris, Adams, & Daniels, 2009), based on input from over 5,000 stakeholders, and found the behavioral healthcare workforce to be lacking in the knowledge and skills needed to implement resilience-focused, recovery-oriented, culturally competent services. The call for competency-based training, for both pre-service and incumbent workers, has been echoed by other experts (Aubry, Flynn, Gerber, & Dostaler, 2005; Chow, Cichocki, & Leff, 2009; Clasen, Meyer, Brum, Mase, & Cauley, 2003; Corrigan, Steiner, McCracken, Blaser, & Barr, 2001; Hoge et al., 2005).

At the direct-service and provider agency levels, an array of concerns and barriers impede competency-based workforce development, including, but not limited to stress and burn-out in incumbent workers; lack of formal training through academic pre-service education; training on the job that is not adherent to evidence-based practices or principles; lack of reciprocal understanding of psychiatric rehabilitation (PsyR) approaches, leading to the development of poorly coordinated support teams; inadequately constructed curriculum design at the academic and provider-training levels; and training that reflects archaic, rather than empirical, traditions (Chow & Cichocki, 2009).

Like the behavior change process for individuals, change within service systems, organizations, and individual practice requires motivation, support, and time. This behavior change process becomes increasingly complex when looking at the heterogeneous composition of the PsyR workforce.

The PsyR Workforce

Outlining required workforce competencies presents a challenge as qualifications of workers in the PsyR field are varied and new job roles and responsibilities have been (and are being) developed for which practitioners were not trained. Advocacy, outreach, and education are vital to the promotion of PsyR principles and values, yet are only minimally included in conventional training curricula, if at all. The face of the PsyR workforce is changing also as more individuals from other health-related disciplines enter and remain in the psychiatric rehabilitation field and as job roles evolve. The most visible newly emergent group of practitioners is peer support specialists or peer providers, who self-identify as living with psychiatric and/or substance use disorders and are trained to assist others in their recovery through a variety of programs.

The rich tapestry of training and experience in the PsyR workforce means that people from various professional disciplines may perform similar or identical tasks. Some consistency across job roles within PsyR suggests common knowledge and skills. Social workers, rehabilitation counselors, occupational therapists, and psychiatric nurses may all meet the requirements for any single job description in this field. While many disciplines are represented in the PsyR workforce, rarely do we find one that includes a focus on psychiatric disabilities in their academic pre-service curricula standards, and when we do, it is often inadequate and contradictory to the strengths-based, function-focused work of PsyR.

There is a need for academic and discipline-based training in recovery-oriented rehabilitation principles, and this is being explored through the federally funded curriculum development project *Recovery to Practice* (Development Services Group Inc., n.d.) as is the introduction of experiential training at the undergraduate and graduate levels (Reddy,

Spaulding, Jansen, Menditto, & Pickett, 2010). Knowledge-based curricula are used in many current academic training programs although a competency-based curriculum better serves the needs of the PsyR profession.

Best Practices in Workforce Development

As noted earlier in this chapter, defining workforce competencies is important to delivering quality services for people living with mental health concerns; yet, beyond defining competencies, there is the task of building a workforce ready to deliver these services. Pre-service preparation, on-the-job training, and supervision of the PsyR workforce are all important components of implementing service delivery based on best practices.

Pre-service preparation

There is a dearth of PsyR educational options in the United States. Though some programs offer PsyR content within the existing curriculum, a focused track is rarely found. One problem often encountered in academia is that strict discipline-specific accreditation requirements dictate what courses must be offered. However, this issue can be overcome through integrating new content into existing courses, offering specialization courses, and designing targeted assignments and practicum experiences (Farkas & Anthony, 2001; Farkas & Anthony, 1993; Farkas, O'Brien, & Nemec, 1988). The University of Medicine and Dentistry of New Jersey has used a different approach and offers bachelors, masters, and doctoral degrees specifically in psychiatric rehabilitation (Gill & Barrett, 2009). The increasing volume of research on and implementation of evidence-based best PsyR practices should provide educators with impetus for curriculum change to educators in the rehabilitation and behavioral health fields.

The Consortium of PsyR Educators was established in 1993 by committed academic educators in order to develop and advance pre-service education in PsyR (Barrett, 2004). The Consortium meets twice annually to exchange ideas, curricula, and training materials to promote and develop educational standards and degree-granting programs in PsyR.

On-the-job training

Since few newly hired workers arrive with a strong background in PsyR, on-the-job training becomes essential:

> [T]he most intensive workforce training is directed at occupations that comprise professional practitioners—only 18 percent of the mental health workforce—whereas the least intensive training is given to direct care, non-professional occupations, that comprise at least 46 percent of the workforce. This analysis is consistent with other research, showing that direct care personnel without advanced professional degrees comprise 40 percent of care staff in mental health organizations, and more than 60 percent of client care staff in state and county psychiatric hospitals. (Leff et al., 2007, p. 7)

Given the large numbers of service providers without a formal academic education and the inadequacy of many academic pre-service programs on-the-job training is critical for introducing PsyR and building skills for effective practice.

Supervision

Supervision provides an opportunity for training, coaching for skill improvement, and performance evaluation. Training in supervision is needed—both generic training on supervision and specific training on how to support the use of any new intervention or approach being adopted (Leff, et al., 2007)—as supervisors are often promoted from clinical practice positions and lack formal instruction on supervision, leadership, or management. Trained supervisors possessing exceptional communication skills are essential in facilitating dialogue and building trust. This is especially important when conflict or resistance is encountered as conflict often leads to new ideas and a more productive environment when acknowledged without judgment.

Educational outreach, or academic detailing, is a focused education and support method designed to coach providers to change practice. The target audience is identified and approached by a knowledge expert who, using minimalist handouts and presentations, informs practitioners about research and current best practices (Nemec, 2011). By staying on topic, engendering trust, repeating the key message, and rewarding improvement on follow-up, academic detailing can prompt service providers to change how they operate. Change is never easy; getting to know the provider's needs and current practices makes the transition from outdated practices to recovery-oriented practices more fluid.

Credentialing

One way of ensuring that a practitioner provides consistent, competent, evidence-based, and quality service is through a credentialing process. Credentials are granted to institutions, programs, individuals, and organizations (Durley, 2005) that have met the stringent, focused educational guidelines set by the corresponding accrediting body. Employers use these credentials as earmarks of professionalism when screening potential employees while people using services often view a credential as a sign of the practitioner's dedication to the expected standards of his/her profession.

The credential most associated with professional practice in behavioral health is the discipline-based academic credential. The academic credential is granted to an individual who has completed coursework or a plan of study approved by a degree-granting institution. In addition, the graduate may have passed some sort of post-graduation assessment leading to certification or licensure. An academic degree is, essentially, a "curriculum-based certificate" (Durley, 2005, p. 6).

For the purpose of this chapter, we will be differentiating accreditation, certification, licensure, and registration. Accreditation often refers to the approval of an organization, such as a pre-service academic program (Nemec & Legere, 2008). Certification, in contrast, is granted to an individual by a non-governmental agency, whereas licensure and/or registration are granted to the individual by a government agency (Durley, 2005).

A practical example illustrates all of these credentials. The University of Arizona receives accreditation from the North Central Association of Colleges and Schools, The Higher Learning Commission—this is the institution level credential. The Rehabilitation Counseling program at the University of Arizona is accredited by the Council on Rehabilitation Education (CORE)—this is the program level. Successful completion of coursework, practicums, and internship leads to the academic credential of Master of Arts in Rehabilitation Counseling— this is the academic level. Successful completion of elective coursework in PsyR and immersion-oriented, independent studies leads to the academic certificate of Specialty/ Emphasis in Working with Individuals with Mental Illnesses—a second academic level. Individuals graduating from the program are eligible to sit for the comprehensive exam that leads to the credential known as Certified Rehabilitation Counselor (CRC) offered by the Commission on Rehabilitation Counselor Certification (CRCC)—this is an individual level exam-based credential. The nationally recognized CRC credential can then be used to apply for state licensure such as Licensed Mental Health Counselor (LMHC)—this is an individual level government-granted credential.

This example is typical of the levels of credentialing in various professional disciplines. In many long-standing and well-known accredited rehabilitation counseling programs, as with other disciplines, coursework in psychiatric rehabilitation is elective rather than a part of the core curriculum, leading to a specialty in working with individuals with psychiatric disabilities. Many academic programs in the various behavioral health disciplines lack coursework and content on PsyR. This deficiency may be addressed by updating national accreditation standards to reflect the evolving practice in behavioral health. This is taking place at the University of Arizona through restructuring of the program currently offered in the rehabilitation counseling department to include required PsyR coursework. However, academic training in PsyR, where it exists, does not ensure competency. For graduates who take and pass a discipline-specific certification exam, and perhaps, go on for licensure, employers and service users can be assured of basic competency and a well-rounded professional education, but have no evidence that the graduate has specific competencies in using a PsyR approach.

Other forms of "certificates" may be considered a part of the credentialing process. Knowledge- and curriculum-based certificates may only require completion of a certain number of hours of seat time in a training program. In contrast, professional certification assesses the KSAs of the participant (Institute for Credentialing Excellence, 2010) and is based on an analysis of competencies that are required for successful performance of job duties in a defined role. Credential maintenance also plays an important part in identifying quality practitioners in that recertification requires demonstration of continued competence in the form of continuing education.

THE CERTIFIED PSYCHIATRIC REHABILITATION CREDENTIAL

The PsyR field, as we currently know it, is made up of professionals and non-professionals with varied training and experience who often work together as teams. This interdisciplinary diversity and collaboration is a positive force in PsyR practice and creates cohesion in the overall care of the individual receiving services. To guarantee our stakeholders that PsyR practitioners possess the qualities required to deliver these services, we need a credential that ensures these practitioners are trained in the competencies vital to this unique field.

Before the creation of the Certified Psychiatric Rehabilitation Practitioner program, credentialing in psychiatric rehabilitation was determined through a voluntary registration process. The International Association of Psychiatric Rehabilitation Services, the predecessor of the Psychiatric Rehabilitation Association, was first established in 1975. In 1992, IAPSRS formed a training and certification committee to "develop standards of practice, a code of ethics, and training curriculum" (Hughes & Weinstein, 2000, p. vi). A study, funded by the National Institute of Disability and Rehabilitation Research, led to a statistical map systemically defining, for the first time, the competencies that PsyR practitioners need to deliver quality services (Hughes & Weinstein, 2000, p. vii).

IAPSRS started a registry for PsyR qualified practitioners in 1996. This voluntary registry was conceived and instituted in such a way that individuals from a diverse set of educational and experiential backgrounds would be included. Eligibility for the registration included four letters of recommendation focused on current and prior work in the field of PsyR, an experiential resume, two essays (one about ethical concerns faced by the applicant and how those were resolved), and a signed testament that the person agreed to apply the IAPSRS Code of Ethics in all aspects of practice. Individuals holding a Bachelor's degree or higher in a related field with work experience in psychiatric rehabilitation were credentialed as Registered Psychiatric Rehabilitation Practitioners (RPRPs) and those with a GED or high school diploma and experience working in the field of psychiatric rehabilitation were awarded the Associate Psychiatric Rehabilitation Practitioner (APRP) credential. The registry was eventually phased out, and the exam-based CPRP was developed and adopted as the new credential. RPRPs were allowed to apply to be grandparented into the new CPRP program, but applications to the registry were no longer accepted after 2001, and the registry was put to bed on June 30, 2005. An exam-based credential was chosen for its criterion-based validity and because test-based credentials are considered more legally defensible—an important element in protecting the stakeholders and the fidelity of the profession (Durley, 2005).

The Certification Commission of PRA was formed in 2002 by the board of directors, and continues today. The purpose of the Commission is to provide the governance, coordination, planning, and operation of the certification process and promote the welfare of people with psychiatric disabilities by establishing professional standards for those engaged in providing psychiatric rehabilitation services. The Commission collaborates with recognized education and research organizations and professional testing companies to maintain high standards of service and competency and stay abreast of new and promising practices in the field.

There are several key steps involved in creating a test-based credential: identification of job-related responsibilities, creation of a test blueprint, development and validation of the exam questions, assembly of the test, and deciding on a pass/fail scoring system (Henderson, 2001). The critical element in the process, from inception to implementation, is the role delineation study or job task analysis (Schroeder Measurement Technologies, n.d.). The job task analysis identifies the competencies that form the blueprint for the examination and ensures that the exam tests on the tasks and duties of a PsyR practitioner (USPRA, 2007). A job task analysis can be performed according to four formats: focus group, traditional survey-based, electronic survey-based, and/or transportability, which involves using other job task analysis results (Castle, 2003a). The results of the job task analysis become a list of domains and corresponding competencies that are used to generate exam questions. The domains allow for the grouping of related competencies so that test development is organized and fluid and represents the foundation for support of a specialized certification in the field.

The first job task analysis for the CPRP was conducted in 2001 by Columbia Assessment Services, now CASTLE, Worldwide, Inc. To ensure the test covered all facets reflected in PsyR practice settings, the psychometricians at CASTLE, under the oversight of Dr. Kenneth Gill, vice president of the PRA Certification Commission at the time and chair of the Psychiatric Rehabilitation Department at the University of Medicine and Dentistry of New Jersey, developed three stages for the job task analysis process (Gill, 2005). First, a role-delineation panel "identified the domains, tasks, knowledge, and skills essential" for a competent PsyR practitioner (Henderson, 2001, p. 1). This was followed by a review and validation of the panel's work by subject matter experts in PsyR. Finally, the findings from this review formed the test specifications for this exam. Questions were developed by expert PsyR practitioners and followed three basic patterns: knowledge, which involves recalling information from memory; application, which requires solving case-study situational problems; and analysis, which involves breaking down the material into its component parts to understand the organizational structure (Henderson, 2001). These exam questions were then reviewed by yet another set of expert PsyR practitioners and revised to guarantee they met the standards of importance, criticality, and relevance (Henderson, 2001). Questions were used for the CPRP exam only after an agreement was made that the questions met these three standards. A criterion-referenced method was then used to determine the passing point for the test. The initial test was composed of 150 multiple-choice items, and this format remains today.

In order for any assessment instrument to maintain its efficacy, it must be reviewed and updated on a regular basis (Institute for Credentialing Excellence, 2010). Industry standards suggest a job task analysis and subsequent content re-evaluation be performed every three to five years (Castle, 2003b). To this end, a new job task analysis for the CPRP was performed in 2007 by Schroeder Measurement Technologies with similar domains and competencies identified and an expansion in the seventh domain for cultural competency, resulting in the competencies outlined in the CPRP blueprint today. As of this writing, a third job task analysis is underway, expected to be completed in 2013.

The CPRP competencies

This section provides a brief overview of the CPRP domains and offers a summary of the corresponding competencies. For the purposes of this discussion, the competencies have been divided into two categories—KSAs, which include interpersonal competencies, professional role competencies, community integration, and diversity and cultural competency; and Practice Domains that seem most related to practitioner actions specific to service delivery, which include assessment, planning, and outcomes); interventions for goal achievement; and systems competencies.

Knowledge, skills, and attitudes (KSA)

All of us communicate in varying ways according to our world view; the way we communicate with others in our environment can impact the quality of our life and the lives of those with whom we interact. As practitioners, we need to keep this in mind as we interact with individuals living with mental health conditions during both individual and group collaborations. Communication skills do not cover only spoken language; it is good to keep in mind that communication includes oral, physical, and written skills. The use of empowering, person-first, recovery-oriented language and behaviors becomes increasingly significant now that we are living in an electronic, global community where an email, social "tweet," or video can become viral overnight, and our thoughts, words, and/or actions may be seen by millions. We are free to speak as we wish, but as representatives of PRA and the PsyR profession, we do our best to practice the skill of person-first communication at all times. It is also our ethical obligation to model this behavior in that it follows the core principles and multicultural values of dignity, respect, advocacy, and empowerment. To this end, PRA has created a set of *Language Guidelines* (International Association of Psychosocial Rehabilitation Services, 2003) to help guide us in adhering, to the best of our abilities, to the principle of "person first."

Interpersonal competency takes on a more professional tone as we work to establish trusting, supporting, and empowering environments for assisting people in changing their lives and meeting their goals. Motivational interviewing skills, including active listening, reflecting, reframing, validation, unconditional acceptance (Miller & Rollnick, 2002), and Prochaska and DiClemente's stages of change (1986) become an important asset for the practitioner—not only for developing this trusting relationship, but also in helping the individuals we serve understand the concept of recovery, recognize their strengths, design their unique goals and objectives, and build a strong non-judgmental support system. These skills are used in both individualized and group settings, thereby necessitating some knowledge of group work on the part of the practitioner.

As with all professions, the PsyR practitioner gathers best-practice KSAs from a variety of sources including, but not limited to, the scholarly professional literature, professional meetings, other practitioners, lived experience, and program observation. A practitioner needs to know where to access relevant information, how to interpret the information, and when to put it into practice. The PsyR profession has practitioners who hail from diverse disciplines, and this works in our favor as we can call upon a variety of learning models when professional advice is needed.

The most used "advice engine" for many health services professions is its own code of ethics, and PRA adopted a code of ethics more than a decade ago (International Association of Psychosocial Rehabilitation Services, 2001), which was last revised in 2012. It is not only vital that we are aware of the content of our code of ethics, but that we apply these guidelines in our professional lives, and when we encounter a dilemma, we should call upon those who have expertise in this area. More than any other document, the code of ethics guides our actions and reactions as they apply to our professional growth, PsyR practice, and collegial and social relationships. Professional growth encompasses more than just continuing education in the field of PsyR. Practitioners need to maintain personal health and well-being to avoid compassion fatigue and occupational burn-out.

Community integration is a PsyR competency area that challenges us to develop our networking skills and build collegial relationships with other organizations delivering services for individuals with mental health concerns. Practitioners delivering PsyR services in the field understand how critical this networking is in attaining stable support systems within the fractured health care delivery system. It is of vital importance that the practitioner acquires knowledge of both system resources and natural indigenous community resources. The acquisition of this knowledge is just the first step, which must be followed by integrating access to these other resources into the holistic assessment and the individualized service plan.

Advocacy also plays a role in community integration. Developing effective negotiating skills will empower the practitioner to combat negative public attitudes, prejudice, and discrimination as well as to model the art of self-advocacy. Self-advocacy does not equate to going it alone. When self-advocacy is modeled correctly, the observer learns to put together a system of community advocacy supports that can be called into action when needed. This system may consist of a variety of advocacy models: peer-directed/run agencies, self-help groups, support programs, disability agencies, independent living centers, and grassroots organizations. It is not unheard of for grassroots operations to spring from an individual's lived experience, and we, the practitioners, can act as the watering system for that grassroots movement.

Our communications skills come into play in advocacy as well as in working with individuals since PsyR professionals are called upon to engage stakeholders in service-improvement dialogue. Not only is this dialogue necessary to the delivery and expansion of PsyR, it allows us the opportunity for service change and quality improvement. As with all dialogue, conflict can arise. Here, our communication skills serve us well as we mitigate the negative and promote the positive aspects of conflict resolution.

We must constantly challenge old and new concepts. Best practices must be researched, adapted, and sometimes abandoned. The practice of PsyR is fluid, and practitioners must be ready to change and adapt. In 2007, the CPRP exam blueprint changed with the addition of the new competency area of cultural competency. In this diverse society, it is necessary that the practitioner continues to challenge his or her worldview. The foremost challenge a practitioner must face is confronting any internalized prejudice. We do not advocate that anyone change his or her core beliefs; only that s/he become aware of them and of how those beliefs may influence any collaborative relationship. When we discover that we do have an internalized prejudice, then it is imperative to discuss this in supervision to avoid letting our values negatively influence our work. Personal and professional growth in this area must be ongoing.

Practice competencies

The KSAs form the foundation of the work of PsyR and make it possible to effectively deliver services. Interpersonal and professional role KSAs are needed to implement the practice competencies and deliver services with respect and dignity, creating an atmosphere where self-respect, self-esteem, and self-efficacy will flourish. Professional role competencies, knowledge and skill in community integration, and awareness and sensitivity to diversity and varied cultures are needed for collaborative development of person-centered and goal-oriented plans and interventions. These competencies also assist us in navigating the systems that deliver the services crucial to meet the individual's goals. The domains of assessment, planning and outcomes; interventions for goal achievement, and systems competencies are not simply "case management." As applied in PsyR, these competencies are used to support the recovery process through an egalitarian collaboration, and not to "manage" anyone.

No single individual or practitioner is able to accomplish putting all these KSAs together successfully every time. Just as the individuals we accompany on their recovery journey need support systems, so do practitioners. The effective practitioner needs a sound professional, emotional, social, spiritual, physical, and environmental support system of his or her own.

State recognition of the CPRP

As of this writing, the CPRP credential is recognized in 15 states in the U.S. by regulations defining and/or qualifying mental health practitioners: Arizona, Florida, Georgia, Hawaii, Idaho, Illinois, Iowa, Louisiana, Maine, Maryland, Minnesota, New Jersey, New York, Pennsylvania, and Virginia. Similar legislation or regulation is in progress in several others. These states have decided that individuals who have shown competency by passing the CPRP exam are better prepared to deliver quality psychiatric rehabilitation services to individuals with psychiatric and co-occurring substance use disorders, although there is no definitive research to date that demonstrates this. We are using Pennsylvania's adoption as an example in this chapter, and their standards are outlined below.

Pennsylvania ties the CPRP to staff qualifications to be met by a provider in order to be reimbursed for psychosocial services under Medicaid. The "staff qualifications" part of the program requirements section reads:

> At least 25% of all staff within each psychiatric rehabilitation program must be registered/ certified through the International Association of Psychosocial Rehabilitation Services

(IAPSRS) as psychiatric rehabilitation practitioners within a two-year timeframe of program start-up. (Commonwealth of Pennsylvania, 2001)

Pennsylvania, among the first to adopt legislation, is a good example of a state that both recognizes the importance of a competency-based workforce and allows staff who do not have their CPRP when hired the time to get the necessary training/education in PsyR to apply for the exam. During this time, new staff without the CPRP can also learn from observation and interaction with their peers who have their CPRP. As a result of these regulation and practices, Pennsylvania has a larger number of CPRPs than any other state. While the cost of credentialing all staff who deliver PsyR services to individuals is challenging with current program budgets and the economic trials in behavioral health funding, Pennsylvania continues to hold to the standards adopted, and the state office of Mental Health and Substance Abuse Services, in alliance with Drexel University College of Medicine, provide a PRA-approved CPRP training program (Commonwealth of Pennsylvania, 2010).

These standards recognize the necessity for competency and continued training, ensuring that the system of care, the PsyR workforce, and the individuals who use services are more likely to achieve successful outcomes overall. This is also a great benefit for PsyR service providers, service users, and family/natural supports to avoid compassion fatigue, maintain higher morale, and experience the benefits of the recovery and resiliency that competent, person-centered systems ultimately yield.

Looking to the Future

With each new role delineation study, the list of competencies for the CPRP is likely to change. For example, with the life expectancy rate for people living with mental illnesses being 25 years less than that of people without mental illnesses (Gill, Murphy, Zechner, Swarbrick, & Spagnolo, 2009), a holistic approach focused on wellness (Swarbrick, 2006) is becoming ever more present in the practice of psychiatric rehabilitation. Perhaps the wellness competency, currently included in the current interventions domain, will emerge as its own subset within this domain or claim a domain of its own. This also may occur for trauma-informed care (Substance Abuse and Mental Health Services Administration, 2011) and crisis alternatives to civil commitment (Bola, Lehtinen, Cullberg, & Ciompi, 2009; Greenfield, Stoneking, Humphreys, Sundby, & Bond, 2008; Mead, 2005).

Now is an opportune time for those states who have not yet adopted the CPRP in legislation or regulations to do so, ensuring that competent, credentialed staff will be in strategic positions. Pennsylvania is in the forefront of this movement, and in setting the minimum standards for delivery of PsyR services, the state requires that PsyR facilities follow PRA practices and values and requires the facility directors, along with 25% of their staff members, to be CPRP credentialed.

Expanding the number of CPRPs will increase the likelihood of recovery-oriented conversations in supervision and an exchange of rehabilitation-focused knowledge, techniques, and interventions at team meetings. As more states formally recognize the CPRP, accrediting bodies will acknowledge the need to make PsyR courses a mandatory part of the curriculum for getting bachelors, masters, and doctorates degrees in any behavioral health discipline.

Given that the Substance Abuse and Mental Health Services Administration has awarded millions of dollars to support systems transformation, states and service provider agencies are coming to recognize that recovery is not only possible, but it is probable when the treatment, rehabilitation, and support services provided are evidence-based, individualized, and recovery-oriented. The broader field of healthcare is struggling with the "new" ideas of person-centered care and shared decision-making—a perspective that has been endorsed and promoted through PsyR for over 35 years. Continued transformation will take time and will occur only through a knowledgeable and skilled workforce.

The structure and process of behavioral health services delivery in the U.S. is in flux as changes are likely to occur as healthcare reform is implemented. It is difficult to predict how PsyR will be included in the design of the medical homes where behavioral health services and medical care will be integrated. Such changes will demand new knowledge and skill while drawing on the currently identified practice domains and competencies for PsyR.

The need for ongoing training and credentialing of the PsyR workforce seems evident. We believe that widespread adoption of the CPRP, with a complementary foundation of training and supervision, would result in an increase in positive service outcomes, a reduction in service costs, and increased satisfaction for service users and service providers alike. Together, these changes would lead to the ultimate goal: a competent workforce that is highly dedicated, trained, and up to date on evidence-based and promising practices.

SUMMARY

The behavioral health field has rapidly evolved over the past century—from institutional-ization to community care; from a medical to a bio-psycho-social-spiritual model; from disease-oriented, population-wide treatment to holistic, individualized care; from a focus on symptoms to a focus on strengths; and from an emphasis on stabilization to an emphasis on improved functioning—leading to expanded roles and community integration for people with psychiatric disabilities. We now encourage individuals who have been "patients" or "clients" to move out of that role and return to work or school via supported employment and supported education. We now embrace individuals who have been using our services as they move into the new roles of peer specialists and colleagues and work as an integral part of a multidisciplinary team. During these transformations, the field has been populated by a diverse workforce with each discipline making unique advancements in the field. Behavioral health workers differ in education, training, experience, and cultural background. This hetero-geneity can be both a base of strength and an opportunity for growth and is reflected in the PsyR workforce. "The future of the [mental health] professions depends on whether they can summon the resolve to respond to their collective challenges, settle internecine conflicts, and develop appropriate plans for adapting to the trends shaping their future" (Substance Abuse and Mental Health Services Administration, 2011, p. 620). PsyR and the CPRP credential provide a model for interdisciplinary collaboration by recognizing a common foundation of knowledge, skills, and attitudes that indicates a unity of purpose and crosses the artificial boundaries of professional discipline.

People with psychiatric disabilities deserve competency and congruency in providers of treatment, rehabilitation, and support in order to achieve their individualized goals of recovery. One way of ensuring this consistency of care is through the development of a workforce that is dedicated to recovery principles and practices and actively engaged in individualized and systemic growth in the understanding and execution of present and emerging best practices.

BEST PRACTICE GUIDELINES FOR ENSURING
PSYR PRACTITIONER COMPETENCIES

• Focus on identifying and defining competencies needed for each job role, drawing on broader competency lists for human service workers, mental health service providers, and PsyR practitioners.

• Make academic pre-service education relevant through collaborative curriculum development that integrates accreditation requirements and the current needs of the field.

• Provide competency-based on-the-job training.

• Use supervisors with relevant training and experience to support ongoing knowledge and skills development for the workforce that is specific to PsyR.

• Require credentials that demonstrate achievement of the competencies actually needed for the job and support staff in gaining and maintaining those credentials.

ABOUT THE AUTHORS

Beth Stoneking, Ph.D., MSW, CPRP is a professor in the Department of Disabilities and Psychoeducational Studies at the University of Arizona. She has worked in the field of community behavioral health for over 25 years, spending 17 years in California prior to moving to Arizona in 1994 to work as the vice president of the Maricopa County Regional Behavioral Health Authority. Dr. Stoneking is a founding member of PRA's Certification Commission for the Certified Psychiatric Rehabilitation Practitioner (CPRP) certificate and served as secretary, treasurer, and chair of the Test Oversight Committee for nine years. Dr. Stoneking has her Ph.D. in both clinical and organizational psychology and a master's degree and license in clinical social work.

Aaron "Arrow" Foster, BS, CRSS is a senior instructional specialist at the Recovery through Integration, Support & Empowerment Recovery Support Specialist Institute Workforce Development Program at the University of Arizona, Family & Community Medicine, a graduate student in rehabilitation counseling, and a counseling intern. Mr. Foster held two large mental health awareness programs in 2007 and 2009, co-authored a chapter for PRA's new best practices manual, and assisted in the successful execution of two PsyR courses offered at the UA.

REFERENCES

Aubry, T. D., Flynn, R. J., Gerber, G., & Dostaler, T. (2005). Identifying the core competencies of community support providers working with people with psychiatric disabilities. *Psychiatric Rehabilitation Journal, 28*(4), 346-353.

Barrett, N. (2004). The psychiatric rehabilitation educators' group. *Recovery and Rehabilitation, 3*(2), 4.

Bola, J. R., Lehtinen, K., Cullberg, J., & Ciompi, L. (2009). Psychosocial treatment, antipsychotic postponement, and low-dose medication strategies in first-episode psychosis: A review of the literature. [Article]. *Psychosis, 1*(1), 4-18.

Castle, R. (2003a). *CLEAR pre-conference workshop testing essentials.* Paper presented at the The Council on Licensure, Enforcement and Regulation 23rd Annual Conference. Retrieved from http://www.smttest.com/web/resources/articles/Introduction%20to%20Job%20Analysis.pdf

Castle, R. (2003b). *Continuous job analysis.* Paper presented at the Association of Test Publishers Conference. Retrieved from http://www.smttest.com/web/resources/articles/Continuous%20Job%20Analysis.pdf

Chow, C. M., & Cichocki, B. (2009). The need for evidence-based training strategies. *Psychiatric Rehabilitation Journal, 33*(1), 62-65.

Chow, C. M., Cichocki, B., & Leff, H. S. (2009). The support for evidence-based training strategies. *Psychosocial Rehabilitation Journal, 33*(2), 156-159.

Clasen, C., Meyer, C., Brum, C., Mase, W., & Cauley, K. (2003). Development of the competency assessment tool: Mental health, an instrument to assess core competencies for mental health care workers. *Psychiatric Rehabilitation Journal, 27*(1), 10.

Commonwealth of Pennsylvania. (2001). *Psychiatric rehabilitation medical necessity criteria and standards.* Retrieved from http://paproviders.org/Pages/MH_Archive/PRS_Med_Neccesity_020801.pdf

Commonwealth of Pennsylvania. (2010). *Adults—recovery oriented services.* Retrieved from http://www.parecovery.org/stj/Adult_ROS.pdf

Corrigan, P. W., Steiner, L., McCracken, S. G., Blaser, B., & Barr, M. (2001). Strategies for disseminating evidence-based practices to staff who treat people with serious mental illness. *Psychiatric Services, 52*(12), 1598-1606.

Development Services Group Inc. (n.d.). Recovery to Practice—Project Overview. Retrieved from http://www2.dsgonline.com/rtp/RTP%20Overview.pdf

Durley, C. C. (2005). The NOCA Guide to Understanding Credentialing Concepts. Retrieved from http://www.credentialingexcellence.org/portals/0/CredentialingConcepts.pdf

Ennis, M. (2008). *Competency Models: A review of the literature and the role of the Employment and Training Administration (ETA). ETA Occasional Paper 2008-13.* Retrieved from http://wdr.doleta.gov/research/keyword.cfm?fuseaction=dsp_puListingDetails&pub_id=2395&mp=y&start=81&sort=2

Farkas, M., & Anthony, W. A. (2001). Overview of psychiatric rehabilitation education: Concepts of training and skill development. *Rehabilitation Education, 15*(2), 119-132.

Farkas, M. D., & Anthony, W. A. (1993). Rehabilitation case management research. In M. Harris & H. C. Bergman (Eds.), *Case management for mentally ill patients: Theory and practice* (pp. 119-141). Langhorne, PA England: Harwood Academic Publishers/Gordon.

Farkas, M. D., O'Brien, W. F., & Nemec, P. B. (1988). A graduate level curriculum in psychiatric rehabilitation: Filling a need. *Psychosocial Rehabilitation Journal, 12*(2), 53-66.

Gill, K. J. (2005). Experience is not always the best teacher: Lessons from the Certified Psychiatric Rehabilitation Practitioner Certification Program. *American Journal of Psychiatric Rehabilitation, 8*(2), 151-164.

Gill, K. J., & Barrett, N. M. (2009). Psychiatric rehabilitation: An emerging academic discipline. *The Israel Journal of Psychiatry and Related Sciences, 46*(2), 94-102.

Gill, K. J., Murphy, A. A., Zechner, M. R., Swarbrick, M., & Spagnolo, A. B. (2009). Co-morbid psychiatric and medical disorders: Challenges and strategies. *Journal of Rehabilitation, 75*(3), 32-40.

Greenfield, T. K., Stoneking, B. C., Humphreys, K., Sundby, E., & Bond, J. (2008). A randomized trial of a mental health consumer-managed alternative to civil commitment for acute psychiatric crisis. *American Journal of Community Psychology, 42*(1-2), 135-144.

Henderson, J. (2001). Development of the CPRP Examination: An Overview. Retrieved January 5, 2011 from http://www.mhrsla.org/providers/opendocument.asp?file=History_of_the_CPRP.pdf&Id=122

Hoge, M. A., Morris, J. A., Daniels, A. S., Huey, L. Y., Stuart, G. W., Adams, N., et al. (2005). Report of recommendations: The Annapolis Coalition Conference on behavioral health work force competencies. *Administration and Policy in Mental Health and Mental Health Services Research, 32*(5), 651-663.

Hughes, R., & Weinstein, D. (Eds.). (2000). *Best practices in psychosocial rehabilitation.* Columbia, MD: International Association of Psychosocial Rehabilitation Services.

Institute for Credentialing Excellence. (2010). Defining features of quality certification and assessment-based certificate programs. Retrieved from http://www.credentialingexcellence.org/d/do/71

International Association of Psychosocial Rehabilitation Services. (2001). Code of ethics for psychiatric rehabilitation practitioners. Retrieved from http://www.psychrehabassociation.org/sites/default/files/images/CPRP-Code_of_Ethics_REV.pdf

International Association of Psychosocial Rehabilitation Services. (2003). *2003 language guidelines.* Retrieved from http://www.psychrehabassociation.org/sites/default/files/images/PRA%20Language%20Guidelines.pdf

Kak, N., Burkhalter, B., & Cooper, M. A. (2001). Measuring the competence of healthcare providers. *Operations Research Issue Paper, 2*(1), 1-28. Retrieved from http://openstorage.gunadarma.ac.id/linux/docs/v01/DEC-USAID/Health-Population/Measuring-the-competence-of-healthcare-providers.pdf

Leff, H. S., Leff, J. A., Chow, C., Cichocki, B., Phillips, D., & Joseph, T. (2007). Evidence-based workforce development strategies for evidence-based practices in mental health. Retrieved from http://www.tecathsri.com.

McClelland, D. C. (1973). Testing for competence rather than for "intelligence." *American Psychologist, 28*(1), 1-14.

Mead, S. (2005). *Intentional peer support: An alternative approach.* United States: Author.

Miller, W. R., & Rollnick, S. (2002). *Motivational interviewing: Preparing people for change.* New York: Guilford Press.

Nemec, P., & Legere, L. (2008). Workforce credentials. *Psychiatric Rehabilitation Journal, 32*(2), 138-140.

Nemec, P. B. (2011). Education and training column: Academic detailing. *Psychiatric Rehabilitation Journal, 34*(3), 257-259.

PRA. (2009). PRA certification exam blueprint. Retrieved October 16, 2013 from http://www.psychrehabassociation.org/sites/default/files/images/2009CPRPExamBlueprint.pdf

Prochaska, J. O., & DiClemente, C. C. (1986). Toward a comprehensive model of change. In W. R. Miller & N. Heather (Eds.), *Treating addictive behaviors: Processes of change* (pp. 3-27). New York: Plenum Press.

Reddy, F., Spaulding, W. D., Jansen, M. A., Menditto, A. A., & Pickett, S. (2010). Psychologists' roles and opportunities in rehabilitation and recovery for serious mental illness: A survey of Council of University Directors of Clinical Psychology (CUDCP) clinical psychology training and doctoral education. *Training and Education in Professional Psychology, 4*(4), 254-263.

Schroeder Measurement Technologies. (n.d.). *Solutions through innovation: Job analysis/role delineation studies.* Retrieved from http://www.smttest.com/web/resources/infoSheets/Job%20Analysis.pdf

Stuart, G. W., Hoge, M. A., Morris, J. A., Adams, N., & Daniels, A. S. (2009). The Annapolis Coalition report on the behavioral health workforce needs of the United States. *International Journal of Mental Health, 38*(1), 46-60.

Substance Abuse and Mental Health Services Administration. (2011) The impact of trauma on wellness: Implications for comprehensive systems change. Retrieved from http://www.promoteacceptance.samhsa.gov/10by10/presentations/ImpactOfTrauma.pdf

Swarbrick, M. (2006). A wellness approach. *Psychiatric Rehabilitation Journal, 29*(4), 311-314.

U.S. Department of Labor. (2011). Competency model clearinghouse. Retrieved December 16, 2011 from http://www.careeronestop.org/competencymodel/default.aspx

RESEARCH, EVALUATION, AND EVIDENCE-BASED PRACTICES

E. Sally Rogers
Jonathan Delman

A B S T R A C T

This chapter examines the role of research in evaluating PsyR service models, processes, and outcomes and describes the importance of sound research methods and measurement of the outcomes of interest in psychiatric rehabilitation programs. New initiatives in the research world, including evidence-based practices (EBP), are highlighted. The chapter defines an EBP and enumerates prevailing approaches to designating evidence based practices and services. Initiatives to aggregate data for end users, providers, and other consumers of research and the importance of "knowledge translation" are offered. The chapter presents the critical importance of participatory approaches to research, particularly Participatory Action Research (PAR), and delineates and defines these approaches. Descriptions of how participatory approaches can be implemented in the world of psychiatric rehabilitation service are also provided.

RESEARCH AND PROGRAM EVALUATION INVOLVE THE GENERATION OF NEW KNOWLEDGE. IN THE PSYR field, that means gaining a better understanding of how the practitioners, program structures, or the organization and delivery of services affect the experiences and outcomes of the individuals served and how they affect the programs or systems themselves. While the terms evaluation and research are often used interchangeably, evaluation activities generally involve the study of existing services rather than the development and testing of an entirely new service or intervention, which is often the focus of research studies. In this chapter, we describe research and evaluation broadly and draw distinctions between them to help the reader understand how those respective initiatives may relate to their work in PsyR programs.

There are many "ways of knowing," such as through experience, intuition, or the knowledge that experts share through anecdotes. Research can be thought of as another "way of knowing" but one that is based on more systematic and rigorous methods. Systematic methods are needed for the generation of new knowledge, so we can improve on our practitioner intuition and our anecdotal understanding of problems. As stated by Kazdin (2003), "scientific research is essential for understanding natural phenomena and for making advances in knowledge. Although there are number of different research methods are available, they have in common careful observation and systematic evaluation" (p. 2). Program evaluation is yet another "way of knowing," and if done well, will allow you to draw conclusions about what would have happened if the program had not been available at all or if another program had occurred in its place (Fitzgibbon & Morris, 1987).

AN INTRODUCTION TO RESEARCH AND PROGRAM EVALUATION

In this section, we describe basic concepts relevant to research, how to frame a research question, important aspects of research design, how to improve the quality of research, and issues in conducting program evaluation.

Framing Research or Program Evaluation Questions

Despite the differences between research and program evaluation, they both generally begin with a clinical or service question that specifies what you want and need to study. Such questions help us to learn what "works for whom and how to get effective interventions implemented and sustained (NIMH, 2006, p.13).

Developing research questions

For the purposes of this chapter, we will consider the research or evaluation question to be the broad issue we are trying to address. From that broad question, we may develop working hypotheses (or best guesses) about how our services affect the outcomes of those with whom we work. These hypotheses must be "tested" in an evaluation or research study before we know if they can provide answers to our questions and inform the future direction of services. For example, broad research or evaluation questions might be: What work outcomes do people experience when they come to our employment services program? Why do people drop out of our programs? Are there services that we should consider providing that we don't provide? Do people have better outcomes when they receive a certain set of services rather than other sets?

For each of these initial and broad research or evaluation questions, we must clearly define or operationalize the exact question we are asking, specify the variables that are of interest, and then develop a research or evaluation plan that will allow us to draw reasonably valid conclusions about the questions.

Identifying independent and dependent variables

In developing a research or evaluation question, one of the very first tasks is to more clearly define the independent and dependent variables that are of interest. The independent variable is either the variable that is controlled or manipulated by the researcher/evaluator— sometimes this control occurs through actually changing something, at other times it is controlled statistically The dependent variable is the outcome of interest or the result of that independent variable. In a simple example, if I am interested in knowing the effect of active outreach to potential service recipients to their later engagement and retention in services, then "active outreach" is my independent variable. As a researcher/evaluator, I can control that variable or I can use it in analyses to examine its effect on outcomes. The dependent variables are the outcomes. In this example the outcomes are "engagement" and "retention" in services. Once identified, I need to operationalize the variables. For example, exactly what do I mean when I say "engagement in services"? Does this mean coming to the program once, twice, or five times? By "outreach" do I mean a combination of five phone calls or in-person visits to attempt to engage the person in services or some other combination of activities?

Specifying the research methods and designs

In this section, we detail the factors that can strengthen a research design. We begin with the notion that might seem evident, but is often not that obvious: It is critical to match the research design or evaluation plan to the question being addressed. There is no one design that is best for every research question. For example, we may be interested in addressing questions about the effects of services, or we may be interested in a more exploratory or descriptive question, such as the long-term outcomes of participating in self-help. In the first situation, we are asking an "effectiveness" question, and there are certain designs that are considered the "gold standard" in those circumstances. In the second case, we are interested in exploring and understanding a phenomenon, but not necessarily addressing a question of the effectiveness of an approach or service, and there are research designs better suited for such questions.

An additional and related consideration is the need to weigh the state of the knowledge about a particular problem, the feasibility of studying that problem with a particular design, and the meaningfulness of the results. A mismatch in any of these areas will not produce satisfactory results. For example, proposing a simple evaluation design to study a problem that is abundantly addressed in the professional literature will serve no purpose. Similarly, proposing a complex design that is beyond the ability of an organization to conduct will only lead to frustration. Finally, conducting a study that critical stakeholders don't consider important in the end will lead to a "so what" experience once the results are compiled.

In addition to balancing these three factors (the state of the existing knowledge, the feasibility of completing the study, and the meaningfulness of the results), we must be mindful of the large array of research and evaluation designs available to us. In selecting the design, it is important to consider the questions asked, the existing state of knowledge, and any issues that might affect the validity of the study.

Validity of research and evaluation

In designing a research or evaluation study, it is critical to address issues of internal and external validity. A study with a high level of internal validity is one in which there is reasonable certainty that the intervention being studied caused the outcome observed because all of the problems that "threaten" the internal validity of the study and all of the potential "confounders" have been well controlled. A confounder is a factor that the researcher may not be paying attention to that could undermine his or her conclusions. For example, in a study of the intensity of employment services and its relation to outcomes, the researcher may need to consider the contributions of age, gender, or education to understanding outcomes. Thus, the first task of a researcher involves both knowing what the potential confounders may be and accounting for or controlling them in the study to the extent possible.

Sources of invalidity that can threaten any study can also include: poor operationalization of the independent and dependent variables you want to study; poor instruments or assessment tools used in the study; a weak intervention or one that is poorly implemented; selection effects where the people you study are not representative of those you are interested in knowing about; a maturation effect in which the individuals being studied improve on their own (You might mistake that improvement as being due to your intervention.); and/or statistical problems where you mistake improvement for flaws or flukes in the statistical analysis. Experimenter bias can threaten a study when the evaluator or researcher does subtle or not so subtle things to make the results favor their prior hypotheses.

Some researchers use the "signal-to-noise ratio" analogy when referring to internal validity. If we have a strong intervention, delivered cleanly and well with the appropriate sample and measures, we can have a powerful signal. Noise is the potential confounders and other threats to internal validity. If we minimize the noise and maximize the signal, we can improve our study because the signal can be seen despite any noise.

External validity or generalizability

The question of external validity (also called generalizability) is whether our findings can be used to draw conclusions beyond the particular, local circumstances in the study. For example, findings of employment outcomes in New York City may not hold up in another geographic location, in another economy, or with another type of service user. There are steps researchers can take to improve the external validity of their research and evaluation activities, but first, the researcher must demonstrate internal validity.

Specifying study participants

In addition to potential threats to internal validity and issues related to generalizability, researchers will often specify inclusion and exclusion criteria for their study as a way of reducing confounding variables. For example, a study on employment services may focus on including adults between the ages of 18 and 65 who are not working and who are literate at a sixth grade level. The study also may want to exclude individuals who have difficulty understanding the implications of being in the study or anyone who is experiencing a high level of psychiatric symptoms. Generally, these inclusion and exclusion criteria are developed to strengthen the study by maximizing the chances for the experimental intervention to work, which will make the findings more interpretable.

Classification of research and evaluation approaches

As mentioned above, there are many schemes for classifying research and evaluation designs and these schemes are somewhat arbitrary (cf, Kazdin, 2003; Campbell & Stanley, 1963; Isaac & Michael, 1995). Four commonly used examples are:

- Correlational versus experimental
- Pre-experimental, quasi-experimental, experimental
- Qualitative versus quantitative
- Process versus outcome

Correlational versus experimental research: In experimental research, the researcher controls or "manipulates" an independent variable to see what the effect will be on a dependent variable. In contrast, correlational research simply explores (statistically or numerically) the relationship of these two variables but does not try to draw cause and effect conclusions. The drawback to correlational research is that one could argue that the correlation may be affected by other factors, and potentially confounding ones that muddy the waters.

Pre-experimental, quasi-experimental, and experimental research: These types of designs are often used when an effectiveness question is being addressed, for example, a question of whether service X is better than service Y in producing the outcomes we care about. Pre-experimental research designs (generally a pre-test and a post test of one group with no comparison group) do not have sufficient controls to make the conclusions very trustworthy, and the potential threats to internal validity are high. Experimental research designs are excellent for addressing questions about the effectiveness of services, provided they are well-executed. Often, experimental designs are referred to as randomized clinical trials (RCT) that involve randomly assigning study participants by chance to an experimental group or a control group. The control condition is often services-as-usual. This random assignment process generally ensures that the two groups are equivalent in all of the important factors that might have an effect on the outcomes and could threaten the internal validity of your study. For a new practice or intervention to have an evidence base, according to certain researchers, there must be two well-conducted randomized trials with unequivocal results for it to be designated an evidence-based practice (as described below).

We mention *quasi-experimental research designs* last because they can approach the quality and rigor of experimental designs, but generally do not involve random assignment of individuals to different groups or conditions. An example of when a quasi-experimental design might be useful is in examining mental health service use in two neighboring counties when there is every reason to believe (and you can demonstrate) that the two counties are not significantly different in terms of demographics, services available, economic base, etc. We could then introduce a new mental health service approach in one county and leave the other county's services as they were. By comparing these two apparently equivalent groups, we could test whether our new approach improves outcomes. A quasi-experimental research design hinges almost entirely on whether the researcher can demonstrate reasonable equivalence or comparability of the groups. If equivalence cannot be plausibly argued, it becomes an apples-to-oranges comparison, which poses many threats to internal validity.

Qualitative versus quantitative research: Quantitative research involves structured measurement and numbers or some other quantification of the constructs being studied. Qualitative research tends to involve less structured approaches such as conveying narratives, stories, or open-ended responses to questions. Qualitative research is a broad, umbrella term that can include a variety of approaches including ethnography, narrative analysis, and case studies. Qualitative research tends to be naturalistic and inductive in the sense that the researcher is searching for relationships among phenomena by exploring those relationships in an open-ended, "bottoms up" way. There is generally no testing of firm hypotheses as tends to be the case in quantitative research.

Many approaches to research now combine quantitative and qualitative approaches into what are referred to as "mixed methods" studies. These studies may come from a deductive, effectiveness testing, hypothesis-driven stance, but may also incorporate a qualitative component to find meaning in the results beyond the numbers and help point the researchers in new directions for needed research.

Process- versus outcome-focused research and evaluation: Studying process means focusing on the who, what, when, and how a service or intervention is delivered. Focusing on outcomes generally means examining the effect of that service or intervention for service recipients. The process of providing case management, for example, might be studied by looking at the activities the case manager engages in; the case manager's training and experience; the specifics of delivering the service, including where the service is delivered; the interactions of the case manager and the person being served; and the components of the intervention that appear to be helpful. All of these factors are important to understanding the process of case management service delivery, irrespective of the outcomes. In some studies, researchers want to link the processes studied to the outcomes experienced. While arbitrary distinctions can be made between process versus outcomes, in practice, evaluators and researchers are often interested in both in the same study.

Other common types of research/evaluation designs in PsyR include:

- *Needs assessment,* a category of program evaluation, is designed to learn more about the needs and wants of service users, possibly using surveys, case studies, and qualitative approaches.

- *Descriptive or exploratory studies* are designed to learn more about a phenomenon of interest, but not to address a question about the effectiveness of an intervention. For example, a researcher might ask how the recovery process differs for different individuals or how people experience receiving emergency services, or what are the various paths to vocational recovery are.

- *Survey research* involves structured sets of questions, largely quantitative in nature, designed to learn about a participant's attitudes, knowledge, and opinions relative to phenomena of interest. Surveys can be used to determine the needs of service users, for example, or their satisfaction with services and tend to be done only once in time. Occasionally, a panel survey will use the same group of individuals over time to ascertain changes in attitudes or other phenomena.

- *Archival/historical research* often relies on administrative or clinical records to collect data retrospectively (meaning back in time) rather than prospectively (as in a planned research study going forward). Archives or historical records can provide information about how people improve over time, what services they received, and what their circumstances were like when beginning a program or service. The quality of this type of research depends on the record keeping culture of an organization. When records or archives are not complete or accurate, the research or evaluation can be compromised.

- *Cost effectiveness studies* can be helpful to address questions of whether an intervention or service has a financial pay off in terms of dollars and cents in addition to recipient outcomes. Such studies often rely on administrative databases of costs and billing within an organization.

- *Case studies* generally focus on a small number of individuals (5-10 people is not uncommon) that allow the research to probe in depth about the phenomena of interest. For example, studying the effect of having a parent with a significant psychiatric condition on an adult child may lend itself to a case study approach. Case studies cannot address questions about the effectiveness of services or interventions, but sometimes can be helpful in determining how to better understand the results of an effectiveness study.

- *Participatory action research* (described below) is not a research design per se, but an approach to conducting studies with the full involvement of the individuals who can be affected by a research study.

Other considerations for selecting the research or evaluation approach

One important way to learn about which design or evaluation approach makes the most sense and which outcomes are most often studied is by examining the current research literature. For example, if you are interested in conducting a needs assessment about housing, it is important to learn from researchers in the field of residential services about what is already known, including finding instruments or surveys that have been used rather than creating a new instrument. In addition to being grounded in the existing professional literature, researchers and evaluators need to secure organizational support for their research and ensure that human subjects are adequately protected regarding their privacy and confidentiality.

Program Evaluation

Program evaluation generally consists of a set of methods and procedures to collect and interpret information about the effects of a program, a service, or a system in which those services or programs exist (cf, King, Morris & Fitzgibbon, 1987; Stecher & Davis, 1987). Although the terms research and program evaluation are used interchangeably, there is no pure distinction between them. They both rely on similar methods of observing, systematizing, collecting, and interpreting information to make judgments about the effects and value of a service, intervention, or program.

Distinctions between research and program evaluation

One important distinction between research and program evaluation is that the latter is done largely with "programs-in-action" in contrast to research studies, which more often focus on new interventions developed for the purpose of the study. Since a control or comparison group is not readily available in most program evaluations, the rigor and robustness of the findings and conclusions may not be as strong as a well-conducted research study. Though often considered less rigorous than research, results from program evaluation are intended to go beyond what we know on a case-by-case basis and gather systematic information on the program or services that can be useful in decision making for administrators, policy makers, providers, and end users.

Another distinction between evaluation and research relates to scope. Program evaluations are usually conducted locally within one agency or organization using funds from the service agency undertaking the evaluation. Research studies are largely funded by federal funding bodies or foundations.

Research projects tend to have a fairly high degree of standardization of the intervention being studied and the procedures used to conduct the study. In the past it was not uncommon to see research funded with little information about the details of an intervention (that is, "the who, what, when, where and how" for delivering the intervention). Now, research funds are rarely provided for studies where the intervention is not well-defined. Research studies strive to understand what intervention is delivered, for how long, and potentially, what particular aspects of the intervention seem to be leading to the outcomes seen (sometimes called the "mechanisms of action" or understanding why a service or intervention is beneficial). There has been a growing movement to understand the details of interventions and in some cases to manualize, or "unbundle" and otherwise open the so-called "black box" of the intervention.

Because program evaluation efforts often do not rely on federal funding, such standardization is not generally undertaken. Services are generally delivered "as usual" without an attempt to ensure that each person has the same amount of services, in the same order, or even of the same quality. While this is more reflective of "programs-in-action," it can lead to difficulties in understanding and parceling out the outcomes that are seen, whether neutral or positive.

Inclusion and exclusion criteria

As noted above, research studies generally specify inclusion and exclusion criteria, which may be necessary to strengthen the study but may limit how the findings can be generalized. In contrast, program evaluations typically include all individuals served by the program in the evaluation. This can make for some messiness in terms of confounding factors, but can also increase the generalizability of the findings because the sample of study participants is not as limited.

Measurement and attention to process

Program evaluation activities often use measurement that is less rigorous than research studies. Sometimes evaluators develop instruments for the purposes of their study, whereas researchers are likely to use established instruments with a high degree of validity and reliability that have been quality-tested and are able to detect actual change. In addition, use of a control or comparison group with random assignment is generally not an option in program evaluation initiatives.

Why conduct a program evaluation?

Program evaluation results can provide accountability of the organization to funding sources and accrediting bodies. Some organizations use program evaluation to improve the management of their organization either to achieve a particular goal or simply because improvement through information is a core value of the organization. Program evaluation can access the voice of the consumer and end user, which is an important value of PsyR. Through a program evaluation, providers of services can get feedback about how they are performing and how they are affecting the lives of individuals they serve. In short, well-conducted program evaluation initiatives can help to make a PSR program more knowledgeable about its own effects and thus more competent, and hence, more competitive.

Useful Program Evaluation Framework

A useful framework for conducting a program evaluation is proffered by King, Morris and Fitzgibbon (1987) who suggest that an evaluation can be focused on the program's inputs, outputs, processes, outcomes, and/or impact. Knowing which of these aspects of evaluation to target can help the evaluator design a useful evaluation. Another useful way of conceptualizing evaluations is whether the focus is primarily "formative" or "summative." A formative evaluation is used for the purposes of determining effectiveness of services expressly for the purpose of making changes to improve the program. A summative evaluation usually aims to make a statement about program effectiveness.

For example, an administrator might want to describe what human and financial resources are needed to run the program (inputs) and what services are delivered for those inputs (outputs). Documenting inputs and outputs is a prelude to other evaluation questions, but also is important in conducting outcome-focused evaluations. Outcomes include the effects of the program or the service on the people receiving services in terms of their living, learning, working, or social outcomes. In studying outcomes, it is important to match the goals and activities of the program and services to the outcomes being measured and to choose the best measurement or assessment of that outcome possible. Finally, studying the impact of PsyR services is useful, but frequently beyond the scope of a traditional program evaluator. Impact studies generally examine the societal effects of an intervention on large swaths of the population. Examples include studying the effects of the "Ticket to Work" initiative on employment rates in individuals with disabilities or studying the effects of welfare reform on parents and children who were recipients of services.

Considerations in Conducting a Program Evaluation

All of the factors and considerations that ensure internal and external validity for a research design are also important for a program evaluation, even if they are less feasible to implement. As with any research study, a program evaluation effort requires that the evaluator match the methodology with the questions being asked. For example, if an evaluator wants to document his or her outputs, he may need to use administrative and historical records, but learning how services affect a person's level of self-esteem will require a more rigorous prospective study with standardized instruments.

Well-defined questions and operational definitions of variables being studies are critical as is using the most reliable and valid instruments possible. It is also important to target the most appropriate sample of service recipients for the study and to attempt to get a sufficiently large and representative sample. As much as is feasible, reliable implementation of the service or intervention is important. Appropriate handling of any data collected during a program evaluation and careful interpretation of findings are also critical. Sometimes outside consulting assistance can be helpful to design and help implement program evaluations in the best way possible and especially to assist with data analysis and interpretation. Using participatory methods as described below is critical for program evaluations. Developing the specific evaluation questions you wish to address is best approached as an iterative process that involves all important stakeholders. Examining existing literature is an important step early on in the process to determine what is known about your evaluation questions and see whether there are strategies, procedures, instruments, and other information that evaluators have employed.

Caveats in Conducting a Program Evaluation

New program evaluation initiatives can be thought of like other organizational change efforts, since they often require shifts at many levels within the agency. Many times, organizational change works best when groundwork can be laid with important stakeholders so that they experience a "felt need" for the evaluation. It can be useful for a program evaluator to examine the literature on organizational change to optimize their evaluation efforts (see, for example, E. Rogers, 1962). Evaluation can be threatening, particularly if practitioners and administrators are concerned that the evaluation results will not be as positive as hoped, so it is important for the evaluator to consider program politics. It is important for the evaluator to plan for possible negative evaluation findings and how they can be presented to stakeholders.

Program evaluations are not easy, and they do not pay off immediately. There are often complaints from service providers and administrators about the burden of evaluation, its relevance, and meaning. One way to minimize the burden of program evaluation is to make the effort serve more than one purpose. Accreditation bodies, funding bodies, management, persons being served may all be able to benefit from similar pieces of information, so the evaluator should take time with stakeholders to think through these information needs. Another potential tactic is to consider a modular approach that breaks up the program evaluation up into components and implementing the components in a stepwise fashion to introduce the burden gradually.

Setting aside resources for outside consultation from researchers or data analysts can also be very helpful for many obvious reasons. When providing results of the program evaluation effort, it is important to take a "knowledge transfer" approach (see section below on this topic). That is, consider the information needs of the audience as well as the mode of delivering that information. Some audiences and stakeholders have only minutes to look at findings from a program evaluation and want brief "bottom line," non-technical, and easily digestible kinds of reports while others prefer anecdotes and narratives. The program evaluation effort cannot be conducted solely by an outside entity. Finally, in any program evaluation effort, as well as in a formal research study, it is important to ensure that human rights process and protections of confidentiality are followed.

IMPORTANT TRENDS IN PSYCHIATRIC REHABILITATION RESEARCH AND EVALUATION

Three important developments in mental health research have emerged over the past decade and have special relevance to practitioners of PsyR and service users. First is the burgeoning emphasis on *evidence-based practices* (EBPs). Second is the emphasis on what is referred to as *knowledge translation*. The third is the relatively recent role of *systematic reviews* of the scientific and research literature.

Evidence-Based Practices (EBP)

The push toward Evidence-Based Practice (EBP) calls for PsyR practices, services, and interventions to be derived from a body of research that informs those practices and services. EBPs require that empirical information be married with clinical expertise to provide the most consistent and effective services (Sackett et al., 1996; Stout & Hayes, 2005). This emphasis on EBP has led governmental policy makers to re-focus and invest their resources in services that can be demonstrated to be effective based on existing research evidence rather than on models or services that have no evidence. The focus on EBPs has grown dramatically in the past two decades in such disparate areas as geriatric mental health care (Bartels et al., 2002), substance abuse treatment (Miller et al., 2006), children's mental health (Hoagwood et al., 2001), and childhood speech disorders (Zipoli & Kennedy, 2005).

The growth of evidence-based practices is possible because of the recent growth of research evidence. In the PsyR world, a handful of practices have been declared as evidence-based, generally meaning they have more than one randomized clinical trial resulting in clear findings related to the outcomes. These EBP include the Program for Assertive Community Treatment (Test & Stein, 1976) the Individual Placement and Support model of supported employment (Bond & Drake, 2008), Illness Management and Recovery (Mueser et al., 2002), family psychoeducation (McFarlane et al., 2003), and integrated treatment for co-occurring disorders (Drake et al., 1998). The Substance Abuse and Mental Health Services Administration has also endorsed permanent supportive housing and consumer-run programs as having an evidence base (http://www.samhsa.gov). As more research accumulates that is of sufficient rigor and quality, additional mental health and rehabilitation practices will undoubtedly be declared "evidence-based practices."

National entities have begun evaluating practices for their evidence base, including the Substance Abuse and Mental Health Services Administration through their National Registry of Evidence Based Programs and Practices (www.nrepp.samhsa.gov), the Agency for Healthcare and Research Quality (www.ahrq.gov), and indirectly, the Cochrane and Campbell Collaborations (www.cochrane.org; www.campbellcollaboration.org). The government-sponsored What Works Clearinghouse evaluates research on educational curricula (Department of Education, What Works Clearinghouse, 2012). The Center for Psychiatric Rehabilitation recently concluded a grant to perform systematic reviews, knowledge translation activities, and develop the "Disability Right to Know" Clearinghouse (http://www.bu.edu/drrk).

Knowledge Translation

The second important trend is the growing number of "knowledge translation" initiatives. Knowledge translation has emerged, in part, because while mental health research has grown, this accumulating body of research and evidence has not always changed service delivery. Failed attempts at changing practice based on research is sometimes referred to as the "knowledge gap" or the "Know-Do" gap (World Health Organization, 2005), or the "Science-to-Service Divide" (National Institute of Mental Health, 1999). Several authors have suggested that an active, well-planned, and inclusive approach to dissemination and adopting innovative practices must be undertaken for that knowledge to be used (Sudsawad, 2007; Grimshaw et al., 2001). The Canadian Institute of Health Research has defined knowledge translation as "an acceleration of the natural transformation of knowledge into use" (Canadian Institute of Health Research, 2005).

One reason for these knowledge gaps may be the difference in perspectives that exists between individuals who generate new knowledge (such as academics and researchers) and those who use new knowledge (such as providers of services, users of services, policy makers). Participatory research methods (see the section on Participatory Action Research; Selener, 1997) and this emerging science of knowledge translation (Sudsawad, 2007) can address the difficulties of helping organizations translate new knowledge into innovative services and practices and promote the adoption of evidence-based practices.

Until recently, those who developed new knowledge or conducted research studies were expected to only engage in "knowledge transfer," a straightforward and linear process by which research studies were conceived, executed, and then made available primarily through professional journals (Landry, Lamari, & Amara, 2001). Proponents of knowledge translation argue that in order to ensure the adoption of new knowledge, research must include early and frequent interactions between researchers and potential end-users of those findings for research results to be credible and meaningful.

Rating the Quality of Research and Systematic Reviews

As mentioned above, there is an enormous proliferation of research studies, much of which is readily available to the general public. "Lay users" of research information, even when they are able to locate the information they seek, are often unable to evaluate its quality, which is important.

With these proliferating bodies of research, standards for determining the quality of that research have become important. Such quality standards began taking hold about two or three decades ago to guide medical care. There are growing initiatives in this area and burgeoning numbers of "systematic reviews" which are designed to review the best available research on a specific question by synthesizing and grading them (www.cochrane.org; www.campbellcollaboration.org). Most systems that rate the quality of research rely on a rating hierarchy. Examples of those ratings include descriptors like Strong Evidence to Moderate Evidence to Some Evidence to No Evidence, or ratings or grades such as A, B, C, D, with an "A" representing "Excellent Evidence", and so on. The Cochrane Collaboration was first to respond to this growing need to rate health research for quality and then to perform systematic reviews, and they now represent the largest such initiative in the world (Starr & Chalmers, 2003; www.cochrane.org).

Participatory Action Research (PAR)

PAR is a process in which researchers and community stakeholders work collaboratively to combine knowledge and action for social change (Delman, 2012). PAR is best concep- tualized as an approach or a stance towards the conduct of research and evaluation rather than as a research design in and of itself (McIntyre, 2008). Community stakeholders who participate are most frequently consumers of services, but also include providers, advocates, family members, and others depending on the specific context of the research or evaluation (Rogers & Palmer-Erbs, 1994). Collaboration requires that community stakeholders have the opportunity to be active participants in all phases of the research, including defining the problem, designing the research methodology, collecting data, and analyzing and dissemi- nating results. Active participation occurs when community members take advantage of opportunities to assert their opinions and ideas with the research team in a way that influences the research process (Checkoway, 2011). A major barrier to active participation is the imbalance in resources between researchers and community members. Hence, one PAR requirement is that there be a redistribution of power between the researchers and the disadvantaged community members (Ochocka et al., 2002). Methods of breaking down this barrier include subcontracts with community organizations and cross training as discussed in greater detail below.

Both formal and informal methods of PAR can be undertaken. By formal, we refer to structured processes whereby stakeholders are solicited and involved in a systematic way. This includes subcontracting with community organizations to support the research participation of their constituency, the direct hiring of community members as research associates, and establishing a steering or advisory committee that includes a significant number of stakeholders. More informal processes may also be useful particularly where key stakeholders and end-users of services are already embedded in the administrative workings of a PsyR program.

Regardless of the approach, it is critical for PAR researchers to allow time and effort to provide training for consumers/stakeholders to understand the research process and the importance of choosing the right design, selecting the best instruments and measures, carrying out the study carefully, and interpreting the data cautiously and thoroughly. With cross-training, consumers/stakeholders also present to the researchers on their knowledge and expertise of the topic.

In comparison to traditional research, PAR leads to findings that are more relevant and accessible to community members, providing greater opportunities for findings to affect public policies. When involved early on, stakeholders are more likely to take ownership of the project and are better prepared to share the findings with other community members and policy makers. In a critical review of PAR, Viswanathan and colleagues (2004) concluded that PAR not only improves the quality of the research, but also has a positive impact on the quality of life of the engaged community researchers. That is, consumer participants often report new or improved skills, greater self-confidence, and the development of a career path.

PAR with people with serious mental illnesses

Researchers in the United States have generally failed to include people with serious mental illnesses (SMI) in the research process in any meaningful way (Campbell, 2009). Historically they have been reluctant to do so because of perceptions that people with SMI are not capable and can be difficult to manage as employees (del Vecchio et al., 2009). However, over recent decades, policy-makers have formally recognized that people with SMI bring a unique experience and expertise that can enrich all aspects of the research process, and with the right supports, they can add great value to the research process. Several studies have shown that study participants with SMI talk more openly with interviewers known to have SMI, and this openness can lead to obtaining more honest and in-depth data (Clark et al., 1999). Further, research shows that people with SMI can assist with dissemination by helping to eliminate jargon in the content and by advising on reporting formats that their peers will find accessible. Accordingly, federal agencies, such as the National Institute of Mental Health (NIMH) and the Substance Abuse and Mental Health Services Agency (SAMHSA), have introduced new funding mechanisms that promote the active involvement of people with SMI in research and evaluation. These include the NIMH's special grant mechanism for community-based participatory action research and SAMHSA's basic requirement that people with SMI participate in project evaluations.

PAR is very consistent with the values of psychiatric rehabilitation services, but it often requires significant role shifts for researchers and for key stakeholders. Using a PAR approach, researchers cannot be seen as the only experts on research. This new paradigm values the "lived experience" (Wadsworth, 1998) and requires that researchers and evaluators take on roles as educators and sometimes consultants to service users and other stakeholders who wish to have an active role in the research process. In one effective approach, researchers have trained 3-5 consumers as qualitative researchers, who then participated in the research team. Consumers/stakeholders can be viewed as invested in the research process and be co-investigators, and at times, co-principal investigators when provided with the resources to share responsibility for completion of the research (Delman & Lincoln, 2009).

However, this means that researchers must open up and share the decision-making process, which is often difficult for traditional social science researchers to do. At the same time, PAR requires that consumers be educated in research methods so that they can become full co-investigators or even co-principal investigators. Delman and Lincoln (2009) have identified key components of that promote the active participation of adults with psychiatric conditions: (1) personal commitment of leadership; (2) additional resources and project flexibility; (3) inclusion; (4) clear communication; (5) respect; (6) education and training; (7) individualized attention; (8) effective hiring practices; and (9) supportive infrastructure. With regard to including young adults with serious mental health conditions, we have learned that additional key supports are adult mentoring, vocational supports, and attention to the generational difference between younger and older adults (Delman, 2012).

SUMMARY

In this chapter, we have provided an overview general research and program evaluation procedures and ways to strengthen any program evaluation initiative in a PsyR program. We have drawn distinctions between research studies and program evaluation efforts, understanding that they are similar in many ways, including the steps that can be taken to make both initiatives robust. We also detailed important initiatives with which all PsyR practitioners and administrators should be familiar: the growth of evidence based practices, the burgeoning efforts to conduct knowledge translation, and the value of systematic reviews of current research. All of these initiatives should lead to improvements in the interventions we deliver and the outcomes that service recipients achieve.

BEST PRACTICE GUIDELINES FOR PSYCHIATRIC REHABILITATION RESEARCH AND EVALUATION

- Read professional, peer reviewed journals to become familiar with important research and evaluation trends.

- Visit organizational websites where systematic reviews are being conducted and stored, such as the Cochrane Collaboration.

- Take steps to plan and implement a program evaluation if your organization is not implementing one; if it is, become more familiar with its processes and goals.

- Ensure that a participatory approach is being used in any evaluation, needs assessment, or satisfaction survey that is done within your organization.

- Build relationships with research organizations that can assist and support your evaluation activities.

ABOUT THE AUTHORS

E. Sally Rogers is director of research and research associate professor at the Center for Psychiatric Rehabilitation at Boston University where she has been conducting research in the mental health field for many years. Dr. Rogers currently serves as co-principal investigator of a Research and Training Center grant, which is funded to carry out research studies on the vocational recovery of individuals with mental illness. In her capacity as director of research she has successfully conducted several randomized trials as well as numerous other studies and evaluations of mental health services. A licensed psychologist in the state of Massachusetts, Dr. Rogers has taught masters and doctoral level research courses and seminars at the College of Health and Rehabilitation Sciences: Sargent, at Boston University. She is the recipient of the Loeb Research Award from PRA and has written numerous peer-reviewed papers and book chapters on various topics related to the recovery of persons with severe psychiatric disability.

Jonathan Delman, Ph.D., J.D., MPH is a behavioral health researcher, evaluator, and policy analyst as well as a person in mental health recovery. Dr. Delman is a principal at the consulting firm Reservoir Consulting Group and a research professor of psychiatry at the University of Massachusetts Medical School, Department of Psychiatry. At UMass, he is the associate director for participatory action research at the Transitions (to adulthood) Research and Training Center and director of recovery research. He is a national expert in consumer/family participation in the research and dissemination practices, recovery-oriented systems of care, peer recovery supports, and integrated healthcare delivery. A 2008 recipient of a prestigious Robert Wood Johnson Community Health Leader Award, one of ten awarded nationally, Dr. Delman received a bachelor of arts in economics from Tufts University, a law degree from the University of Pennsylvania, and a Ph.D. in health policy and management from the Boston University School of Public Health.

REFERENCES

Agency for Healthcare and Research Quality. (2011). *Advancing excellence in healthcare.* Retrieved from http://www.ahrq.gov/clinic/epc/epctopicn.htm

Agency for Healthcare Research and Quality. (2002). *Systems to rate the strength of scientific evidence* (No. Evidence Report 47). Rockville, MD: U.S. Department of Health and Human Services.

Bartels, S. J., Dums, A. R., Oxman, T. E., Schneider, L. S., Areán, P. A., Alexopoulos, G. S., et al. (2002). Evidence-based practices in geriatric mental health care. *Psychiatric Services, 53*(11), 1419-1431.

Bond, G. R., Drake, R. E., & Becker, D. R. (2008). An update on randomized controlled trials of evidence-based supported employment. *Psychiatric Rehabilitation Journal, 31*(4), 280-290.

Campbell, D. T., & Stanley, J. C. (1963). *Experimental and quasi-experimental designs for research.* Boston, MA: Houghton Mifflin Company.

Campbell, J. (2009). Methods. In J. Wallcraft, B. Schrank, & M. Amering (Eds.), *Handbook of service user involvement in mental health research* (pp. 113-138). Chichester, UK: John Wiley & Sons, Ltd. doi: 10.1002/9780470743157.ch9

Canadian Institute of Health Research. (2005). *About knowledge translation.* Retrieved from http://www.cihr-irsc.gc.ca/e/29418.html

Checkoway, B. (2011). What is youth participation? *Children and Youth Services Review, 33*(2), 340-345.

Clark, C. C., Scott, E. A., Boydell, K. M., & Goering, P. (1999). Effects of client interviewers on client-reported satisfaction with mental health services. *Psychiatric Services, 50,* 961-963.

Delman, J. (2012). Participatory action research and young adults with psychiatric disabilities. *Psychiatric Rehabilitation Journal, 35*(3), 231-234.

Delman, J., & Lincoln, A. (2009). *Service users as paid research workers: Principles for active involvement and good practice guidance.* Indianapolis, IN: John Wiley and Sons.

Delveccio, P., & Blyler, C. (2009). *Beyond involvement: Looking for a common perspective on roles in research in mental health research.* Indianapolis, IN: John Wiley and Sons.

Drake, R. E., McHugo, G. J., Clark, R. E., Teague, G. B., Xie, H., Miles, K., et al. (1998). Assertive community treatment for patients with co-occurring severe mental illness and substance use disorder. *American Journal of Orthopsychiatry, 68*(2), 201-215.

Fitz-Gibbon, C. T., & Morris, L. L. (1987). *How to design a program evaluation.* Newbury Park, CA: SAGE Publications.

Grimshaw, J. M., Shirran, L., Thomas, R., Mowatt, G., Fraser, C., Bero, L., et al. (2001). Changing provider behavior: An overview of systematic reviews of interventions. *Medical Care, 39*(8, Supplement 2), 112-145.

Hoagwood, K., Burns, B. J., Kiser, L., Ringeisen, H., & Schoenwald, S. K. (2001). Evidence-based practice in child and adolescent mental health services. *Psychiatric Services, 52*(9), 1179-1189.

Isaac, S., & Michael, W. B. (1995). *Handbook in research and evaluation: For education and the behavioral sciences* (3rd ed.). San Diego, CA: Edits Publishers.

Kazdin, A. E. (2003). *Research design in clinical psychology.* Boston, MA: Allyn and Bacon.

King, J. A., Morris, L. L., & Fitz-Gibbon, C. T. (1987). *How to assess program implementation.* Newbury Park, CA: SAGE Publications.

Landry, R., Amara, N., & Lamari, M. (2001). Utilization of social science research knowledge in Canada. *Research Policy, 30*(2), 333-349.

McFarlane, W. R., Dixon, L., Lukens, E., & Lucksted, A. (2003). Family psychoeducation and schizophrenia: A review of the literature. *Journal of Marital and Family Therapy, 29*(2), 223-245.

McIntyre, A. (2008). *Participatory action research.* Thousand Oaks, CA: SAGE Publications.

Miller, W. R., Zweben, J., & Johnson, W. R. (2006). Evidence-based treatment: Why, what, where, when, and how? *Journal of Substance Abuse Treatment, 29*(4), 267-276.

Mueser, K. T., Corrigan, P. W., Hilton, D. W., Tanzman, B., Schaub, A., Gingerich, S., et al. (2002). Illness management and recovery: A review of the research. *Psychiatric Services, 53*(10), 1272-1284.

National Institute of Mental Health. (1999). *Clinical treatment and services research workgroup: Bridging science and services.* Rockville, MD: National Institute of Mental Health.

National Institute of Mental Health. (2006). *The road ahead: Research partnerships to transform services.* Rockville, MD: Department of Health and Human Services.

NREPP. (2012). SAMHSA's national registry of evidence-based programs and practices. Retrieved March 1, 2012 from http://www.nrepp.samhsa.gov

Ochocka, J., Janzen, R., & Nelson, G. (2002). Sharing power and knowledge: Professional and mental health consumer/survivor researchers working together in a participatory action research project. *Psychiatric Rehabilitation Journal, 25*(4), 379-387.

Rogers, E. (1962). *Diffusion of innovations.* New York: The Free Press.

Rogers, E. S., & Palmer-Erbs, V. (1994). Participatory action research: Implications for researchers in psychiatric rehabilitation. *Psychosocial Rehabilitation Journal, 18*(2), 3-12.

Sackett, D. L., Rosenberg, W. M. C., Gray, J. A. M., Haynes, R. B., & Richardson, W. S. (1996). Evidence based medicine: What it is and what it isn't. *British Medical Journal,* 71-72.

Selener, D. (1997). *Participatory action research and social change.* New York: Cornell University Press.

Starr, M., & Chalmers, I. (2003). The evolution of the Cochran Library, 1988-2003. Retrieved from http://siivola.org/markku/krit/jarkytyksen_jalkipuinti_Cochrane_history.pdf

Stecher, B., & Davis, W. A. (1987). *How to focus an evaluation* (Vol. 2). Newbury Park, CA: SAGE Publications.

Stout, C. E., & Hayes, R. A. (2005). *The evidence-based practice: Methods, models, and tools for mental health professionals.* Somerset, NJ: John Wiley and Sons.

Sudsawad, P. (2007). *Knowledge translation: Introduction to models, strategies, and measures.* Austin, TX: Southwest Educational Development Laboratory, National Center for the Dissemination of Disability Research.

Test, M. A., & Stein, L. I. (1976). Practical guidelines for the community treatment of markedly impaired patients. *Community Mental Health Journal, 12*(1), 72-82.

The Campbell Collaboration. *What helps? What harms? Based on what evidence?* Retrieved from http://www.campbellcollaboration.org

The Center for Psychiatric Rehabilitation. *Disability right to know.* Retrieved from http://www.bu.edu/drrk

The Cochrane Collaboration. (2012). *Working together to provide the best evidence for health care.* Retrieved from http://www.cochrane.org

The Department of Education. (2012). *What works clearinghouse.* Retrieved from http://ies.ed.gov/ncee/wwc

Viswanathan, M., Ammerman, A., Eng, E., Gartlehner, G., Lohr, K. N., & Griffith, D. (2004). *Community-based participatory research: Assessing the evidence.* Rockville, MD: Agency for Healthcare Research and Quality.

Wadsworth, Y. J. (1998). What is participatory action research? *Action Research International* (Paper 2). Retrieved from http://www.aral.com.au/ari/p-ywadsworth98.html

Whyte, W. F. (1991). *Participatory action research.* Newbury Park, CA: SAGE Publications.

World Health Organization. (2005). *Bridging the "know-do" gap: Meeting on knowledge translation in global health.* Retrieved from http://www.who.int/kms/WHO_EIP_KMS_2006_2.pdf

Zipoli, R. P., & Kennedy, M. (2005). Evidence-based practice among speech-language pathologists: Attitudes, utilization, and barriers. *American Journal of Speech-Language Pathology, 14*(3), 208-220.

CHAPTER 5

PERSON-CENTERED PLANNING

Janis Tondora
Chacku Mathai
Diane Grieder
Larry Davidson

ABSTRACT

This chapter reviews emerging practice guidelines in person-centered planning (PCP) from a process perspective (how roles, relationships, and planning meetings look different when conducted in a person-centered fashion) as well as a documentation perspective delineating how the person-centered process is reflected in a written plan. How these practices are then implemented in real-world service settings is illustrated through the review of a progressive state-based program with person-centered planning as its quality foundation. Strategies for managing the complex issues that frequently hinder PCP implementation, including how to honor the person's right to maximal self-determination while also satisfying certain external regulatory, compliance, or legal expectations, are presented. Contrary to the common myth that person-centered planning is "soft," this chapter demonstrates the potential for PCP to be an effective strategy for creating service plans in partnership with persons in recovery while also maintaining rigorous standards for treatment planning and documentation.

IT IS WIDELY ACCEPTED THAT RECOVERY-ORIENTED PSYCHIATRIC REHABILITATION MUST BE GROUNDED IN a person-centered approach to service delivery. Adherence to person-centered principles has diverse implications across the mental health system as a whole. However, increasing emphasis has been placed on the power of person-centered planning (PCP) to transform systems so that they are maximally responsive to the rights and preferences of persons with psychiatric disabilities.

IMPORTANCE OF PERSON-CENTERED PLANNING FOR RECOVERY

"You keep talking about getting me in the 'driver's seat' of my treatment and my life ... when half the time I'm not even in the damn car!"

The above quote is an excerpt of a story told to the authors many years ago when we first began attempting to understand the experiences of persons in recovery as it related to the process of service planning. The words are a humorous, yet at the same time a sobering, reflection of the reality that mental health services in this country—including the pivotal process of recovery planning—continue to be oriented primarily to the requirements of bureaucracies rather than to the goal of providing individuals real and meaningful opportunities for choice and self-determination. The service plan, in fact, is commonly seen as little more than a technical document completed to satisfy accrediting or reimbursement bodies and is perceived as useful neither to the provider nor to the service user. In such cases, the plan is completed with marginal input from the person in recovery and is filed away in the medical record while playing little, if any, role in actually guiding the care provided.

It is doubtful whether anyone involved would argue that this is an ideal way of providing services or occupying the time of dedicated mental health practitioners. Nor is it consistent with the spirit and values of psychiatric rehabilitation as articulated throughout this book. In this chapter, we propose an alternative vision of person-centered planning—one created through a process of partnership and shared discovery—and suggest that such a process and plan should be, in the words of the New Freedom Commission on Mental Health (2003), "at the core of the consumer-centered, recovery oriented mental health system" (p. 12). Rather than being a bureaucratic task that takes time away from the real work of service provision, the collaborative creation of the PCP is an intervention in and of itself as it becomes the very heart of the psychiatric rehabilitation process.

The potential transformative power of person-centered planning has led to a call for its wide-spread adoption by many stakeholders in the mental health community as well as one of the most esteemed of organizations in American healthcare, the Institute of Medicine (National Research Council, 2006). Around the country, people in recovery demand it, public service systems endorse it, training programs are encouraged to teach it, and researchers investigate it. Yet, people struggle to understand exactly what *"it"* is and what *"it"* might look in practice. Despite a general consensus regarding the more abstract principles on which person-centered planning is based (including promotion of self-determination, community inclusion, and strength-based, individualized service delivery), there has been little guidance regarding the translation of these principles into concrete practice. The absence of such guidance has served to perpetuate what is perhaps the most formidable barrier in PCP implementation—the complacency that comes with this assumption: "Person-centered planning? Of course, we already do that."

The voices of persons in recovery say otherwise. Focus groups conducted around the country suggest that individuals typically have a limited role in service planning and systems fail to provide important information that could enable them to more fully participate in the process (Koyanagi et al., 2008). This chapter describes how we as a field are moving beyond the rhetoric of person-centered care toward the discernible implementation of person-centered practices in routine service settings. Put simply, when the rubber hits the road, how will we know when we have fulfilled our promise to deliver PCP? In order to address this challenge, this chapter articulates the so-called nuts and bolts practices of person-centered planning and includes a review of their application in a select state-based PCP implementation effort. This material provides practical strategies for those who are earnest in their commitment to person-centered planning but are uncertain regarding how to move forward with implementation.

Person-centered planning is defined as an ongoing collaborative process between an individual and his or her team members (including clinical and rehabilitation professionals as well as natural supporters) that results in the development and implementation of an action plan that will assist the person in achieving his or her unique recovery goals. The person-centered planning document is a meaningful road map for pursuing these valued life goals and the milestones that are achieved along the way. In this sense, the plan becomes a useful tool that has direct relevance in guiding the work of the team over time. It can be consulted as needed in order to ensure that all parties stay on course and revised as needed if the person encounters roadblocks along the way or reaches certain landmarks and wants to set a new destination.

Below, a series of practical strategies for creating this road map are presented from both a process perspective focused on how roles, relationships, and planning meetings look different when conducted in a person-centered fashion as well as a documentation perspective centered on how a person-centered process is reflected in a written plan. For the reader's reference, the practices described here are also summarized in a quality indicators tool, the Person-Centered Care Questionnaire (Tondora & Miller, 2009).

Best Practice Principles for Person-Centered Planning
The following principles summarize current best practice in person-centered planning.

Person-centered plans recognize the power of strengths-based assessment.
Practitioners striving to implement person-centered planning frequently make the mistake of jumping to the tasks of goal setting and service matching. This tendency runs the risk of significantly compromising the overall quality of the plan as planning should be preceded and fully informed by a comprehensive, strengths-based assessment. The plan is only as good as the assessment on which it is based (Adams & Grieder, 2005). Interests, talents, and coping strategies uncovered in the assessment process should be documented and then actively used in the context of the plan. For example, if an individual uses meditation, exercise, journaling, or other self-directed wellness methods, these should be explicitly documented alongside those action steps that will be carried out by clinical and rehabilitation professionals.

Individuals have maximum participation, choice, and control in the planning process.
Consistent with the "nothing about us, without us" dictum of the consumer movement, providers actively partner with the individual in all planning meetings regarding his or her recovery services and supports. While it is recognized that some individuals may not want

to participate for a variety of reasons, it is important for practitioners to make an effort to understand the reasons behind a person's reluctance prior to defaulting to the position that the person simply refused to be involved.

People are given advance notice of the planning meeting so that they have adequate time to invite/include significant others, reflect on progress, and consider priorities moving forward. To inform a person when s/he arrives for a regular appointment that "today is the day we are going to decide your hopes dreams and desires for the next six months" does not allow the person to actively partner in the process or to involve natural supporters who may be critical to the future success of the plan.

The individual has reasonable control as to the location and time of planning meetings as well as to who is involved. Planning meetings are conducted at a time that does not conflict with other activities that support recovery, such as employment. The individual can extend invitations to any person she or he believes will be supportive of his or her efforts toward recovery, including natural supporters and/or collaborating rehabilitation providers, such as a job coach. The model must flex to remain responsive to personal and cultural preferences, such as when the individual values a more collective model of decision-making and planning and prefers to invite, and perhaps even defer to, family members.

Information on rights and responsibilities is provided at all recovery planning meetings, including mechanisms through which individuals can provide feedback to the provider and/or agency. If necessary, the person is provided with support before the meeting so that s/he can be prepared and participate as an equal (Osher & Keenan, 2001). In the spirit of true partnership and transparency, all parties must have access to the same information so that they can effectively carry out responsibilities associated with the recovery plan. All individuals are automatically offered copies of their written plans as this is a tool of accountability that outlines not only what the person can expect from professional and natural supporters, but also what s/he has personally committed to. We have found that this concrete offering of the written plan is a simple, yet powerful, person-centered intervention. Knowing ahead of time that a copy will be shared with the service user can dramatically impact both the language of the plan and the content within it.

Person-centered plans recognize the value of natural supports and community connections.

The focus of planning and care is on how to create pathways to meaningful community life, and not just on how to maintain clinical stability or abstinence. Person-centered recovery plans document areas like physical health, family and social relationships, employment, education, spiritual life, housing satisfaction, recreation, community service, and civic participation, unless such areas are designated by the person as not-of-interest. This is consistent with the broader recovery-oriented vision of mental health services put forth by both the President's New Freedom Commission on Mental Health (2003) and the guidelines issued by the Centers for Medicare and Medicaid Services (Smith, Kennedy, Knipper, O'Brien, & O'Keefe, 2005).

The plan identifies a wide range of both professional supports and alternative strategies to support the person's recovery, particularly those that have been helpful to others with similar struggles. Information about medications and other treatments is mingled with information about self-help, peer-support, exercise, nutrition, daily maintenance activities, spiritual practices, homeopathic remedies, and other alternative interventions.

Achieving interdependence with natural community supports is a valued goal for many people in recovery who express a strong preference to live in typical housing, to have friendships and intimate relationships with a wide range of people, to work in regular employment settings, and to participate in school, worship, and recreation alongside other community members (Reidy, 1992). Person-centered plans seek to maximize engagement in typical community settings as opposed to segregated services designed solely for persons with mental illnesses. Given this focus on life and community context, one tool required in PCP is adequate knowledge of the person's local community, including its opportunities and potential barriers.

Recovery plans respect the fact that services and professionals should not remain central to a person's life over time. Criteria for discharge to an independent community life or a lower level of care are clearly defined and are worked toward actively in the context of the service plan. This should not be confused with a get-tough approach to planning, but seen, rather, as an attempt to send a consistent positive message of the expectation for growth and recovery.

Person-centered plans support the "dignity of risk" and the "right to fail" (Deegan, 1996).

Prior to any acts of imposing power, providers use persistent and varied efforts to engage the individual and support his or her ability to make active choices. Each individual is presumed competent and entitled to make personal decisions until such time this right has been suspended by law. Only in situations involving imminent risk of harm to self or others would a professional override the decisions of the individual and his or her support team. Person-centered care does not take away the provider's right and responsibility to take action to protect the person or the public in the event of emergency or crisis situations. However, it does suggest that in such situations, the provider should maximize the use of person-directed recovery and crisis planning tools such as formal psychiatric advance directives (see the National Resource Center on Psychiatric Advance Directives, 2011) or the crisis planning section of the Wellness Recovery Action Plan (Copeland, 1997).

Person-centered principles are reflected in the recovery planning document.

The language used in person-centered plans is neither stigmatizing nor objectifying. At all times, person first language (IAPSRS, 2003) is used to acknowledge that the diagnosis is not as important as the person's individuality and humanity. Employing person-first language does not mean that a person's diagnosis is hidden or seen as irrelevant; however, it is not the sole focus of any description about that person. The language of the plan should be understandable to all participants, including the service user and his or her natural supporters. Where professional terminology is necessary, this is explained to all participants involved.

Goal statements on the plan are about having a meaningful life in the community, not only symptom reduction or compliance. They should be written in the person's own words and based on the individual's interests, preferences, and strengths. Objectives and interventions are clearly related to the attainment of these stated goals.

Planning focuses on the identification of concrete next steps that will allow the person to move toward his or her vision for the future. These concrete steps are captured in the crafting of the short-term objectives statements. Well-written objectives serve to divide larger life goals into more discrete, manageable tasks and provide time frames for benchmarking progress. Given these functions, it is essential that the objective include a target date and reflect a concrete and measurable change in behavior, functioning, or status that is meaningful to the person in recovery. Simple service participation, e.g., *Colleen will regularly attend day treatment over the next three months,* is not considered a quality objective as it does not necessarily equate with meaningful change in the person's life and functioning. Instead, objectives should focus on how participation in day treatment helps Colleen to overcome mental health and/or addictions barriers to achieve measurable improvements in things that she values.

Within the planning process, a diverse and flexible range of options must be available so that people can choose those supports that will best assist them in their recovery. These service options are clearly explained to the individual and documented in the interventions section. In addition to professional services, a comprehensive PCP also includes any action steps or tasks that unpaid natural supporters or the individual person will own and act upon. This is consistent with the emphasis that PCP places on building a sense of self-agency and on maximizing the focus person's connections to meaningful community activities and natural support relationships.

Following the completion of the initial plan, the team reconvenes as necessary to address life goals, accomplishments, and barriers. Planning is characterized by celebrations of successes, and meetings can occur beyond regular established parameters such as six-month reviews or at times of crisis when service providers must meet to address hospitalization or relapse.

CHALLENGES FOR IMPLEMENTING PERSON-CENTERED PLANNING

Both service providers and service users identify challenges—either experienced or anticipated—when asked to participate in a person-centered planning process. Basically, it is important to appreciate that the *practice* of PCP can only grow out of a *culture* that fully embraces the principles embodied in these types of changes. When this foundational culture does not exist, systems often face implementation challenges.

Program Implementation: Providers' Perspectives

A nuts and bolts understanding of person-centered planning does not necessarily prepare mental health practitioners and administrators for the myriad of implementation challenges they are likely to face as they attempt to apply these practices in routine service settings. The challenges raised range from the abstract and philosophical (how to build the organizational recovery culture that is necessary in order for PCP to take hold or how to handle staff who simply do not believe persons with mental illnesses should make their own decisions) to the concrete and practical (how to write a person-centered plan and meet medical necessity criteria or to promote choice with someone whose choices legally belong to a conservator or guardian). Next, we discuss these and other challenges, phrased as statements commonly heard from service providers, and offer suggestions regarding ways in which to respond.

Challenge 1: "Person centered care is based on someone's own goals, but the people I work with don't have goals. They seem comfortable with where they are and don't want to be pushed."

While people with psychiatric disabilities (like many human beings) may find it awkward to articulate their goals and aspirations, they nonetheless will have ideas about what could make their lives better. Do they, for example, want to work and make money? Would they perhaps like to have a better place to live? What gives them pleasure or a sense of success?

This type of dialogue differs significantly from the more restrictive conversation in which the person is expected to report on symptoms and side effects, or patterns of eating, sleeping, and taking medications.

For many people receiving mental health services, it may, at first, feel dangerous to allow themselves to dream once again—with so many of their previous dreams having been abruptly interrupted by illness or dashed by a legacy of low expectations. Based on these experiences, individuals may initially report that they have no goals or aspirations. Such a response should not be taken at face value, but seen as representing the years of difficulties and failures they may have endured and the degree of demoralization that has resulted. In such circumstances, providers need to take the first steps by assisting the person in getting back in touch with his or her previous interests and talents and drawing upon these to imagine a brighter tomorrow.

The consumer/survivor literature has argued that much of what providers view as apathy, passivity, or a lack of motivation to engage in person-centered planning is actually due to the learned helplessness that stems from years of having other people take control and assume decision-making authority over their lives. Just as the process of sharing power and responsibility in treatment planning is a sometimes disconcerting shift in roles among mental health practitioners, many persons with psychiatric disabilities may truly want to exert greater control but feel unprepared to do so. To the degree that this contributes to the person's discomfort with taking the wheel in the recovery planning process, s/he might benefit from some driver's education regarding PCP and how to be a partner within it. A toolkit for this purpose (Tondora, Miller, Guy, & Lanteri, 2009) has been used in multiple states, often with the support of trained peer specialists to enhance the active involvement of persons in recovery in the PCP process.

Challenge 2: "PCP sounds great for people who are well on their way to recovery, but the people I work with are too impaired to do this. First, they need to be stabilized; then we can revisit the idea of a job, classes, or a new apartment."

Despite the positive changes brought about by recovery-oriented systems transformation, it is still common for individuals to be expected to jump through clinical hoops and demonstrate stability before moving on to pursue broader life goals. For example, an agency might require six months of medication compliance before a person is eligible for support to move into his or her own apartment or might dictate a certain compliance level with clinical groups before a resident on an inpatient unit is allowed to participate in the hospital's treatment mall rehabilitation programming or might insist that establishing symptomatic stability is a standard prerequisite for entry to supported employment services. Ironically, engagement in these personally preferred activities is often the factor that ultimately increases individuals' desire to acknowledge, and begin to work on, the core clinical treatment issues that are interfering with their progress. More important, expecting all individuals to rigidly move through a pre-determined continuum of care is a subtle yet pernicious form of coercion that has no place in a person-centered system of care.

Challenge 3: "If given choices, some people make bad ones; then wouldn't the blame be on me? Doesn't PCP increase our exposure to risk and liability?"

The implementation of person-centered planning can be hindered by the risk-averse culture that frequently dominates the policies and protocols of mental health service systems. Practitioners, administrators, and even natural supporters may fear that an individual is about to make a risky decision. In such circumstances, they may feel it is justified to step in and exert influence or control under the well-intentioned belief they are acting in the individual's best interest. However, we have found it necessary and helpful to draw a clear distinction between what we call risk versus safety issues. Risk issues are more subtle areas of concern when a practitioner or loved one or conservator believes an individual is making a decision that would jeopardize his or her recovery. Some risky decisions include moving out of a group home, returning to work, and requesting a medication reduction; yet there are often no imminent safety issues present (involving dangerousness to self or others). In a person-centered system, responsible risk-taking is both tolerated and encouraged as a mechanism for growth and recovery. Safety issues, in contrast, refer to unique circumstances, narrowly defined by each state's statutory laws, where an individual presents an imminent risk to self or others when in the midst of a psychiatric crisis. In such safety circumstances, person-centered planning does not override a provider's ethical and societal obligation to intervene on a person's or the community's behalf. How one intervenes might look dramatically different if operating in a person-centered manner, and it might include the use of recovery-oriented risk-management tools such as psychiatric advance directives and shared decision-making technologies.

Challenge 4: "I have to complete paperwork on a timeline, and we don't have the luxury of discussing everything first—especially when the person doesn't show up half the time."

Mental health practice in today's fiscal climate operates on razor-thin margins. Budget deficits and staff shortages across the country make this seem like an ill-advised moment to advocate for the expansion of person-centered planning. While we acknowledge that conversations regarding goals, strengths, and aspirations may take more time up front, these conversations are an investment in a collaboration that stands to be time saving in the long run. With the focus on personal responsibility and action, providers can shift from a *do for* perspective to a *do with* approach fostering increased independence on the part of the individual and a shift toward maximizing natural community connections rather than relying on institutional ones. Furthermore, research and program evaluation findings on PCP planning models suggest that this approach to care may serve not only to enhance quality of life outcomes, but also to interrupt the reactive cycle of crisis response, thereby leading to reduced hospitalizations, incarcerations, and assaultive or self-injurious behaviors (New York Care Coordination Program, 2010).

Challenge 5: "But will I get reimbursed? How can I write a plan that honors the person and still satisfies the chart?"

While person-centered planning strives to capitalize on a person's strengths, it is also true that the roadblocks interfering with goal attainment often take the shape of mental health symptoms or experiences. Barriers should be acknowledged alongside assets and strengths as this is essential not only for the purpose of justifying the medical necessity of the professional supports we provide, but also because a clear understanding of what is getting in the way informs the psychiatric rehabilitation interventions that then might be offered to the individual in the service of his or her recovery. The difference is that the mental health barrier does not become the exclusive focus of the plan. It only takes on meaning to the extent that it is interfering with the attainment of larger life goals, such as wanting to return to work, finishing school, or being a better parent.

Despite our assertions that we are not advocating "throwing the baby out with the bath water," practitioners routinely identify the perceived constraints of regulatory and funding bodies as a core barrier to the implementation of person-centered planning. We believe this derives from two fundamental misconceptions: (1) the belief that PCP is somehow soft and (2) the belief that funders will not pay for life goals, such as helping someone to finish school or return to work. Contrary to the common myth that person-centered planning is soft, emerging practice guidelines explicitly call for the documentation of (a) comprehensive clinical formulations, (b) mental health-related barriers that interfere with functioning, (c) strengths and resources, (d) short-term, measurable objectives, and (e) clearly articulated interventions that spell out who is doing what on which timeline and for what purpose (Adams & Grieder, 2005). Based on hundreds, if not thousands, of chart reviews done by the authors and our colleagues, we suggest that these standards for PCP documentation are on par with, if not superior to, the level of rigor that actually exists in most clinical and rehabilitation plans around the U.S. Second, the belief that funders will not pay for non-clinical life goals is actually a correct one, but not because of the nature of the goal itself. Technically, funders do not pay for goals at all. Rather, funders pay mental health practitioners for the interventions and professional services they provide to help people overcome the mental health barriers that are interfering with their functioning and the attainment of valued recovery goals. This is admittedly a broad-brush review, and the authors acknowledge that each state is subject to its own unique funding and regulatory expectations. Furthermore, we have experienced personally that these expectations are often applied inconsistently in the field during audits/site visits or accreditation surveys depending on the training and orientation of the reviewer. However, we maintain that medical necessity and person-centered care are not wholly incompatible constructs. Service plans can be created in partnership with persons in recovery while also maintaining rigorous standards around treatment planning and documentation.

Program Implementation: Service Users' Perspective

There are a number of concerns from the person and family perspective that the practitioner should be prepared to address. They are listed in this section as statements commonly heard from people using services.

Person-centered planning is a direct practice that facilitates recovery. One of the challenges we face is that most people with psychiatric disabilities and their families do not necessarily know or believe that recovery is in fact possible, especially from what we may perceive as the most tragic circumstances and/or disabling conditions. An important part of this process is to recognize the need to orient people to the values, principles, and processes of person-centered planning. An adequate orientation informs people and their families that PCP is an intentional effort to rediscover (or discover for the first time) our own personhood through the pursuit of previously abandoned hopes and dreams, such as a owning a home, getting an education, becoming employed, getting married, or raising children. This is accomplished through an active exploration of our culture, strengths, values, and competencies that may have previously been disregarded. The reawakening of hope can be a scary process, and it is truly a journey of the heart (Deegan, 1995) on which many have closed the door for years.

The person-centered planning process also opens doors to a new life beyond the service system. Plans may be developed to re-engage communities that we feel most excluded from as a result of our past experiences. Believing that these communities can be re-engaged, or that new communities can be discovered, is a valued outcome and a critical motivator for involvement in PCP planning activities.

Ultimately, those of us with psychiatric disabilities and our families need to understand and experience PCP as a tool to re-author the way we see and experience ourselves. Our long held beliefs and narratives as mental patients, rejects of society, and even as criminals are not easily left behind.

Concern 1: "Will my provider really let me make my own decisions? It sounds like just another way to get me to do what they want."

The first time a person or family member is informed about choice and self-determination may be met with skepticism and doubt about the motives and roles of the practitioner or system involved. This is a critical stage of the relationship and presents an opportunity for a meaningful conversation about what has happened in previous services and in the current service relationship. Activities that may have been framed as involvement were really coercive experiences from the perspective of the service user. Developing a new and shared understanding about what involvement, choice, and self-determination can really mean in the existing relationship is a springboard from which every future conversation about the plan, and a person's role in it, can build. An open conversation such as this may also lead to a practitioner needing to take responsibility for past approaches, coercive practices, or mistakes that need to be rectified. The ability to simply apologize demonstrates a tremendous amount of respect and builds a strong foundation of trust on which the relationship can move forward.

Concern 2: "I have a legal guardian and am court ordered to outpatient treatment; how do I get person-centered treatment planning?"

A transparent conversation about the roles and responsibilities of the respective parties involved is especially critical when an individual's level of choice and self-determination is limited by criminal justice involvement or the authority of a legal guardian or conservator. In such circumstances, the individual needs to develop an internal, personal view of what engagement in the recovery process really means to him/her. Compliance with externally imposed mandates does not necessarily equal engagement in the recovery process; however, a person can still take responsibility for his/her own recovery even when involved in court-ordered services or when subject to the authority of a guardian. In terms of the practitioner's role, if there is any enforcement or reporting responsibility associated with that role, full transparency of these responsibilities and how these may impact the relationship is an important area to talk about and negotiate with the service user. The extent to which a person's plan actually includes the priorities of the person and his/her family, even within court-ordered parameters, is a critical indication of whether a plan may be experienced as person-centered. Some degree of choice, even from a restricted range of options, is better than no choice at all. An important conversation and task may also be to develop an understanding of what it will take to remove such court orders, mandates, or guardianship, which may include changing the perceptions of those who believe we are not compliant or adequately engaged in the recovery process. Where necessary, it is important for the practitioner to support the individual's self-advocacy efforts as such efforts to express self-determined ideas are often prematurely judged by others as reflecting non-compliance or resistance to treatment. Practitioners who are able to step out of the role of compliance enforcer and instead, develop a relationship that involves assisting a person to envision a life beyond their mandates and restrictions will foster engagement and strengthen the partnership on which PCP must be based.

Concern 3: "I'm willing to try it, but I'm just not that goal-oriented a person. It feels like I'm forcing it, and it seems kind of unnatural when we make these plans so concretely. The approach doesn't even fit well with my beliefs about how life works. I just wanted someone to talk to during some tough times, and the next thing you know, my life was being planned out for me."

Most people are not as future-oriented as the person-centered planning process would suggest. Engaging people and families in understanding the benefits of assessing their own needs and developing plans that are based on future-oriented quality of life goals may require some additional orientation time. Some of these benefits include having support in identifying barriers or patterns that consistently get in the way of achieving quality of life goals and recognizing and celebrating when objectives or milestones have been achieved. It is also important to clarify values and beliefs that a person or family may experience as being in conflict with future-oriented or self-determined planning efforts. These values and beliefs should be discussed openly to ensure that they are respected in how service planning is conducted and in how decisions are made in that process.

Concern 4: "What if my provider doesn't follow through? How do I hold my provider accountable to our plan?"

The role of the person-centered plan in promoting accountability amongst those who commit to certain action steps is another area important to include in the service-user's orientation to PCP. Information regarding how progress, or lack of progress, will be reviewed, and how new directions or services will be negotiated as well as how grievances can be aired and addressed are all essential parts of person-centered planning.

Concern 5: "What happens if I don't meet my objectives? Will I get kicked out of the program if I don't meet my goals?"

One of the unspoken fears that inhibit people and families from participating in person-centered planning is the concern that the goals and objectives we set will not be reached and that the barriers that have previously held us back will continue to hold us back. Practitioners may need to provide consistent reassurance to service users that the person-centered planning process exists to facilitate their participation and progress. And, when set-backs do occur, these are not judged as a failure on the part of the service user, but as a natural part of the change and growth process for all human beings. If goals and objectives are not met, this is simply an opportunity to revisit the plan together so that the team as a whole can discuss what is and what is not working, and make adjustments accordingly. The focus on evaluating progress is not intended to put undue pressure on the individual or on members of the team. Rather, it represents an important opportunity to send the hopeful message that through the collective efforts of all involved, the realization of valued recovery goals is ultimately possible and expected even if the journey is not always a smooth one.

SUCCESSFUL IMPLEMENTATION: WHAT DOES IT TAKE?

Often, the initial impulse of administrators and clinical leaders is to provide training to direct care staff with the belief that this is sufficient to support the implementation of person-centered planning. Unfortunately, training initiatives in mental health tend to rely on outdated and ineffective models of didactic lecture and teaching, and they rarely employ evidence-based implementation strategies (Stuart, Tondora, & Hoge, 2004). Proven strategies include things such as experiential/interactive training, onsite technical assistance with continuous feedback, the identification and use of internal agency champions to promote change, active involvement of persons in recovery in the design and delivery of training and technical assistance, and clinical supervision and strengths-based coaching in day-to-day work.

While the incorporation of these evidence-based strategies could significantly improve the impact of training on staff competency development, it is also true that training, even best-practice training, is not sufficient in and of itself to support the implementation of person-centered planning. True practice change is only achieved with multi-level interventions that go far beyond the need for competency development amongst practitioners (Berwick, 2002).

Equally, if not more, important is the need to consider both the first-hand experiences of service users and their families and also the external and regulatory environments within which care is provided. In an effort to illustrate how best-practice training can combine with multi-level systemic and service-user interventions, we now offer an example of a PCP implementation effort that has been underway in the State of New York for the past several years within the context of their state-wide Personalized Recovery-Oriented Services (PROS) program (http://www.omh.state.ny.us/omhweb/PROS). Many states, including Wisconsin, Connecticut, North Dakota, California, and Massachusetts, have launched significant PCP initiatives with considerable impact. However, New York's efforts have been unique in their ongoing commitment to both best-practice training models and the types of multi-level systems change interventions that are necessary to facilitate broad scale dissemination and uptake of person-centered planning. Furthermore, they have done so within the context of a health care environment that is simultaneously subject to the rigorous fiscal and regulatory requirements of the Centers for Medicare and Medicaid (CMS).

In 2004, the New York State Department of Health received approval from CMS to establish the Personalized Recovery Oriented Services program (PROS) as a Medicaid-reimbursable, recovery-oriented alternative to more traditional day treatment models. PROS is a comprehensive program that supports recovery from serious mental illnesses by integrating evidence-based practices, clinical treatment, recovery-oriented services, and psychiatric rehabilitation in one single person-centered environment. PROS is based on the core belief that anyone can achieve a measure of recovery and work toward attaining desired life role goals. PROS views the practitioner's role as one of supporting the attainment of these goals rather than one of simply working to reduce problematic clinical symptoms. Of particular importance to the topic of this chapter is the emphasis that PROS places on the individualized recovery plan (IRP) as the foundation of quality across the program and in each participant's experience of care within it. State leadership wisely recognized that significant support and multiple interventions would be needed to support all stakeholders (agencies, practitioners, and service users and families) in collaborating on a more recovery-oriented approach to service planning. Next, we briefly describe several key elements of New York's training and dissemination plan that appear to have been central to the progress the PROS program has made in its implementation of higher quality person-centered planning.

First, from a systems perspective, it is significant that collaborative individualized recovery planning is formally recognized as a defined PROS service within the menu of allowable interventions that practitioners can offer in support of a person's recovery. Practitioners are able to count the time dedicated to recovery planning as a part of what they are paid to deliver to PROS participants. This reinforces the value of the PCP plan as being more than just a paper document to satisfy the chart, and it removes a significant disincentive to collaborative planning efforts that exists when this task/time is not covered. In addition, efforts have been made to orient state auditors/reviewers in PCP to minimize the mixed messages that practitioners often point to as a key obstacle in implementation.

From a workforce development perspective, the New York Office of Mental Health (OMH) has committed to providing practitioners with the necessary skills-based training that is pivotal in PCP implementation, and the authors of this chapter have had the opportunity to contribute to that effort. Training for PROS programs typically begins with a two-day skills-based introduction to the topic of PCP where staff are educated about person-centered values as well as the concrete practices in planning meetings and in documentation that reflect those values in action. Following the didactic learning, and consistent with evidence-based adult-learning strategies (Dale, 1969), the trainers facilitate a highly experiential exercise where participants have an opportunity to practice what they have learned and receive feedback on their performance. Using hypothetical case-based assessment data, small groups of participants role play a PCP meeting, craft a written IRP, and present their work to the larger group; after which, trainers critique the plan and offer suggestions for further enhancement. In the authors' experience, it is important to distinguish between a critique and a criticism, as the former reflects a more strengths-based approach to teaching that parallels the strengths-based approach staff are asked to adopt with the individuals they serve.

To support the transfer of learning from the classroom to routine service settings, participating PROS agencies often have the opportunity to receive a series of follow-up technical assistance phone-calls and/or return site visits. Follow-up is tailored to address each individual agency's unique implementation opportunities and barriers and may include the following: case review of written IRPs in accordance with the best-practices covered in the introductory skills training, attendance at actual IRP planning meetings to provide coaching and mentoring, consultation to administrators regarding the balance of person-centered documentation with medical necessity and other regulatory expectations, input regarding the design of planning software and/or electronic health records, development of how-to workbooks and provider tip-sheets that reinforce the best practices of PCP, and education regarding emerging innovative methods and tools that might support the further implementation of person-centered planning. For example, the New York OMH, through a collaboration with the New York Care Coordination Program (NYCCP), has encouraged PROS providers to actively participate in the NYCCP's learning collaborative as well as its online interactive PCP tool, the Recovery Skill Builder (NYCCP, 2012). This tool gives staff the opportunity to practice building PCPs that maintain their person-centered quality while also satisfying rigorous fiscal and accreditation requirements.

Finally, New York State has done significant work to both solicit feedback from and provide support to service users and their families so that they can be better prepared to assume a more active role as partners in person-centered planning. Spreading awareness has been achieved through collaboration with state and local advocacy groups, consumer and family advisory councils, and the New York Association of Psychiatric Rehabilitation Services (NYAPRS). NYAPRS, a statewide coalition of people who use and/or provide community based mental services, is a peer-run organization that is widely recognized for its development of training and technical assistance programs that support recovery, best-practice rehabilitation, and the rights of people with psychiatric disabilities. Several NYAPRS staff trainers have themselves received extensive training in person-centered planning so that they can, in turn, provide support and build PCP capacity amongst their constituents. This has been a significant factor in the sustainability of PCP in the State of New York, and while much work remains to be done, there are many lessons to be learned from this effort as it relates to the transfer of person-centered planning from theory to practice.

SUMMARY

The practice of PCP as outlined in this chapter suggests that the plan of care has the potential to be, and should be, far more than a paperwork requirement. The co-created recovery plan is a manifestation of a respectful partnership as well as a roadmap that outlines a more hopeful vision for the future and how all parties will work together to achieve it. Successful implementation of person-centered planning often requires practitioners and agencies to address multiple complex philosophical and organizational barriers. Yet, motivation to fuel this ongoing transformation effort can be found in the simple truth that person-centered planning is, at its core, about the attainment of goals that are universal to typical human experiences—goals that appreciate our common humanity, our common aspirations and dreams, and our common sense of responsibility to become contributing members of society (Nerney, 2005, p. 4). We hope that we have provided practical guidance regarding the creation of recovery plans that honor the person while also satisfying the chart. Finally, while best practice person-centered planning is a marked departure from more traditional styles of service planning, we hope we have left you with a sense of optimism that this PCP is, in fact, possible provided we all recognize our obligation to, in the words of Dale DiLeo (2008), "stop accepting what is … and start creating what should be."

BEST PRACTICE GUIDELINES FOR PERSON-CENTERED PLANNING

- Begin with a strengths-based assessment.
- Provide individuals using services with opportunities to maximize participation, choice, and control in the planning process.
- Include natural supports and community connections in developing and implementing the plan as desired by the person served.
- Support the "dignity of risk" and the "right to fail."
- Develop a service planning document that is obviously based on person-centered planning principles.

ABOUT THE AUTHORS

Janis Tondora, Psy.D. is assistant professor at the Yale School of Medicine, Program for Recovery and Community Health. Janis' professional interests focus on the design, implementation, and evaluation of services that promote self-determination, recovery, and community inclusion among individuals living with behavioral health conditions. She has provided training and consultation to over a dozen states seeking to implement person-centered planning models, and has shared her work in a variety of publications including a 2009 book co-authored with several colleagues entitled *A Practical Guide to Recovery-Oriented Practice: Tools for Transforming Mental Health Care.*

Chacku Mathai is associate executive director of the New York Association of Psychiatric Rehabilitation Services. Chacku has over twenty-five years experience in mental health and addiction community based services in a wide variety of roles including peer advocate, peer support meeting facilitator, self-help educator, community organizer and educator, community residence manager, psychiatric rehabilitation practitioner, trainer and program administrator. He is an implementation partner for the New York State Center of Excellence for the Integration of Care (CEIC), the SAMHSA Northeast Addiction Technology Transfer Network, the SAMHSA Recovery to Practice Resource Center for Behavioral Health Professionals and the SAMHSA Bringing Recovery Supports To Scale Technical Assistance Center Strategy (BRSS-TACS). He served as a founding board member and advocate for Friends of Recovery—New York, a statewide coalition of people in recovery from addiction and is a former member of the Commission that oversees the Psychiatric Rehabilitation Association (PRA) Certification Program for Certified Psychiatric Rehabilitation Practitioners (CPRP).

Diane Grieder is owner of AliPar, Inc., a behavioral health consulting firm committed to improving organizational performance, and co-author of *Treatment Planning for Person-Centered Care: The Road to Mental Health and Addiction Recovery,* a textbook with Elsevier/Academic Press with Neal Adams MD, published in late 2004. She is a co-author with Dr Adams of a chapter in the *Handbook of Community Psychiatry,* "Collaborative Person-Centered Planning," published by Springer in 2012. She is also a consultant with the National Council of Behavioral Healthcare and with NASMHPD. She was an accreditation surveyor with CARF for more than 17 years, has conducted at least 100 accreditation surveys, served on several CARF National Advisory Committees to develop and revise standards, and provided training at four CARF International Conferences on Behavioral Health.

Larry Davidson, Ph.D. is professor of psychiatry at the Yale School of Medicine where he directs the Program for Recovery and Community Health. His research and practice has focused on understanding processes of recovery in serious mental illnesses and substance use conditions and translating that understanding into the development and evaluation of recovery-oriented policies, systems of care, and innovative, community-based practices, including person-centered care planning, strength-based assessment, and community inclusion.

REFERENCES

Adams, N., & Grieder, D. (2005). *Treatment planning for person-centered care: The road to mental health and addiction recovery.* Burlington, MA: Elsevier.

Berwick, D. (2002). A user manual for the IOM's "quality chasm" report. *Health Affairs, 21,* 80-90.

Copeland, M. E. (1997). *Wellness recovery action plan.* West Dummerston, VT: Peach Press.

Dale, E. (1969). *Audio visual methods in teaching* (3rd ed.). New York: Dryden Press.

Deegan, P. (1996). Recovery as a journey of the heart. *Psychiatric Rehabilitation Journal, 19,* 91-97.

DiLeo, D. (2008, December). Proceedings of the 14th annual Conference for People with Disabilities. Indianapolis, IN.

IAPSRS. (2003). *Language guidelines.* Linthicum, MD: Psychiatric Rehabilitation Association. Retrieved from http://www.psychrehabassociation.org/sites/default/files/images/PRA%20Language%20 Guidelines.pdf

Koyanagi, C., Alfano, E., & Carty, L. (2008). *In the driver's seat: A guide to self-directed mental health care.* Washington, DC: Bazelon Center for Mental Health Law & UPENN Collaborative on Community Integration.

National Research Council. (2006). *Improving the quality of health care for mental and substance-use conditions: Quality chasm series.* Washington, DC: National Academies Press.

National Resource Center on Psychiatric Advance Directives. (2011). *Getting started.* Retrieved from http://www.nrc-pad.org/content/section/6/41

Nerney, T. (2004, March). *Quality issues in consumer/family direction.* Paper prepared for the SAMHSA Consumer Direction Summit, Washington, DC.

New York Care Coordination Program. (2010). *August 2010 program evaluation results.* Retrieved December 15, 2011 from http://www.carecoordination.org/docs/Results%20Book%202010.pdf

New York Care Coordination Program. (2012). Recovery skill builder. Retrieved February 5, 2012 from http://www.carecoordination.org/recoveryplanning

Osher, D., & Keenan, S. (2001). From professional bureaucracy to partner with families. *Reaching Today's Youth, 5*(3), 9-15.

President's New Freedom Commission on Mental Health. (2003). *Achieving the promise: Transforming mental health care in America, final report.* No. Pub. No. SMA-03-3832. Rockville, MD: U.S. Department of Health and Human Services.

Reidy, D. (1992). Shattering illusions of difference. *Resources, 4*(2), 3-6.

Smith, G., Kennedy, C., Knipper, S., O'Brien, J., & O'Keefe, J. (2005). *Using Medicaid to support working for adults with serious mental illnesses in the community: A handbook.* Washington, DC: U.S. Department of Health and Human Services. Retrieved from http://aspe.hhs.gov/daltcp/reports/ handbook.htm

Substance Abuse and Mental Health Services Administration. (2010). *Shared decision-making in mental health care: Practice, research, and future directions.* Rockville, MD: U.S. Department of Health and Human Services. HHS Publication No. SMA-09-4371.

Stuart, G., Tondora, J., & Hoge, M. (2004). Evidence-based teaching practice: Implications for behavioral health. *Administration and Policy in Mental Health, 32*(2), 107-130.

Tondora, J., & Miller, R. (unpublished measure, 2009). *Person-centered care questionnaire (PCCQ), person in recovery & provider version.* New Haven, CT: Yale Program for Recovery and Community Health. Retrieved December 15, 2010 from http://www.yale.edu/PRCH/documents/toolkit. draft.3.5.11.pdf

Tondora, J., Miller, R., Guy, K., & Lanteri, S. (2009). *Getting in the driver's seat of your treatment: Preparing for your plan.* New Haven, CT: Yale Program for Recovery and Community Health. Retrieved from http://www.yale.edu/PRCH/documents/toolkit.draft.3.5.11.pdf

CHAPTER 6

ASSESSMENT

Deborah B. Pitts
Stephania L. Hayes

ABSTRACT

Assessment is considered to be a necessary first step and ongoing process in psychiatric rehabilitation practice. Through a highly individualized strengths-based assessment, a person labeled with a psychiatric disability and a psychiatric rehabilitation practitioner mutually identify the individual's personal strengths and environmental supports available to move recovery forward. In addition, they identify the personal needs that must be met or developed and the environmental barriers that require action. This chapter addresses the importance of assessment for promoting recovery; best practices in psychiatric rehabilitation assessment, including its focus on strengths; and challenges and concerns related to the assessment process in psychiatric rehabilitation.

ASSESSMENT IN PSYCHIATRIC REHABILITATION PRACTICE IS AN ONGOING *PROCESS* THAT THE PERSON IN recovery and his/her psychiatric rehabilitation practitioner engage in mutually to determine the need for and direction of change in the person's daily living skills and/or in his/her living, learning and working environments, as well as to guide the collaborative design of interventions or actions intended to facilitate that change (Corrigan, Mueser, Bond, Drake, & Solomon, 2008, p. 65; Liberman, 2008; MacDonald-Wilson & Nemec, 2006; Pitts & St. George, 2006; Vaccaro, Pitts, & Wallace, 1992; Wallace, 1986). This chapter addresses how assessment can support recovery, offers best practice guidelines for assessment in psychiatric rehabilitation, and describes challenges experienced by practitioners and concerns of people in recovery related to the assessment process.

IMPORTANCE OF STRENGTHS-BASED ASSESSMENT FOR PROMOTING RECOVERY

It is now well understood that recovery for persons labeled with psychiatric disabilities is a complex, dynamic, and personal process that emerges out of an interaction between the individual's unique strengths and vulnerabilities, and the nature of the environmental and contextual supports and barriers the person experiences over time (Davidson et al., 2005; Deegan, 1996; Ridgway, 2001). If psychiatric rehabilitation practitioners are to facilitate recovery for the individuals with whom they are working, they need a way to understand what the individual's recovery goals are, what personal strengths the individual brings to the recovery effort, and what personal needs the person must have met to meet his or her recovery goals as well as what social support and material resources are available to facilitate that recovery. Further, it is well accepted in the psychiatric rehabilitation practice community that the only effective means of reaching such understanding is through a highly individualized strengths-based assessment (Larry Davidson, Tondora, Lawless, O'Connell, & Rowe, 2009; Rapp & Goscha, 2006).

Best Practices in Psychiatric Rehabilitation Assessment

A comprehensive approach to psychiatric rehabilitation assessment is generally understood to include an assessment of (1) the person's readiness and preferences for life changes; (2) the person's everyday functional strengths and needs within the contexts of the persons daily life; and (3) the nature of the person's resource supports and barriers (MacDonald-Wilson & Nemec, 2006; Pitts & St. George, 2006). What counts as a "best practice" in psychiatric rehabilitation assessment has developed over decades and has been informed by the assessment philosophies and practices of various disciplines, including rehabilitation counseling, occupational therapy, psychology, social work, and psychiatry. In addition, it has been informed by the philosophical and structural shifts in mental health services, including the move from institutional settings as the locus of care to community-based interventions delivered in the person's natural environment; the move away from a medical model deficit perspective to a strengths-based recovery perspective; and the move away from relying solely on academically prepared mental health providers to inclusion of mental health consumers and family members as service providers. These shifts have influenced what gets assessed, how the assessment is conducted, *who* or what practitioner conducts which part of the assessment as well as when and where the assessment is completed. The next section of the chapter briefly reviews a current perspective on the components of and methods for assessment in psychiatric rehabilitation, specifically assessing the person's readiness for rehabilitation, strengths and needs, and finally, resource supports and barriers.

Assessing rehabilitation readiness

Early approaches to psychiatric rehabilitation assessment incorporated the notion of assessing a person's readiness for change into the overall process of assessment. It was understood that this was a necessary dimension of practitioners' reasoning needed to design the rehabilitation plan and facilitate behavioral change. In fact, it was seen as part of the professional obligation of the practitioner to either protect the person from taking on too much given the nature of his/her psychiatric disability or to ensure that public resources were used responsibly for persons ready to engage in rehabilitation. As the recovery and strengths (Rapp & Goscha, 2006) perspectives grew in their influence on psychiatric rehabilitation practice, psychiatric rehabilitation researchers and practitioners challenged this traditional notion of readiness (Cohen, Anthony, & Farkas, 1997). They argued that "readiness is a reflection of consumers' interest in rehabilitation and their self-confidence, not of their capacity to complete a rehabilitation program" (p. 644). Drawing on contemporary understanding of how to understand and facilitate behavioral change, Farkas, Soydan, and Gagne (2000) developed an approach to assessing and developing a person's readiness for psychiatric rehabilitation.

The approach is informed by specific assumptions, including an understanding that readiness for rehabilitation can change over time in response to changes in the person's internal and/or external experience and is specific to the environment so that a person might be "ready" to make changes in the home, but not in his/her work/school environment. Another assumption is that the readiness assessment process requires full engagement on the part of the person in recovery. A critical skill set for every psychiatric rehabilitation practitioner is the capacity to create the interpersonal context for engaging in the readiness assessment process. Further, this perspective on rehabilitation readiness is not intended to exclude persons in recovery from service, but rather to provide guidance to the practitioner and the person in recovery for "how best to begin the rehabilitation process" (p. 32). Specifically, when engaged in the process of assessing rehabilitation readiness, the practitioner and the person in recovery explore the:

1. Need for Change or the extent to which a person is either unsuccessful or unsatisfied in his or her current situation;

2. Commitment to Change or the extent to which a person is committed to making changes in his or her life;

3. Personal Closeness or the extent to which he or she is open to connecting with others;

4. Self-Awareness or the extent to which the person has some level of understanding about himself or herself; and

5. Environmental Awareness or the degree to which a person is aware of the differences between environments (Farkas et al., 2000, p. 34).

Through a facilitated reflective dialogue that draws on the practices of motivational interviewing (Miller & Rollnick, 2002) and/or narrative interviewing (Davidson, 2003), the practitioner assists the person in recovery in considering each area as it relates to his/her current life circumstances. This requires sensitive interpersonal and skillful interview skills that facilitate a context of trust and safety. It is important for psychiatric rehabilitation practitioners to develop such interviewing skills. The practitioner should be mindful of sociocultural factors that may affect dialogue about behavioral change, utilization of health services, and prioritization of life domains. All life domains should be explored, including relationships, health and wellness, self-care, housing, productivity, and leisure. Narrative interviewing (Davidson, 2003), in particular, is effective in eliciting life stories that facilitate an understanding of the meaning of particular life experiences to the person in recovery.

Specific interview protocols have been developed that may provide effective guidance for facilitating the reflective dialogue that the assessment of rehabilitation readiness requires. For example, Slade (2009) outlines a recovery-focused interview guide consistent with this perspective in his *Personal Recovery and Mental Illness: A Guide for Mental Health Professionals.* Another example is the *Occupational Performance History Interview–II* (Kielhofner et al., 2004), which was developed for use by occupational therapists. The OPHI-II in particular draws on a clear theoretical framework consistent with the recovery perspective, uses a narrative interview approach, has been found to effective by both practitioners and persons in recovery (Ennals & Fossey, 2007), and has been demonstrated to support recovery (Ennals & Fossey, 2009). More information on this assessment can be obtained from the Model of Human Occupation Clearinghouse (http://www.moho.uic.edu).

Interview protocols can also be paired with self-report measures that can elicit the person's perspective, and sometimes using self-report measures helps facilitate the interview dialogue. Several self-assessments that explore a person's experience with recovery have been developed in recent years. The Evaluation Center at HSRI (www.tecathsri.org) produced two reports listing such measures (Campbell-Orde, Chamberlin, Carpenter, & Leff, 2005; Ralph, Kidder, & PHillips, 2000) and providing summaries of some of these tools.

Assessing functional strengths and needs

The focus of the functional assessment component of a psychiatric rehabilitation assessment is the behavioral routines and skills needed for the life domains targeted for change by the rehabilitation readiness assessment. The starting point for the functional assessment is always the person's expressed goals. Once the person in recovery and the psychiatric rehabilitation practitioner are clear on the person's recovery goals, they will know where to begin the functional assessment.

A person's successful enactment of the behavioral routines and skills needed for specific life domains is influenced by his/her motivational state for those behavioral routines or skills; the context in which the behavioral routine or skill is needed; the person's past successful enactment of the behavioral routine or skill; and his/her cognitive, interpersonal, and physical abilities at the time when the routine or skill needs to be enacted. Motivation and, to some extent, the person's perception of his/her past functional success are assessed primarily through the rehabilitation readiness assessment addressed above. The assessment of the context or environment is addressed in the next section. In completing an assessment of the person's functional strengths and needs, the psychiatric rehabilitation practitioner must gather information about (1) the person's past functional successes and challenges in the major life domain or role that is being assessed, (2) the person's current functional successes and challenges, and (3) the actual demands of the daily living tasks related to the major life domains or roles in which the person is engaged. Functional assessments must help the psychiatric rehabilitation practitioner to know and understand both what skills the person has as well the likelihood that the person will use those skills as needed. Skill areas most typically assessed include communication/interaction, personal/self-care, home-care/domestic routines, community mobility, leisure/recreation, and work/education.

Developing an understanding of a person's past functional successes and challenges is not intended to diminish the practitioner's hopefulness, nor should this information be used to limit the person's access to rehabilitation. Rather, this information is often helpful in understanding times in the person's life when s/he was more able to do the things that s/he needed and wanted to do. Some information regarding the person's past functional success in major life roles may be captured during the readiness assessment; if not, the psychiatric rehabilitation practitioner should gather this information during the functional assessment. In addition, some of this information may be captured during the initial evaluation, including the diagnostic evaluation conducted as part of eligibility determination or entry into publicly funded mental health services. Although these initial evaluations may address past function, it is rarely at a level of detail that is helpful to the psychiatric rehabilitation practitioner. Getting a sense of the person's past functional successes is most typically elicited through an interview with the person and/or with people who have been in the person's life for some time. As in the readiness assessment, the narrative and phenomenological interviewing approach—one that encourages reflection on the meaningfulness of their personal experience—may be helpful here. The practitioner is essentially trying to get a sense of the person's perception of what s/he was able to do before, what types of activities or daily living tasks s/he engaged in, how successful s/he was, what the environment was like in which the person engaged in those daily tasks, what kind of help or supports were available, etc.

Because, as human beings, we often under- or over-estimate our ability to do things, eliciting the person's perception of his/her functional ability, although critical, is not a sufficient means of understanding the person's best ability to function. Therefore, there is a need for performance-based assessments. Performance-based assessments are assessments in which the person in recovery is actually engaged in doing the activity, and the psychiatric rehabilitation practitioner is observing the person's engagement in the task or activity. Most optimally, this observation is being done in the actual context in which the behavioral skills or routines are used or needed. Just as the practitioner must master interviewing skills that build trust and rapport in the initial dialogue about readiness for change, it is important to be mindful of how an assessment is tolerated and to always maintain a supportive environment during the administration of performance-based tests, which can be demoralizing for those who perceive that they are not successful. Occupational therapists and psychologists can provide consultation to other psychiatric rehabilitation practitioners as they both have a long tradition of developing and administering such assessments, which are also referred to as situational assessments.

In recent years, there has been a growing understanding of the critical impact of cognitive functioning on a person's overall ability to successfully complete daily living tasks necessary for success in major life roles (Green, Kern, Braff, & Mintz, 2000; Green & Nuechterlein, 1999). As a result, there has been an increase in the development of performance-based assessments that address both daily life tasks and cognition. For example, the *Test of Grocery Shopping Skills* (Brown, Rempfer, & Hamera, 2009; Brown, Rempfer, Hamera, & Bothwell, 2006) was developed as an in-vivo assessment of a person's level of success with grocery shopping in the local market. For more information on such assessments, the psychiatric rehabilitation practitioner is encouraged to consult with an occupational therapist or neuropsychologist or seek reviews of performance-based assessments and situational assessments in the professional literature.

Finally, it is important for the psychiatric practitioner to have an understanding of the actual cognitive and physical demands required to complete specific daily living tasks. This is essential in order to know what behavioral skills or routines the person will need, or what changes or modifications in the task or activity will be needed to match the person's existing skill set. For this aspect of the assessment process, the practitioner must rely on his/her observation skills as well as on a general understanding of the demands of daily living tasks. Practitioners can also seek consultation from an occupational therapist that has expertise in task or activity analysis. In the area of work, the practitioner can also consult with a vocational rehabilitation counselor or employment specialist, given their expertise in job task analysis.

Assessing environmental resources and barriers

The focus of the environmental assessment component of the psychiatric rehabilitation assessment deals with the socio-cultural, physical, community, financial, and other material resources that will facilitate or impede recovery. Just like in the functional assessment component of the psychiatric rehabilitation assessment, the starting point for the environmental assessment is the person's recovery goals. By having a full understanding of the specific recovery goals, psychiatric rehabilitation practitioners will be able to focus their environmental assessment on particular resources and barriers.

During the rehabilitation readiness assessment, it is likely that some information about the person's preferences for his/her daily living environments were identified. Given that the assessment process is ongoing, the person's preferences for and experiences of his/her daily living environment will need to be continually reassessed as environments are dynamic and constantly changing. Small changes in the social and physical environment can be experienced as profound and, as a result, have significant impact on the person's sense of satisfaction as well as his/her actual functional success within a particular context. It is important for psychiatric rehabilitation practitioners to regularly note material changes in the social and physical contexts as well as to elicit the person's perception of that change.

As psychiatric rehabilitation practitioners provide services within a specific geographic location, they will build familiarity with the local communities in which they are working. This information will include the location of specific resources as well as the specific nature of supports provided and/or the barriers that exist within particular settings within that community. This type of understanding is critical to facilitating the best match for the person in recovery. This is knowledge that develops over time and is often passed from one psychiatric rehabilitation practitioner to the next. Attempts to document this information in some way often fails because the contexts themselves are so dynamic. This is particularly true for housing supports because as landlords or tenants change and/or staff or roommates in residential care homes change, the social dynamics of a particular context changes. What was once thought likely to be a "perfect" match for the person in recovery may no longer make sense given the person's needs and the nature of the supports now available.

Significantly fewer formal assessment tools have been developed and published for assessing the environment and/or context than for the other two components of the psychiatric rehabilitation assessment process. Some aspects of the environmental assessment are captured in many initial assessments used by mental health agencies. These include information about available material and financial resources like income source (e.g.,

Social Security), access to transportation, or presence of and access to family. The breadth and specificity of this information is likely to be modest, so the psychiatric rehabilitation practitioner will need to go well beyond this to complete a thorough environmental assessment.

CHALLENGES IN IMPLEMENTING ASSESSMENT BEST PRACTICES

Challenges to the implementation of assessment best practices can be experienced by the specific psychiatric rehabilitation program or by the psychiatric rehabilitation practitioners themselves. Although levels interact and influence the other, it is helpful to review the unique challenges of each.

Program-Level Challenges

At the program level, some challenges to implementation of psychiatric rehabilitation assessment best practices are the same as those at the organization level, in particular ensuring that all staff are sufficiently trained in the use of the assessment tools and practices adopted by the agency. At the program level, however, the challenge becomes specific, meaning that the program needs to have staff trained in the use of assessments that meet the needs of that particular program. Because distinct psychiatric rehabilitation programs may target particular major life domains or roles (living, learning, or working), each program will need to have some assessment tools and practices that address specific strengths and needs in that domain. In addition, because many different assessment tools have been developed, a specific program will need to continually evaluate the effectiveness of the assessment tools in use. As with the organization level, this evaluation process can sometimes be facilitated by engaging in accreditation. When deciding which specific assessment tools to use to conduct each component of the psychiatric rehabilitation assessment—readiness, functional, and/or environmental assessment—psychiatric rehabilitation programs must answer the following questions:

- Is the tool relevant to the needs of your program and the people you serve? Does the assessment tool generate information that fits your needs? Does the assessment elicit information that addresses the overall purpose of the evaluation? Is this the right assessment for this particular program as well as the person in this context at this time?

- Is the assessment feasible to use given the unique resources of the program? Can the assessment tool be used with available resources? Do you have the competency, time, materials, support, etc., to use the assessment? Certain assessments are time-intensive to learn how to use as well as to administer, some may only be administered by a practitioner with particular credentials, or they may require specific equipment and materials that are costly, technical, or non-portable.

- Will the information gathered by the assessment be useful? Who benefits and how do they benefit? Many assessments are time-intensive and therefore costly to the persons being served and to the organization that serves them. Therefore, the information gathered by using that particular assessment should have value both to the person in recovery and the program. It is important that the information gathered will result in critical information that will improve the likelihood that the recovery plan will be successful.

• Is there evidence to support the use of the tool? Have reliability and validity studies been conducted to show that it can accurately reflect a true performance of the individual and that it does measure what it proposes to measure? Have there been studies that demonstrate the effectiveness of the assessment tool with persons in recovery participating in programs like yours?

Practitioner-Level Challenges

Psychiatric rehabilitation practitioners may experience challenges in their efforts to implement best practices for readiness, functional, and environmental assessments. Psychiatric practitioners vary significantly in the life experiences from which they can draw to understand the demands of various daily life tasks, such as the psychiatric rehabilitation and other mental health settings in which they have worked and now practice as well their actual formal and informal learning of and experience with specific assessment tools and approaches to psychiatric rehabilitation assessment. For many, the first formal introduction to assessment processes comes when they enter their first jobs as psychiatric rehabilitation providers. They may not have completed an undergraduate or graduate degree in a psychiatric rehabilitation or mental health/health care field, such as occupational therapy, social work, rehabilitation counseling, nursing, or psychology. They may come to their roles as psychiatric rehabilitation practitioners because of their life experiences, which are important for supporting the person in recovery, but they may be limited in their understanding of assessment best practices.

In addition, depending on the setting in which they are working, practitioners may or may not have the opportunity for formal learning sessions and/or apprentice experiences for learning how to use the assessment tools and processes adopted by that agency. In some settings, there may be a much more informal or self-directed learning expectation—a kind of "learn by the seat of your pants" approach to becoming proficient in the assessment tools and practices used by that particular agency or setting. It may also be the case that the agency does not use formal or standardized assessment tools and processes, but may have developed forms or may use official forms required by the local mental health authority on which information about the person in recovery is to be documented while leaving it up to the provider to determine how to gather the information required.

CONCERNS IN IMPLEMENTING ASSESSMENT BEST PRACTICES

Common concerns that persons in recovery may have regarding the implementation of psychiatric rehabilitation assessment best practices include (1) how the assessment is implemented, in particular the temporal, spatial, and interpersonal dimensions of the assessment; and (2) how the information that is elicited through the assessment process is used by the individual practitioner, the mental health or psychiatric rehabilitation organization, and/or by the mental health system itself. As noted early in this chapter, assessment is understood as the first step in the psychiatric rehabilitation process. No matter how formal or informal that assessment process is, it is something that the person in recovery can experience as helpful or not and has the potential to influence his/her utilization of psychiatric rehabilitation services to support recovery.

Concerns for How the Assessment Is Implemented

Persons in recovery have called upon practitioners to see them as people first, and the field of psychiatric rehabilitation has long held this principle as well. The psychiatric rehabilitation practitioner can enact this principle by attending to the temporal, spatial, and interpersonal dimensions of the assessment process. Despite funding and other organizational constraints, adequate time is needed to develop a full understanding of a person's readiness and motivation as well as his/her functional and resource strengths and needs. Practitioners should not let the time demands for conducting and documenting assessment information override the very real person-to-person interaction that is occurring. This is especially important when interacting with persons that Deegan (1996) describes as "hard of heart" or having lost hope. Each encounter that a person who is "hard of heart" has with a supportive, understanding practitioner has the potential to facilitate engagement. By focusing solely on filling out the forms and getting them submitted on time, the practitioner risks reinforcing a feeling of hopelessness in the person served.

Since the focus of psychiatric rehabilitation is on the daily life of the person in recovery, psychiatric rehabilitation practitioners often conduct the assessment process in the natural environment. This may help the psychiatric rehabilitation practitioner to keep the person first principle in mind. However, whether you are conducting the assessment process at your agency or in the natural environment, it is important to attend to characteristics of the space. For example, when conducting an interview, is there privacy if needed or desired by the person in recovery? Is there social support available if desired by the person? Are there minimal distractions? When the practitioner is using a standardized interview assessment tool, there will be guidelines for optimizing the success of the interview, including those that address "person first" characteristics. As with the temporal dimensions, attending to the spatial dimensions of an interview can influence how the person in recovery experiences the assessment process. Don't let the very real challenges that may be created by the specific physical layout and characteristics of your psychiatric rehabilitation program distract you from attending to the "person first" principle during the assessment process.

There is significant guidance in most psychiatric rehabilitation programs regarding the importance of the interpersonal relationship in supporting recovery. It is clearly understood that psychiatric rehabilitation practice is, at its most basic, an interpersonal practice. That said, it is the interpersonal behavior of practitioners that persons in recovery often find most troubling. Persons in recovery often describe feeling disrespected and demeaned by practitioners, for example, being ignored when they are in need or talked to as if they were children. Being mindful and reflective are important skills to develop and enact to reduce the risk of engaging in interpersonal interactions that do not support recovery, particularly when completing the psychiatric rehabilitation assessment.

Concern for How Assessment Information Is Used

Another broad area of concern that persons in recovery have regarding the assessment process is how the information that is elicited during an assessment will be used by the individual practitioner, the program, or organization with whom the practitioner works and/or the mental health system itself. Information obtained during an assessment and the interpretations that practitioners make about that information are frequently used to make determinations about access to psychiatric rehabilitation services. Because assessment information may be used for such decision making, persons in recovery often worry that if they respond in a particular way or describe particular experiences or do not communicate a particular enthusiasm or desire for change, they will not be referred or approved for entry into a psychiatric rehabilitation program. This is especially concerning when there are limited opportunities available in a local community for particular services or programs, and this is often the case given the limited availability of many best practice psychiatric rehabilitation programs. For example, supported housing programs can have more than ten applicants for each individual housing unit that is available. Individual practitioners and organizations must be sensitive to this concern when conducting assessments, especially when they use assessment information to make admit/reject decisions. This sensitivity is particularly important given our limited ability to use assessment information to accurately predict who will or won't be successful in a given program.

Persons labeled with psychiatric disabilities may participate in a range of psychiatric rehabilitation and other mental health programs during their journey of recovery. Given the structure and funding of mental health services in the United States, this means persons may receive services from several different agencies or organizations even when they maintain their services within a small geographic area. As they move from program to program, they are engaged in assessment processes conducted by each single agency, program, and/ or practitioner with whom they work. These assessment processes may be very similar even within the same agency. In addition, it is a common practice in agencies to allow each program to engage in a unique assessment process to ensure the best fit between the person in recovery and the program. Even when separate agencies have well-established referral processes and staff who have collaborated with each other over several years, the agency receiving the referral still conducts a new assessment. It is unusual to rely solely on the assessment conducted by the referring agency. Having to participate in assessment after assessment can be a frustrating and degrading experience for the person in recovery, especially if after participating in the assessment, a determination is made to not accept the referral.

Documentation of the information captured or elicited during an assessment is a necessary part of all health and mental health care services. Although some mental health funding sources, non-Medicaid and private insurance primarily, may have substantially modest documentation requirements, they still require some documentation. Even though HIPAA protections are in place for disclosure of documentation, the mere fact that psychiatric rehabilitation assessments are documented means that a person's daily life experiences of success and difficulty can be accessed. Further, because documentation is more than just recording facts, and usually only represents the practitioner's interpretation of the person's daily life experiences (few official record keeping systems include the person in recovery's documentation of their own experiences), information may be incomplete and/or represent misunderstandings of the person's experience. Most practitioners are sensitive to the problems inherent in current documentation systems, even those that require the practitioner to include the words of the person served (e.g., Commission on Accreditation of Rehabilitation Facilities accreditation requirements). In addition, the adoption of the person-centered, strengths-based, recovery-oriented practices increase the likelihood that the interpretative work that practitioners must engage in during the assessment process limits the risk of misunderstandings of the person's experience.

EXAMPLE OF SUCCESSFUL IMPLEMENTATION

Southland Community Mental Health Center (CHMC) provides publicly funded community-based mental health services to persons at risk for and/or labeled with psychiatric disorders across the life span. The state, as well as the county in which Southland CMHC is located, has adopted the recovery perspective promoted by the Substance Abuse and Mental Health Administration (SAMHSA) as an organizing framework for its adult services. In addition, the state has mandated that agencies prioritize the delivery of evidence-based interventions. As part of its ongoing performance improvement activities, the leadership team wanted to improve their psychiatric rehabilitation assessment practices. Although they felt confident about their diagnostic and crisis response assessment activities, they wanted to be better able to help the persons they serve identify their recovery goals and provide staff with more effective tools to better understand their clients'/members' unique strengths and needs as well as their resources and barriers.

The leadership team appointed an ad hoc workgroup of volunteer representatives from the peer support/supported education program, the assertive community treatment teams, and the supported employment programs with the charge of reviewing the current psychiatric rehabilitation assessment processes and making recommendations for improvement. The work group began by looking at the current psychiatric rehabilitation assessment processes and found that each program had its own separate assessment activities. These activities were more influenced by (1) the requirements of funding sources (e.g., Medicaid, Department of Rehabilitation) for certain kinds of information (e.g., medical necessity) and/or (2) the specific practice experience, knowledge, and preferences of the specific provider (i.e., peer provider, occupational therapist, nurse, employment specialist, etc.) rather than by the best evidence regarding psychiatric rehabilitation assessment. Although funding source requirements clearly had to be addressed and each provider's expertise was a vital resource, the work group determined that more consistency across programs would benefit the agency. It would improve the quality of the assessment process and could serve to reduce redundancies. Since service providers often moved from program to program during their tenure with the agency, as did the people who used services, efficiencies in staff training and service user transitions could be achieved by having a more integrated approach to assessment.

The work group then completed a thorough review of the psychiatric rehabilitation literature and web resources for best practices in psychiatric rehabilitation assessment. They also sought out expertise from the local university, which had psychiatric nursing, occupational therapy, and social work professional education programs for which the agency had long served as field practicum sites. In addition, the university had a SAMSHA-funded mental health research center that focused on recovery-oriented psychiatric rehabilitation interventions. The work group recommended that the agency adopt the framework proposed in this chapter for a psychiatric rehabilitation assessment. They then completed a thorough review of various evidence-based assessment tools that could be used to facilitate the readiness, functional, and environmental assessment components of the assessment. The work group used agency-specific criteria to ensure that there was a good match between the tools that they selected and the needs of the target population, the nature of the evidence-based interventions they were providing as well as the agency's staffing, regulatory, and financial resources. Several tools were selected, some of which were to be used with each new service user, and others that would be used on an as-needed basis or only by staff qualified to administer that particular assessment.

This process took several months, but the work group eventually produced new policies and procedures and successfully obtained funding from a local community foundation to procure copies of the assessment manuals and provide staff with training in their use. They also received support from the university faculty as well as agency staff that had expertise in the use of some of the assessments. The agency had previous experience in adopting and transitioning to evidence-based interventions, and used the same process for rolling out and enlisting staff commitment for implementation of the new psychiatric rehabilitation assessment process. During a one-year period, the agency successfully implemented the new psychiatric rehabilitation assessment process.

A Description of the Assessment Process

Marcia is an occupational therapist by education and worked on one of the ACT teams. She graduated from the local University's entry-level Master's professional occupational therapy program and completed her professional education fieldwork with one of the agency's other ACT teams. She represented her team on the ad hoc work group that developed the new psychiatric rehabilitation assessment process, and took the lead with her team in implementing the new process. Given her expertise, she had been particularly involved in identifying the performance-based assessments that the agency had decided to adopt as part of the assessment of functional strengths and needs component.

The team had just received a new referral and one of the other team members had completed the readiness assessment. Josh was referred to the ACT team to assist him in moving out of the IMD (Institute for Mental Disease) in which he had been living and receiving treatment for the past year. The staff at the IMD had determined that he no longer needed the functional support provided by their program and made the referral to the ACT team. To complete the *readiness assessment,* the ACT team member used a recovery-focused interview guide (Slade, 2009), one of the assessment tools that was selected by the agency work group. Here is the outcome of the initial readiness assessment, which focused on Josh's housing preferences:

> Josh was happy to be leaving the IMD. He had not been satisfied with his stay because of the restrictions and requirements to go to groups. He really enjoys listening to the radio, but the staff didn't let him do that as much as he wanted. He had never been a very active person and had never liked school, and the groups remind him of sitting in a classroom. He wasn't really sure where he wanted to live, but remembered having lived in board and care homes before he came to the IMD. He liked the companionship and the availability of meals at the board and care home. He also liked having a house manager to help him with his medication and laundry. Although he had been taking his medication with the help of the staff at the IMD, he remembered that in the past, he would stop taking his medication. He thought that was why he had to leave the board and care homes where he had been living. He likes the doctor he was working with at the IMD because she listens, and was happy that she works with the ACT team as well. He thought that this would be helpful.

The team decided to have Marcia complete the assessment of functional strengths and needs, given her expertise as an occupational therapist. The readiness assessment had identified Josh's awareness of his need for support to take his medication, and he had past unsuccessful attempts at living in the community and his recent long stay in a high-support facility. As a result, Marcia decided that it was important to assess Josh's functional cognition. By doing so, she could discover information about how Josh's cognitive abilities, such as language usage, memory, and attention, affect his performance in day-to-day tasks. This would help the team identify what type of cognitive supports Josh would need and what level of housing would be the best fit. This assessment allowed Marcia to capture both Josh's perception of his functional strengths and needs as well as those of the IMD staff with which he had been working. In addition, the results served as a performance-based assessment, which had been prioritized by the agency work group. Here is the outcome of the functional assessment:

When Marcia arrived at the IMD, she learned that the staff at the IMD used a cognitive support approach, known as Cognitive Adaptation Training (Velligan et al., 2000) to help them individually tailor the cognitive supports to Josh's needs. Marcia was familiar with this approach and rather than re-assessing Josh using the assessment tools that her team had selected, she used the information from the IMD staff as it provided her team with what they needed to know to support Josh in his transition. Josh was able to perform all of his self-care tasks with targeted cognitive supports, such as daily checklists and reminder alarms for his medications. He expressed pride in how he had changed since he first came to the IMD.

In assessing the environmental resources and barriers for Josh's transition from the IMD, the team explored with Josh both a small group home and a supported housing apartment. During the readiness assessment, Josh had expressed a preference for a living arrangement where he would have companionship and help with some of his daily routines. In addition, because he had Supplemental Security Income (SSI), but not a Section 8 housing voucher, the team identified two small group homes that had openings for Josh to visit. Josh decided that he preferred the group home that had a big backyard where he could hang out and was within walking distance of the local library. He also felt more comfortable with the house manager at that home as she talked about enjoying listening to the radio.

OTHER CONSIDERATIONS, ISSUES, FACTORS, IMPLICATIONS

Other considerations in the adoption and implementation of psychiatric rehabilitation assessment for organizations includes having sufficient resources for initial and ongoing staff training and development, developing and maintaining processes to ensure that assessment best practices are consistently implemented across programs and providers, and being responsive to the changing requirements of funders.

Given the nature of the funding for most psychiatric rehabilitation and mental health agencies, resources for initial and ongoing staff training are limited. Agencies must make thoughtful decisions about what training needs they target and about how to design an effective and sustainable training program. It is often both financially and operationally difficult to pull a provider "off-line" to participate in training despite its importance in many staff competencies. In addition, there is always ongoing staff turnover, either when practitioners are moving from one program to another within the same agency or when they leave the agency all together. As a practitioner moves from one program to another, s/he will likely require new training for assessment tools and practices unique to that specific program, and of course, when staff leave the agency, training of new staff is required as well. Further, agencies must invest in the development and maintenance of mechanisms that ensure the consistent quality of the assessment practices they adopt. This is often achieved by participating in a formal accreditation process with organizations like the Commission on Accreditation of Rehabilitation Facilities (www.carf.org) or the International Center for Clubhouse Development (www.iccd.org). Standards for the focus and approach to the assessment of persons the agency serves are usually defined by such organizations, and in order to achieve accreditation, the agency must meet those standards.

Many funders require agencies to be able to demonstrate how well they have helped the persons they serve to meet their recovery goals, and this is often demonstrated by showing changes in functional status. Unfortunately, most of the tools that are used to measure change in functional status do not provide psychiatric rehabilitation practitioners with the kind of information that they will need to help the person in recovery make those changes. These tools, called outcomes measures, rate a person's level of function at a particular time and are often targeting global levels of functioning. For example, they may indicate whether a person is working or not, but provide little information about the person's perceived readiness to meet their recovery goals, the person's behavioral skills and routine strengths and needs, or the person's environmental resources and barriers. Staff time must often be used to complete these outcomes measures because their documentation is mandated by the funder. Although there has been some effort to develop assessment tools that serve as outcomes measures and help develop recovery plans, these are rarely the ones mandated.

SUMMARY

As noted in the introduction to this chapter, in the psychiatric rehabilitation process, assessment is a necessary first step. When done effectively, it provides the person in recovery and the psychiatric rehabilitation practitioners with whom they are working guidance for their work together. This chapter drew on the psychiatric rehabilitation literature and described the psychiatric rehabilitation assessment as a strengths-focused assessment that includes three components: (1) a readiness assessment, (2) an assessment of the person's functional strengths and needs, and (3) an assessment of the environmental and/or contextual resources and barriers. Best practices for each component were noted, including the importance of using well-delivered interviews for eliciting the person's perspective and the use of real-world, natural environment assessments to understand the person's functional strengths and needs. It was emphasized that the common cognitive challenges persons labeled with psychiatric disabilities experience may mediate successful daily functioning and should be assessed. The importance of using evidence-based assessments was also noted in keeping with the broader emphasis on evidence-based practices in healthcare. Finally, concerns experienced by persons in recovery and challenges experienced by practitioners were considered. It was emphasized that from the perspective of persons in recovery, practitioners must be attentive to how assessments are conducted as well as how the information is used and communicated to facilitate recovery.

BEST PRACTICE GUIDELINES FOR PSYCHIATRIC REHABILITATION ASSESSMENT

• Use a strengths-focused assessment that includes three components: a readiness assessment, an assessment of the person's functional strengths and needs; and an assessment of the environmental and/or contextual resources and barriers.

- Elicit the person's perspective through a series of engaging interviews that build trust while gathering information.

- Use real-world, natural environment assessments to understand the person's functional strengths and needs.

- Include a consideration of the common cognitive challenges experienced by persons labeled with psychiatric disabilities and how those may mediate successful daily functioning.

- Use evidence-based assessment tools whenever available.

- Attend to how assessments are conducted as well as how the information is used and communicated to facilitate recovery.

ABOUT THE AUTHORS

Deborah B. Pitts, PhD, OTR/L, BCMH, CPRP is an assistant professor of clinical occupational therapy with the USC Department of Occupational Science and Occupational Therapy. She has developed an expertise in the philosophy and practice of psychiatric rehabilitation. She has provided consultation to providers of community-based psychiatric rehabilitation services in California. She has conducted numerous workshops and published in the occupational therapy, psychiatric rehabilitation, and mental health literature on these topics as well.

Stephania L. Hayes, MA, OTR is an occupational therapist with direct practice experience in community mental health settings. She is currently a doctoral student at the University of California, Berkeley School of Social Welfare and an affiliate of the Mack Center on Mental Health and Social Conflict. Her recent work focuses on self-help, consumer-operated mental health services, and the validation and use of recovery-oriented assessments with adults seeking support.

REFERENCES

Brown, C., Rempfer, M. V., & Hamera, E. (2009). *Test of grocery shopping skills.* Bethesda, MD: American Occupational Therapy Association.

Brown, C., Rempfer, M. V., Hamera, E., & Bothwell, R. (2006). Knowledge of grocery shopping skills as a mediator of cognition and performance. *Psychiatric Services, 57*(4), 573-575. doi: 10.1176/appi. ps.57.4.573

Campbell-Orde, T., Chamberlin, J., Carpenter, J., & Leff, H. S. (2005). *Measuring the promise: A compendium of recovery measures, Volume II.* Cambridge, MA: The Evaluation Center @ HSRI.

Cohen, M., Anthony, W., & Farkas, M. (1997). Assessing and developing readiness for psychiatric rehabilitation. *Psychiatric Services, 48*(5), 644-646.

Corrigan, P. W., Mueser, K. T., Bond, G. R., Drake, R. E., & Solomon, P. L. (2008). *Rehabilitation assessment principles and practice of psychiatric rehabilitation: An empirical approach* (pp. 79-114). New York: The Guilford Press.

Davidson, L. (2003). *Living outside mental illness: Qualitative studies of recovery in schizophrenia.* New York: New York University Press.

Davidson, L., Borg, M., Marin, I., Topor, A., Mezzina, R., & Sells, D. (2005). Processes of recovery in serious mental illness: Findings from a multinational study. *American Journal of Psychiatric Rehabilitation, 8*(3), 177-201.

Davidson, L., Tondora, J., Lawless, M. S., O'Connell, M. J., & Rowe, M. (2009). *A practical guide to recovery-oriented practice: Tools for transforming mental health care.* New York: Oxford University Press.

Deegan, P. (1996). Recovery as a journey of heart. *Psychiatric Rehabilitation Journal, 19*(3), 91-97.

Ennals, P., & Fossey, E. (2007). The occupational performance history interview in community mental health case management: Consumer and occupational therapist perspectives. *Australian Occupational Therapy Journal, 54*(1), 11-21. doi: 10.1111/j.1440-1630.2006.00593.x

Ennals, P., & Fossey, E. (2009). Using the OPHI-II to support people with mental illness in their recovery. *Occupational Therapy in Mental Health, 25*(2), 138-150.

Farkas, M., Soydan, A. S., & Gagne, C. (2000). *Introduction to rehabilitation readiness.* Boston, MA: Boston University Center for Psychiatric Rehabilitation.

Green, M. F., Kern, R. S., Braff, D. L., & Mintz, J. (2000). Neurocognitive deficits and functional outcome in schizophrenia: Are we measuring the "right stuff"? *Schizophrenia Bulletin, 26*(1), 119-136.

Green, M. F., & Nuechterlein, K. H. (1999). Should schizophrenia be treated as a neurocognitive disorder? *Schizophrenia Bulletin, 25*(2), 309-319.

Kielhofner, G., Mallinson, K., Crawford, C., Nowak, M., Rigby, M., Henry, A., & Walens, D. (2004). *Occupational performance history interview–II (Version 2.1).* Chicago, IL: Model of Human Occupation Clearinghouse, Department of Occuaptional Therapy, College of Applied Health Sciences, University of Illinois.

Liberman, R. P. (2008). *Functional assessment recovery from disability: Manual of psychiatric rehabilitation* (pp. 89-152). Washington, DC: American Psychiatric Association.

MacDonald-Wilson, K., & Nemec, P. B. (2006). Assessment in psychiatric rehabilitation. In B. Bolton (Ed.), *Handbook of measurement and evaluation rehabilitation* (4th ed). Baltimore, MD: Paul Brookes.

Miller, W. R., & Rollnick, S. (2002). *Motivational interviewing: Preparing people for change.* New York: The Guilford Press.

Pitts, D., & St. George, L. (2006). Assessment. In M. S. Salzer (Ed.), *Psychiatric rehabilitation skills in practice: A CPRP preparation and skills workbook.* Linthicum, MD: USPRA.

Ralph, R. O., Kidder, K. A., & Phillips, D. (2000). Can we measure recovery? A compendium of recovery and recovery-related instruments. Cambridge, MA: The Evaluation Center @ HSRI.

Rapp, C., & Goscha, R. (2006). *The strengths model: Case management with people with psychiatric disabilities* (2nd ed.). New York: Oxford University Press.

Ridgway, P. (2001). ReStorying psychiatric disability: Learning from first-person recovery narratives. *Psychiatric Rehabilitation Journal, 24*(4), 335-343.

Slade, M. (2009). *Personal recovery and mental illness: A guide for mental health professionals.* New York: Cambridge University Press.

Vaccaro, J. V., Pitts, D. B., & Wallace, C. J. (1992). Functional assessment in psychiatric rehabilitation. In R. P. Liberman (Ed.), *Handbook of psychiatric rehabilitation* (pp. 78-94). New York: MacMillan Publishing Company.

Velligan, D. I., Bow-Thomas, C., Huntzinger, C., Ritch, J., Ledbetter, N., Prihoda, T. J., & Miller, A. L. (2000). Randomized controlled trial of the use of compensatory strategies to enhance adaptive functioning in outpatients with schizophrenia. *The American Journal of Psychiatry, 157*(8), 1317-1328.

Wallace, C. J. (1986). Functional assessment in rehabilitation. *Schizophrenia Bulletin, 12*(4), 604-630. doi: 10.1093/schbul/12.4.604

CHAPTER 7

PSYCHIATRIC REHABILITATION INTERVENTIONS

Patricia B. Nemec
Steve LaMaster
Lisa Halpern

ABSTRACT

Interventions include the actions taken by service providers to help individuals achieve their personal recovery goals. By viewing interventions as different from services or program models, service providers are better able to specify needed interventions on an individual's service plan to obtain positive outcomes. Psychiatric rehabilitation interventions aim to build skills and supports. This chapter gives a brief overview that differentiates psychiatric rehabilitation interventions from treatment, crisis intervention, and service coordination services and emphasizes the importance of ensuring integration across interventions and service types. Since engaging a person in services is a critical first step in the psychiatric rehabilitation process, this chapter also briefly discusses engagement strategies and activities geared towards discovering and enhancing motivation. Delivering rehabilitation interventions requires trained staff and ongoing supervision as well as compatible program structures and documentation requirements.

INTERVENTIONS ARE THE ACTIONS SERVICE PROVIDERS TAKE TO HELP INDIVIDUALS ACHIEVE THEIR personal recovery goals, and in a service plan, they indicate the methods by which goals and objectives are achieved. This chapter provides an overview of interventions that are commonly considered part of psychiatric rehabilitation. As described here, interventions are seen as independent of service domain (e.g., vocational, residential, educational) and of service model (e.g., clubhouse, inpatient facility, recovery/wellness center, supported employment program). Service models define a program structure that describes how services are delivered (staffing, hours, location, etc.). An intervention, as the term is used here, describes the types of interactions and activities to be used when delivering services and may include recommended tools and techniques. An intervention can be used in a variety of service models, and a single service model can make use of a variety of interventions.

Interventions are the things service providers do to provide rehabilitation service to promote recovery and help individuals make progress towards their own personal goals. Ultimately, service providers are paid to deliver interventions. Assessment and planning are for the purpose of deciding what interventions are likely to be effective because if the intervention doesn't work, then there's no reason to be doing it.

Psychiatric rehabilitation promotes recovery with the ideal of helping people with psychiatric disabilities achieve a life of meaning and purpose. How that meaning and purpose is defined is unique to each person, but once clarified, provides a target for service delivery. The processes of assessment and planning help define the target (goals and objectives) as well as any barriers to reaching the target. Interventions are selected to remove those barriers and build the person's resources and abilities so that reaching that ultimate target is possible.

WHAT MAKES SOMETHING A "PSYCH REHAB" INTERVENTION?

Psychiatric rehabilitation interventions are typically defined as building the skills and supports needed to help people choose and achieve their personal goals (Anthony, Cohen, Farkas, & Gagne, 2002) and are considered analogous to physical rehabilitation interventions (Anthony, 1982). Other types of interventions and services may be required as many people with psychiatric disabilities have multiple service needs that need to be addressed. In addition to psychiatric rehabilitation services or interventions, a person may benefit from crisis prevention and management services, which focus on immediate problem resolution; treatment services focused on symptom reduction, and service coordination (also known as "case management") services focused on accessing resources and collateral services (Cohen, Nemec, Farkas, & Forbess, 1988). All of these service types are important and should be delivered in a collaborative and coordinated manner that addresses the needs of a particular individual. Often described as integrated services, this cross-service coordination is a recognized principle of several of the SAMHSA-endorsed evidence-based practices (Drake, Merrens, & Lynde, 2005).

Psychiatric rehabilitation interventions are focused on meeting the needs and desires of an individual, not on a diagnostic category or label. Psychiatric rehabilitation practitioners recognize that the person is not the condition, but has personal strengths as well as disability-related limitations. Sensitive recovery-oriented language should be expected in documentation and in all interactions to create a positive climate and to keep the focus on strengths. Psychiatric rehabilitation interventions build on the person's existing strengths and develop new strength areas, while aiming to eliminate, lessen, or compensate for any limitations.

WHAT IS A BEST PRACTICE INTERVENTION?

Some service providers and many people who use services are confused about the terms best practice and evidence-based practice. A best practice meets several broad criteria. It is valued by the people who use it, has been evaluated as effective through high quality research, and has been implemented correctly by a competent practitioner (Drake et al., 2005). No universal definition exists for what level of effectiveness or correctness (technically termed fidelity) must be achieved in order for a method to be considered a best practice.

Evidence-based practice (EBP) is the term of choice in psychiatric rehabilitation and in this field, generally refers to a service model rather than a specific activity one practitioner would use in delivering services. In publicly funded mental health services, the choice of service models often rests with the funder rather than the practitioners or programs responsible for implementing the service model. As commonly used, the concept of evidence-based practice recognizes the importance of understanding and following research recommendations, while taking into account the service provider's clinical expertise and the goals, preferences, interests, values, and characteristics of the people using the service (Drake, Merrens, & Lynde, 2006). Empirically supported treatment (EST) is a slightly different concept that typically refers to a type of intervention (not a service model) that has been proven effective (Chambless & Ollendick, 2001), such as cognitive behavior therapy for treatment of depression.

Evidence-based medicine (EBM), a third way of thinking about evidence-based practice, refers to the process an individual practitioner follows in selecting the appropriate intervention for one individual diagnosed with a particular condition who is experiencing specific symptoms. The practitioner uses a structured and shared decision-making process that takes into account the existing research supporting a particular intervention, the characteristics of that person, such as age, co-morbid conditions, and treatment history; and the person's goals, values, and preferences. EBM, then, describes a process of interaction, not just a label for a particular intervention or service model.

In psychiatric rehabilitation, some experts argue the concept of best practice needs to consider both practices and processes (Anthony, 2003; Stanhope & Solomon, 2008), recognizing that the medium for service delivery is the relationship between the person providing services and the person using services. Regardless of the specific intervention used, attending to the relationship development processes is critical for success. An American Psychological Association task force (Norcross, 2002) concluded that effective individual psychotherapy requires three relationship components: demonstrating empathy, monitoring the alliance, and achieving goal consensus. These relationship factors are likely important in psychiatric rehabilitation as well, but are not always explicitly included in descriptions of EBPs and ESTs.

Demonstrating empathy involves letting the other person know that you understand his or her experience. When a person feels understood and accepted, the door is open to building a relationship of trust. Monitoring the alliance refers to keeping an eye on how the relationship is developing. Is the person using services an active participant who expresses preferences and makes decisions? Do the service provider and service user work as partners or at cross purposes? Achieving goal consensus means that the service provider and service user agree on the purposes of any interventions. Such consensus has long been a foundational principle in psychiatric rehabilitation as represented in the established values of choice and self-determination as well as the newer concepts of person-centered planning and shared decision making.

This chapter presents three broad categories of psychiatric intervention, skill development, support development, and engagement, which vary in the degree to which they might be considered evidence-based. The first, skill development, has been found effective in the area of social skills (see, e.g., Bellack, Mueser, Gingerich, & Agresta, 2003; Corrigan, Mueser, Bond, Drake, & Solomon, 2008). Support development has not been as well defined as skill development, nor has it been studied as thoroughly. The third, engagement, remains poorly defined and virtually unstudied.

Skill Development

A skill is a complex action, made up of both knowledge and behavior (Cohen, Danley, & Nemec, 1985). A behavior is a simple observable action (like sitting or waving) and is conceptually smaller than a skill. An activity is composed of many skills. For example, smiling is a behavior, but introducing yourself to a stranger is a skill. Communication is an activity that includes the skills of introducing yourself and starting a conversation. Maintaining personal hygiene is another activity composed of many skills, such as the skills of shampooing hair, brushing teeth, and shaving. A skill typically involves a number of simple actions, such as squeezing the shampoo bottle, scrubbing, and rinsing. This distinction may seem silly and/ or confusing, as "the words themselves retain their superficial simplicity [but] the familiar becomes unfamiliar as implicit, connotative meanings are replaced by highly operationalized, rehabilitation-specific meanings" (Lilleleht, 2005, p. 9). However, differentiating these terms helps practitioners understand that activities need to be broken down into skills in order to be taught and to make it possible to deliver a skill development intervention that is targeted to a person's actual need.

The two most comprehensive and best defined methods of skill development are skills training (Bellack et al., 2003) and direct skills teaching (Cohen, Danley, & Nemec, 1985; Nemec, McNamara, & Walsh, 1992). While skills training and direct skills teaching differ somewhat in design and delivery (Nemec, McNamara, & Walsh, 1992), they are both based on fundamental principles of skill development, including learner choice and involvement, individualization, the importance of structure and preparation, the need for instructor expertise, practicality and manageability of the instructional lesson, and the need for independence of performance for the skill being taught (freedom from prerequisites or demonstrated mastery of any prerequisite skills).

Both methods of skill development incorporate behavioral techniques and practices related to effective adult education and social learning theories, including modeling and general-ization. Modeling means that a competent performer shows the learner how the skill is done (Bellack et al., 2003) and often includes explanations and descriptions of the critical aspects of performance. Generalization means ensuring successful performance outside the classroom in the real life circumstance where the skill is required.

As developed by the Boston University Center for Psychiatric Rehabilitation, direct skills teaching is a highly structured process:

> One segment follows another in a logical fashion. The prepared lesson plan leads the learner from hearing about the skill, to seeing the skill performed, to practicing the skill in the learning setting. Preparing the lesson requires that the instructor think through the elements of the skill: its definition, the benefit of performing the skill, the conditions under which the skill is performed, and its component behaviors. This preparation requires the instructor to have a thorough understanding of the skill and results in a clear focus for teaching. Accurate identification of which critical behavioral components to teach requires that the instructor know the learner well. This enables the instructor to differentiate the parts of the skill with which the learner needs help from the parts that she or he can perform with ease…. [T]he skills taught are practical, that is, they are manageable both to teach and to learn. What is of manageable "size" varies, depending on the level of functioning of the learner. For example, instruction may be needed in money management, weekly budgeting, identifying fixed expense categories, or simply writing a check. The determination of the relevant "size" of the skill is based on information about the person as well as the environment in which the skill is to be used. (Nemec, McNamara, & Walsh, 1992, p. 178)

In the ideal circumstances, direct skills teaching is highly individualized and is based on clearly identified learning needs. Instruction targets those needs adapting any pre-existing lesson or curriculum to the learner's preferred learning style, reason for needing and wanting to learn the skill, and current competence in the skill or related skills. In psychiatric rehabilitation, skills teaching addresses skills that a person has identified as relevant to achieving his/her personal goal (Farkas & Anthony, 2010), ensuring that motivation to learn is already present.

In keeping with the psychiatric rehabilitation philosophy of partnership, and following the principles of adult education (Knowles, 1970), it is important to orient the learner(s) at the beginning of the lesson. A thorough orientation to the teaching process is beneficial, including a description of how skills teaching is different from therapy or counseling (Bellack et al., 2003). By engaging the learner(s) in a discussion of the purpose of the lesson, the instructor is able to specifically link the lesson to the learner's personal goals (Cohen et al., 1985), connecting successful performance to desirable advantages within the person's experience and connecting lack of successful performance to disadvantages (Bellack et al., 2003). Finally, defining the roles of instructor and learner helps the learner be clear about any expectations, such as participation, practice, and self-evaluation.

Self-determination, choice, and active participation are key components of the direct skills teaching process:

> In order to avoid the problems that arise from low motivation, the skills taught through the direct skills teaching process are based on those skills the person needs and wants to learn. Motivation is inherent in a process where individuals identify skills as necessary for their success and satisfaction in a particular environment they have chosen. Skills that make the lives of service providers easier but have no relevance to [a person's] desires will be seen by [the person] as irrelevant or, at worst, 'force-feeding.' Beyond the obvious ethical considerations, assisting people in pursuing their own goals makes practical sense. (Nemec, McNamara, & Walsh, 1992, p. 177)

Effective skills teaching makes use of educational best practices, such as multi-modal learning and performance practice with feedback. The use of multiple "modes" or methods of delivering information (e.g., written, auditory, pictorial, experiential) facilitates learning and remembering (Halpern & Hakel, 2000). When presenting on the component steps or critical behaviors of the skill, practitioners need to teach each step or behavior separately as part of teaching the whole skill using the process of tell-show-do. Tell refers to written and oral descriptions of what needs to be done, along with any tips about how to do a behavior or how to select and use the tools, equipment, or supplies needed for the skill (e.g., how to choose a brand of laundry soap when washing clothes). Show refers to the instructor or some other person modeling a demonstration of a skill or a component behavior for the learner (e.g., showing how to sort clothes and which ones are darks or lights). Do is giving the learner(s) a chance to practice the skill or component behavior (e.g., measuring the laundry detergent). Ideally, each component behavior or step is taught with tell-show-do, and the skill in its entirety is explained, demonstrated, and practiced as well.

Learning, generalization, refinement, and maintenance of skill performance often benefit from reinforcement and shaping (Bellack et al., 2003). Reinforcement in the form of verbal praise supports effort and accuracy. Shaping means reinforcing gradual changes towards successful performance. Prompts and coaching during practices can help the learner do better.

Role plays for practicing a skill (the do) come after modeling an example (the *show*) to give the learner(s) an image of successful performance (Bellack et al., 2003). To set up a role play, the practitioner should provide clear instructions on what each person in the role play is expected to do. When teaching in a group setting, the practitioner, or instructor, should request participation in a role play from specific individuals rather than asking for volunteers, and when using role plays in groups, it is best to start with the person who is the most skilled and who is the most likely to follow instructions and support others (Bellack et al., 2003). This allows the practice (do) to serve as a demonstration as well (show). As part of the feedback process after a practice, the practitioner, or instructor, should encourage self-assessment before offering any observations (Cohen et al., 1985). For a person who needs additional improvement, a follow-up role play opportunity needs to be accompanied by very specific instructions about what to do differently. Any feedback given should be balanced (+/-), neutral (non-emotional), and specific and should be clearly related to how the skill was taught. Each role play ends with a short and positive statement about the person's performance.

The use of a feedback loop format for evaluating performance can be beneficial. This feedback process begins with the teacher asking the learner, "How do you think you did?" By beginning with the learner's self-assessment, the teacher can evaluate the learner's ability to recognize a correct performance. Learners who perform poorly but who can describe exactly what they did well and what they need to improve have the potential to self-correct and improve on their own. If a person cannot do a skill and also cannot recognize his/her lack of ability, then additional instruction and feedback is necessary.

Following the general self-assessment, the teacher probes for specifics about what the learner sees as plusses and minuses of his/her performance. Tying the feedback to the lesson is useful and reinforces knowledge about the components of the skill. For example, the teacher might ask, "We just went over the three steps of the skill. Let's take them one at a time. How do you think you did with [step 1]?" Only after some discussion does the teacher offer an evaluative critique. Even then, the teacher's feedback should be tied as closely as possible to the learner's self-assessment (e.g., "I agree that you did X well, but I disagree about how well you did Y...").

Homework assignments direct the learner(s) to practice the skill independently in a real-life situation (Bellack et al., 2003) after learning the skill in a structured and supervised setting. When arranging for practice homework, the instructor gives clear and specific instructions and sets up a time for reviewing performance and follow up. Follow up discussions are used to explore any obstacles to completing the assigned homework or doing the skill and also to evaluate changes in skill performance. It is important to keep in mind that any lack of improvement may be due to poor quality skill instruction, and re-teaching may be needed.

Programming skill use (Cohen et al., 1985) is a one-to-one counseling-type skill intervention used when a person has demonstrated the ability to competently perform the skill, but is not using that skill as needed in real life. In some instances, the ability to perform the skill was demonstrated during the functional assessment indicating that skills teaching is not necessary. At other times, skill performance is demonstrated during or after the direct skill teaching lesson. Implementing a skill use program before the person attempts to apply the skill in a real life environment might help prevent an experience of failure. On the other hand, programming skill use might be more relevant after the person has attempted to apply the skill as that experience can prompt discussion about actual events and circumstances rather than hypothetical situations.

There are two broad steps in programming skill use: identifying barriers and developing the program. Identifying barriers begins with an exploration of the problems in using the skill. Like any exploration, it is often most helpful to request examples, such as asking the person to describe a time when s/he did the skill well and when s/he didn't do it well, to describe someone who is excellent at this skill, and to identify what someone would see him/her doing differently if s/he could do the skill consistently well. For example, for the skill of initiating conversation, a person might express a problem like this: "When I try to start a conversation, it often falls flat. I get the opening question out OK, but when the person answers, I freeze up." By exploring the reasons for a problem, specific barriers can be identified.

Knowing the four common types of barriers (Cohen et al., 1985) can help the practitioner structure the exploration. Any or all of these types of barriers (lack of planning, lack of resource, lack of knowledge, or lack of confidence) can contribute to difficulties in using a skill. For example, for the person who freezes up when initiating a conversation, the helper might consider exploring possible barriers using one or more of these paraphrases:

- "You feel stuck because you didn't plan a comment or follow-up question." (suggests a lack of planning)

- "You feel pressured because you don't know what topics might interest the other person." (suggests a lack of knowledge or perhaps a lack of planning)

- "You feel anxious because you don't have a good collection of small-talk topics." (suggests the lack of a resource)

Once the barriers to using the skill are understood, the next step is to involve the person in identifying and then ordering the actions the person will take to overcome the barriers. Steps are often suggested by the barriers themselves. For example, the lack of a resource suggests adding a step to get that resource; lack of knowledge suggests the need for some sort of research to acquire the necessary knowledge; and lack of planning indicates a need to build in more preparation. The barrier of "lack of confidence" does not have a clearly matched step for "get confidence," but can often be addressed through rehearsal and successive approximation where the person's repeated practice can develop a sense of mastery (Cohen et al., 1985).

Developing the program in programming skill use involves sequencing the steps in the order they will be performed. Often there is a natural or logical order where some steps must be done before other steps. At other times, the steps might be sequenced according to the person's ability (easiest first) or the person's motivation (highest motivation goes first). When completed, the steps should address the barriers and result in performing the skill as needed. Completing the program involves adding supports that will strengthen the person's motivation to perform the steps, such as target dates, monitoring or follow up to assess progress, and rewards or celebrations of accomplishments to help increase motivation and acknowledge success (Cohen et al., 1985).

Support Development

Supports are the people, places, things, and activities that keep people going from day to day. For people-type supports, most practitioners use a combination of paid professional supports such as physicians, tax preparers, child care providers, and natural supports, such as family, friends, colleagues, and neighbors. For many people with psychiatric disabilities, however, the people who are their paid professional supports tend to far outnumber their natural supports (Pattison & Pattison, 1981). Also, because many people with psychiatric disabilities live in poverty, they may be limited in their access to supported places, things, and activities. If psychiatric rehabilitation aims to help people develop meaning and purpose in their lives and to become integral parts of a community, then developing supports will be an important type of intervention.

In some instances, building support requires concurrent attention to building skills. For example, good social skills are needed to build a large and strong network of friends. Accessing a free community exercise class might require skills such as navigating public transportation and organizing one's schedule to get to the class consistently and on time. In addition, building support may require additional resources, such as a bus pass to get to the exercise class, a good pair of sneakers, and a buddy to make the class less scary.

Interventions to build supports come in three broad categories: acquiring resources, linking to resources, and creating resources. Resource acquisition involves helping a person access or obtain an existing thing or activity—usually on a one-time basis (for example, buying an alarm clock or getting a discounted bus pass). Acquiring a small resource is often a simple process (like buying a 7-day pill box), and would not really be considered an intervention. Some resources are easy to come by (like a library card); others take time and seem complex (like getting a government-funded housing subsidy). However, the process of resource acquisition is basically the same for both—decide what is needed, find out where to get it, and take the necessary steps to buy, apply for, request, or borrow the needed resource.

Linking to an existing resource, also known as resource coordination or service coordination (Cohen, Nemec, Farkas, & Forbess, 1988), involves making a connection to an existing service or support and is more complicated than resource acquisition. Like resource acquisition, linking requires deciding what is needed and finding out where to get it, but the process of linking may involve negotiating eligibility requirements or selling oneself to the potential support. Selling is an awkward term for this sort of people-work, but accurately captures the needed approach of marketing, persuasion, and negotiation. If a new medical practice is looking for people who have insurance of any kind, then selling yourself as a potential patient would be easy, provided you have insurance they will accept. If a neighbor is already busy with her large family and rarely comes out of her house, however, then selling yourself as a potential friend would be challenging. Part of linking, then, is trying to find a resource that would be a good fit for the person and then figuring out how to help the person sell herself to the resource. Marketing (Cohen et al., 1988) includes identifying and presenting assets from the point of view of the resource (like the buyer in contrast to the seller). Effective marketing also will include preparing strategies to address any potential objections (Cohen et al., 1988). Negotiation (Fisher & Ury, 1981) may be needed to achieve consensus and settle on an agreement about how/when services or supports are provided.

Linking to professional resources, such as helping someone get a dentist appointment, is a common psychiatric rehabilitation practitioner task. Accessing community resources also is common, and providers may feel confident in their ability to help someone get groceries from a food bank or a scholarship to a local gym. Many providers are less confident in helping someone get to know his neighbors, choose a religious community, discover an enriching hobby, or find a date; yet the support of friends, rewarding leisure pursuits, and spiritual communities are often the very things that give a person's life meaning and purpose.

Interventions focused on resource use and increased community integration need to build the individual's own capacity to make the needed connections and use them effectively, but also need to build opportunities for people to develop new relationships. Building opportunities requires time to find and develop connections with minimal or no blaming in any direction if opportunities fail to unfold or somehow a relationship goes bad (O'Brien & Towell, 2003). Not every community member or community resource will pan out, so focus on working with people who are willing, and "some reluctant people will become more willing when they can see what happens for others" (O'Brien & Towell, 2003, p. 8).

Accompanying people to places, events, and appointments (Cohen, Nemec, Farkas, & Forbess, 1988) can provide more than just transportation or monitoring to be sure the person actually arrives. Supported socialization (Davidson, Shahar, Stayner, Chinman, Rakfeldt, & Tebes, 2004), offering the support of a companion or the assistance of a coach, can help build confidence and skills and is underused in psychiatric rehabilitation.

Recognizing that gaps and limitations within the service system do occur, service providers may need to advocate for the development and modification of services to better meet the expressed needs and preferences of people using services. Resource creation becomes necessary when a service or support is needed but does not currently exist. Documenting a service need facilitates system advocacy when a number of people using services have similar unmet needs. Working for systems change on behalf of an individual or a group of people with similar needs can require creating a coalition and planning a strategy for change (Cohen, Nemec, Farkas, & Forbess, 1988).

Engagement Strategies

Recovery is not something a provider does *to* a person who uses services; that person has to own the recovery process and take some personal responsibility for setting and achieving goals (SAMHSA, 2006). At times, though, finding ways to engage someone in services, in rehabilitation, and in the recovery journey becomes a challenge. As many as one-third of people using mental health services will disconnect themselves from services (Kreyenbuhl, Nossel, & Dixon, 2009); most often they are people who are younger, are male, or belong to a cultural or ethnic minority group, and people who struggle with social connections, are isolated, and lack natural social supports. Service systems and programs can provide structures that facilitate getting and staying engaged, such as appointment reminders and assertive outreach (Kreyenbuhl et al., 2009), peer bridgers who help support people at the time of discharge from an inpatient setting (Bluebird, 2004; NYAPRS, 2010), and a person-centered care philosophy (Kreyenbuhl et al., 2009).

Strategic interventions to increase engagement focus on discovering motivation and increasing empowerment, giving a person an opportunity to take responsibility for setting and achieving his/her personal goals. Services that focus primarily on maximizing adherence to provider-generated requirements are unlikely to promote engagement and can cause relationship ruptures and future avoidance of service providers.

As part of the process of psychiatric rehabilitation developed at the Boston University Center for Psychiatric Rehabilitation, readiness assessment and readiness development focus on how to engage someone in the rehabilitation process (Farkas, Cohen, McNamara, Nemec, & Cohen, 2000). Rehabilitation readiness specifically refers to how prepared a person is to begin the goal-setting process in one or more life domains (living, learning, working, socializing). It does not look at whether a person is likely to succeed or fail at any particular goal, such as getting or keeping a job. Someone can be more or less ready, and readiness can fluctuate with a person feeling more or less motivated to set or achieve a goal on any given day. Motivation or readiness does not have an on/off switch like turning on a light. Just because a person feels ready or motivated on one day, it doesn't mean he will feel equally ready the next day.

Motivational interviewing (Miller & Rollnick, 2002) is an approach that is supported by evidence and might be considered a strategic intervention for engagement. The actual process of motivational enhancement or readiness development does not offer specific prescriptions for specific assessment profiles. It is important to consider what service providers do that either facilitates or hinders readiness and motivation and to brainstorm ideas for developing readiness or connection with a particular individual. Rather than random outreach attempts by varied practitioners, service providers should develop a complete strategy. Strategic engagement requires identifying a systematic approach to fostering a connection with someone who is disengaged. By preparing a strategy in advance with identified markers that would be evidence of success, service providers will be able to determine if the intervention was delivered as planned and if it had the desired effect. Brainstorming strategies work especially well in a team to generate new ideas for how to work with someone who has been difficult to engage.

In addition to using skills teaching to develop skills that are critical to success and satisfaction in a person's goal environment and to facilitate using community resources, skills teaching can be beneficial in developing the skills needed for active participation in rehabilitation and recovery. Participation in rehabilitation activities requires such interpersonal skills as asking questions, physically attending (showing interest through body language), and expressing opinions as well as more complex skills related to problem-solving and decision-making. In addition, some people may need help in improving their attention span, concentration, and ability to resist distractions (Bellus, Kost, & Vergo, 2000; McGurk, Mueser, & Pascaris, 2005). Cognitive rehabilitation interventions hold some promise for building capacity to participate in rehabilitation and to achieve goals (Farkas & Anthony, 2010).

CHALLENGES FOR PROGRAM IMPLEMENTATION

The biggest barrier to effective and consistent implementation of psychiatric rehabilitation interventions is that they require trained practitioners. Most service providers entering the mental health field do not arrive with competency in skill development and in linking people to supports. They often lack the basic counseling skill competencies to effectively engage people in services. Finding the time, funding, and staff coverage to make intensive training possible is an ongoing challenge. Retaining trained staff is difficult in a field that pays so little.

Vinfen Corporation in Cambridge, MA, addresses staff development through several strategies. A focused and competency-based training program is required for all new employees in the psychiatric rehabilitation division. This intensive four-day training introduces concepts related to psychiatric rehabilitation and recovery-oriented services and teaches specific skills to support engaging people in services, initiating skill development, and linking to resources. In addition to the typical staff supports from supervisors and service team leaders, Vinfen ensures ongoing availability of rehabilitation consultation through rehabilitation coordinators who operate within each team. These staff members have demonstrated expertise in psychiatric rehabilitation competencies and are turned to by various congregate housing sites and by their teams to provide guidance, consultation, and feedback to service providers.

Recent changes in state-wide service design and funding for community mental health services has uncovered new needs for staff development at Vinfen. Creating a tool bank is one new way of improving staff capacity to plan for and deliver individualized interventions. This bank is a centralized online collection of worksheets and process descriptions for staff to use to deliver interventions under multiple categories. An analysis of identified needs and available interventions suggested the following intervention categories: advocacy for an individual, extended assessment and service planning, crisis prevention and management (including relapse prevention), strategic engagement (including motivational enhancement), role discovery, resource and service coordination, environmental modification, psychoeducation, and skill development. Each intervention is described in the online collection and includes tips to help practitioners use the intervention type effectively.

As new intervention tools are identified or developed, staff members need to update their knowledge. Vinfen's latest approach to educating staff, known as an interventions fair, has been well received. Modeled on a job fair, or other fairs where booths offer different information or products, participants rotate from station to station where they have a chance to try out or observe various intervention tools. A simple four-station set-up provides an opportunity for 40 staff to rotate through the stations in groups of 10 in timed intervals of 10-15 minutes (about 1 hour total). A facilitator is at each station, handing out copies of the tool and/or descriptions of the intervention activity. The leader works through the activity with one or more of the participants while the others observe, and the small group then has a few minutes to discuss how they might use the tool back at their work sites.

Service system pressures for documentation and a natural aversion to risk tend to create an atmosphere that chokes out efforts to offer choice, foster empowerment, and honor the dignity of risk. Vinfen has adopted the *Intentional Care Performance Standards* (Deegan, 2003) as a guide for staff in understanding the importance of risk taking for success, shared risk for building responsibility, harm reduction for maximizing engagement while minimizing risk, and ensuring safety while staying connected. The standards are introduced to new employees during training, are available at each program site, and are referred to in ongoing supervision as needed.

Vinfen's long-standing commitment to recovery-oriented services is evident in the creation of a role for a director of recovery—a person with lived experience who has responsibility for creating and maintaining an organizational culture that nurtures and models recovery at every level. Affirmative hiring of people with personal experience with psychiatric conditions occurs in roles throughout the agency as well as in the designated role of the peer specialist (called peer coordinators at Vinfen) included on every service team. Peer specialists provide support interventions as well as implement the Wellness Recovery Action Plan (Copeland, 1997).

In addition to ensuring that staff members deliver effective interventions, implementation challenges include the need to document those interventions in the service plan and the service notes. Documentation of interventions needs to capture the relevance of the intervention to the person (not the service system) and should include information on how the person participated in choosing the intervention, the person's reaction to the intervention, and the resulting progress towards achieving the person's desired goals and objectives. Too often, service providers document what they do, but neglect to capture how what they do actually helps the people they serve. Detailed staff training at Vinfen includes practice opportunities and is supplemented with an extensive documentation handbook for ongoing reference. Staff training is skill-based and uses the same tell-show-do approach used with people the agency serves. Developing local site-based expertise in documentation, along with giving team and program leaders responsibility for ongoing program documentation audits, provides a two-way communication flow about training needs and guidance for documentation improvement.

Working with people who have significant psychiatric disabilities can be discouraging as positive changes may be small and slow. The idealism of the novice provider can quickly turn to pessimistic cynicism that blames the person using services for being unmotivated and resistant. Service providers must recognize that lack of progress following delivery of an intervention is an intervention failure, not a personal failure of the service provider and not a shortcoming of the person served. Staff must remain open to learning new ways of providing skill and support development, which requires service provider agencies to create an organizational culture where change is the norm and lifelong learning is a clear expectation.

SUMMARY

What we know about how to help people recover will continue to evolve over time. Psychiatric rehabilitation practitioners need to be able to deliver the interventions that will help people achieve their own personal goals. In addition, psychiatric rehabilitation practitioners must be lifelong learners who expect that the best practices of today will not necessarily be the best practices of tomorrow. Interventions need to support people with psychiatric disabilities in crossing the boundary between the mental health service system and the communities where they choose to live and work (O'Brien & Towell, 2003). Making that happen will require practitioners who are trained in intervention methods and who are willing and able to provide the individualized and specialized services necessary to support people in achieving their own goals.

BEST PRACTICE GUIDELINES FOR PSYCHIATRIC REHABILITATION INTERVENTIONS

1. Design interventions to help individuals make progress towards their personal goals rather than assigning the same generic interventions to multiple people.

2. Use psychiatric rehabilitation interventions that build the skills and supports needed to help people choose and achieve their personal goals.

3. Include in skill development interventions activities designed to address using each skill in the person's real-life environment.

4. Use educational best practices in skills teaching, such as multi-modal learning and performance practice with feedback.

5. Include support development interventions as needed to strengthen the use of natural supports and decrease reliance on professional mental health services.

6. Plan strategic interventions to increase engagement and discover motivation as well as increase empowerment and responsibility for setting and achieving personal goals, not maximizing adherence to provider-generated requirements.

7. Document interventions in ways that capture the relevance to the person (not the service system), and include information on how the person participated in choosing the intervention, the person's reaction to the intervention, and the resulting progress towards achieving the person's desired goals and objectives.

8. Recognize that lack of progress following delivery of an intervention is an intervention failure, not a personal failure of the service provider and not a shortcoming of the person served.

ABOUT THE AUTHORS

Pat Nemec is an independent trainer and consultant in psychiatric rehabilitation, and holds an adjunct faculty appointment at the University of Medicine and Dentistry of New Jersey. From 1984-2008, she was on the faculty of the rehabilitation counseling program at Sargent College of Health and Rehabilitation Sciences at Boston University where she was responsible for the graduate level psychiatric rehabilitation specialization. While at Boston University, Nemec worked on the team developing the Psychiatric Rehabilitation Training Technology at the Center for Psychiatric Rehabilitation. She is the recipient of numerous awards, including the 2007 John Beard Award from the Psychiatric Rehabilitation Association. In 2012, she was appointed as a PRA Dincin Fellow.

Steve LaMaster, M.S., CPRP serves as Vinfen's director of psychiatric rehabilitation services, supporting programming that helps 2,600 people live, learn, work, and belong in their communities. Steve's primary activities fall into the areas of person-centered planning, service intervention, adherence efforts related to state Medicaid Rehabilitation Option financing, and ensuring fidelity to IPS-modeled employment services. Steve is currently president of the Massachusetts Chapter of RPA and a member of PRA's CPRP Certification Commission.

Lisa Halpern, MPP, CPRP, CPS is the director of recovery services at Vinfen where she is responsible for providing training to staff, developing programs and educating the community in the areas of recovery and empowerment of people with mental illness. Lisa gives group supervision to all peer coordinators on Collaborative Action for Recovery outreach teams and also supervises the program directors of Vinfen's Recovery Learning Centers. Before joining Vinfen, Lisa was state coordinator and a national trainer, and continues to serve as a speaker, for *In Our Own Voice,* a recovery-based speaking program of the National Alliance on Mental Illness. Prior jobs included a dual diagnosis PACT team, the Massachusetts Department of Mental Health, and the PBS NewsHour with Jim Lehrer.

REFERENCES

Anthony, W. A. (1982). Explaining psychiatric rehabilitation by an analogy to physical rehabilitation. *Psychosocial Rehabilitation Journal, 5*(1), 61-65.

Anthony, W. (2003). Studying evidence-based processes, not practices. *Psychiatric Services, 54*(7), 7.

Anthony, W. A., Cohen, M., Farkas, M., & Gagne, C. (2002). *Psychiatric rehabilitation* (2nd ed.). Boston, MA: Boston University Center for Psychiatric Rehabilitation.

Bellack, A. S., Mueser, K. T., Gingerich, S., & Agresta, J. (2003). *Social skills training for schizophrenia.* New York: Guilford Press.

Bellus, S. B., Kost, P. P., & Vergo, J. G. (2000). Preparing long-term inpatients for community re-entry. *Psychiatric Rehabilitation Journal, 23*(4), 359-363.

Bluebird, G. (2004). Redefining consumer roles: Changing culture and practice in mental health care settings. *Journal of Psychosocial Nursing & Mental Health Services, 42*(9), 46-53.

Chambless, D. L., & Ollendick, T. H. (2001). Empirically supported psychological interventions: Controversies and evidence. *Annual Review of Psychology, 52,* 685-716.

Cohen, M., Danley, K. S., & Nemec, P. B. (1985). *Psychiatric rehabilitation training technology: Direct skills teaching.* Boston, MA: Boston University Center for Psychiatric Rehabilitation.

Cohen, M. R., Nemec, P. B., Farkas, M. D., & Forbess, R. (1988). *Psychiatric rehabilitation training technology: Case management.* Boston, MA: Boston University Center for Psychiatric Rehabilitation.

Copeland, M. E. (1997). *Wellness recovery action plan.* Brattleboro, VT: Peach Press.

Corrigan, P. W., Mueser, K. T., Bond, G. R., Drake, R. E., & Solomon, P. (2008). *Principles and practice of psychiatric rehabilitation.* New York: Guilford Publications, Inc.

Davidson, L., Shahar, G., Stayner, D. A., Chinman, M. J., Rakfeldt, J., & Tebes, J. K. (2004). Supported socialization for people with psychiatric disabilities: Lessons from a randomized controlled trial. *Journal of Community Psychology, 32*(4), 453-477.

Deegan, P. (2003). *Intentional care performance standards.* Framingham, MA: Advocates, Inc. Retrieved from http://www.intentionalcare.org

Drake, R. E., Merrens, M. R., Lynde, D. W. (Eds.). (2005). *Evidence-based mental health practice: A textbook.* New York: WW Norton & Company.

Farkas, M., & Anthony, W. A. (2010). Psychiatric rehabilitation interventions: A review. *International Review of Psychiatry, 22*(2), 114-139.

Farkas, M., Cohen, M., McNamara, S., Nemec, P. B., & Cohen, B. (2000). *Psychiatric rehabilitation training technology: Assessing readiness.* Boston, MA: Boston University Center for Psychiatric Rehabilitation.

Fisher, R., & Ury, W. (1981). *Getting to yes: Negotiating agreement without giving in.* Boston, MA: Houghton Mifflin.

Halpern, D. F., & Hakel, M. D. (2000). Applying the science of learning to university teaching and beyond. *New Directions for Teaching and Learning,* No. 89. San Francisco, CA: Jossey-Bass.

Knowles, M. (1970). *The modern practice of adult education.* New York: Association Press.

Kreyenbuhl, J., Nossel, I. R., & Dixon, L. (2009). Disengagement from mental health treatment among individuals with schizophrenia and strategies for facilitating connections to care: A review of the literature. *Schizophrenia Bulletin, 35*(4), 696-703.

Lilleleht, E. (2005). Paradox in practice? The rhetoric of psychiatric rehabilitation. *International Journal of Psychosocial Rehabilitation, 10*(1), 89-103. Retrieved from http://www.psychosocial.com/IJPR_10/Paradox_in_Practice_Lilleleht.html

McGurk, S. R., Mueser, K. T., & Pascaris, A. (2005). Cognitive training and supported employment for persons with severe mental illness: One-year results from a randomized controlled trial. *Schizophrenia Bulletin, 31*(4), 898-909.

Miller, W. R., & Rollnick, S. (2002*). Motivational interviewing: Preparing people to change addictive behavior* (2nd ed.). New York: The Guilford Press.

Nemec, P. B., McNamara, S., & Walsh, D. (1992). Direct skills teaching. *Psychosocial Rehabilitation Journal, 16*(1), 13-25.

Norcross, J. C. (Ed.). (2002). *Psychotherapy relationships that work: Therapist contributions and responsiveness to patients.* New York: Oxford University Press.

NYAPRS (New York Association of Psychiatric Rehabilitation Services). (2010). *Peer Bridger project.* Retrieved from http://www.nyaprs.org/peer-services/peer-bridger

O'Brien, J., & Towell, D. (2003). *Person-centered planning in its strategic context: Towards a framework for reflection-in-action.* Minneapolis, MN: University of Minnesota Research and Training Center on Community Living. Retrieved from http://rtc.umn.edu/person/publ.asp

Pattison, E. M., & Pattison, M. L. (1981). Analysis of a schizophrenic psychosocial network. *Schizophrenia Bulletin, 7,* 135-143.

SAMHSA (Substance Abuse and Mental Health Services Administration). (2006). *National consensus statement on mental health recovery.* Retrieved from http://www.samhsa.gov

Stanhope, V., & Solomon, P. (2008). Getting to the heart of recovery: Methods for studying recovery and their implications for evidence-based practice. *British Journal of Social Work, 38,* 885-899.

CHAPTER 8

PEER SUPPORT SERVICES AND THE EXPANDING PEER SUPPORT WORKFORCE

Larry Fricks
Sherry Jenkins Tucker

ABSTRACT

This chapter focuses on the emerging new peer workforce that provides recovery-oriented services covered by Medicaid funding as envisioned in the Surgeon General's Mental Health Report (USDHHS, 1999). Commonly known as Certified Peer Specialists or Peer Support Specialists, this new peer workforce has the unique opportunity to model the lived experience of recovery to promote hope and teach skills for self-directed recovery and mind-body whole health and resiliency. As mounting research recognizes the positive impact of peer support specialists, their demonstrated competencies also challenge deep-rooted beliefs that perpetuate societal stigma and negative self-images. The chapter concludes with highlights from three summits held in 2009, 2010, and 2011 at the Carter Center in Atlanta, GA, attended by representatives from a majority of the state mental health authorities. These summits, entitled the *Pillars of Peer Support Services Summits,* generated reports that address the barriers and strengths to supporting and expanding the peer workforce and related Medicaid-billable services nationwide, including an emerging new role in integrated physical and behavioral health, also known as "whole health."

PEER SUPPORT THAT PROMOTES MUTUAL SUPPORT AND SELF-HELP ORIGINATES IN THE UNITED STATES with Native Americans forming social support groups to deal with alcohol use problems as early as 1772. Those support groups, in which group members organized and solved their own issues through mutual support, were led by the group members themselves. The experiences of Native American peers evolved into some of the very first literature on recovery and the first peer mutual-support groups with a focus on achieving and maintaining sobriety (White, 1998).

THE MOUNTING EVIDENCE ON PEER SUPPORT SERVICES

Research evidence on peer support services in mental health suggests positive recovery outcomes as good as, and in some cases, superior to services from non-peer providers (Cook, 2011). The growing evidence includes reduced hospitalizations (Eiken & Campbell, 2008), reduced use of crisis services, improved symptoms, larger social support networks, and improved quality of life as well as benefits to the people providing the peer services. Outcomes of team-based case management services improve when peer specialists are included on the teams, and vocational outcomes also can be improved through peer-provided services (Solomon, 2010). Research also demonstrates that peer providers can increase empowerment (Eiken & Campbell, 2008), decrease substance use, reduce days in the hospital, and increase use of outpatient services at least as long as the peer support continues (Davidson, Chinman, Sells, & Rowe, 2006).

Definitions of Peer Support and Peer Support Services

As states develop and approve curricula to train the peer workforce, peer support and peer support services are differentiated from one another so that participants begin to understand their unique role, some role challenges, and how their role may differ from the role of traditional staff working in mental health systems. Peer support is a process of sharing mutuality, giving and receiving hope, strengths, and lived experiences. Peer support can be done anytime or anywhere when two or more peers are in a mutual, supportive relationship. In contrast, peer support services are programs, discussions, events, groups, etc. within the mental health system that are led by people in recovery and are based on the philosophy of peer support. Peer support services usually occur within the structure of an agency or organization and are provided as a service by trained peer workers who teach skills to unlock the potential within an individual to self-direct his or her own recovery and whole health.

It is the teaching of skills that helps define the new role of peer support services delivered by a peer workforce. For example, if someone is experiencing a deep sense of hopelessness about his or her life, meeting with a peer at a coffee shop to share hope, strengths, and lived experiences may reduce that sense of hopelessness. It is likely both peers have experienced the stigma and discrimination associated with mental illness and simply acknowledging that shared lived experience fosters a sense of understanding regarding the sense of hopelessness. And, if either peer has a lived experience of recovery from hopelessness, that lived experience is also shared and can ignite hope that the sense of hopelessness could improve. Beyond that mutual sharing, a peer specialist may also have the lived experience of being trained in the skill of "Combating Negative Self-Talk: Catch it! Check it! Change it!" The setting may be a peer center rather than a coffee shop, but the peer specialist still shares personal hope, strengths, and lived experiences plus the skill to combat negative self-talk.

Mental Health Systems Transformation

Training of the peer workforce requires providing insight into the potential boundary and power/conflict issues that could arise for a peer support services provider. For example, if shared mutuality is essential to peer support, is that mutuality negatively impacted by the more structured role and responsibilities of trained peers working as providers of peer support services teaching skills for self-directed recovery? Does the more structured role and billing for skills shared by a peer specialist erode the sharing of hope, strengths and lived experiences? If so, it is important for the peer workforce to be aware of this potential conflict and strive to continue building mutually shared relationships focused on sharing hope, strengths and lived experiences. Similar issues of power and conflict also have to be addressed in psychiatric rehabilitation programs that promote equality and shared decision making. One of the earliest power issues that surfaced as Certified Peer Specialists were hired as staff was the segregation of staff and consumer bathrooms. Even some of the most established of psychiatric rehabilitation programs were embarrassed to realize they were not sending the message of hope, social inclusion, and strength-based recovery by having segregated bathrooms, but were perpetuating stigma, discrimination, and exclusion. Hiring peer specialists quickly brought these contradictions to light.

Aside from the awareness of potential power and conflict issues addressed in peer training, there is mounting research that the peer workforce delivering peer support services has significant impact on promoting holistic recovery, and the stage is set for widespread implementation of this new workforce (Cook, 2011). The unique role of trusted peers connecting with each other to foster hope and build on strengths is emerging as a key transformational factor in mental health services (Sells, Davidson, Jewell, Faizer, & Rowe, 2006).

Recovery-oriented services require changing deep-rooted beliefs to foster hope and promote strengths and resiliency rather than emphasizing symptoms and illness. The country's rapidly growing workforce of Certified Peer Specialists is a dynamic force of change agents transforming mental health systems to promote recovery, resiliency, and mind-body whole health, and by virtue of its very existence, conveying messages of support and competence rather than expectations of lost lives and disability.

Evidence demonstrates that the lived experiences of recovery and competent recovery skills that are gained from training can combat the negative beliefs that perpetuate societal stigma and the negative self-image that can spiral into despair and hopelessness. Certified Peer Specialists are taught that what one believes about mental illness may be more disabling than the illness itself. Stigma, discrimination, and prejudice are still our biggest challenges. The former First Lady, Rosalynn Carter (2010), offers the following insight: "Stigma is the most damaging factor in the life of anyone who has a mental illness. It humiliates and embarrasses; it is painful; it generates stereotypes, fear and rejection; it leads to terrible discrimination" (p. 1). Mrs. Carter concludes her book with a message of hope, heralding the unique role of Certified Peer Specialists to challenge stigmatizing beliefs and grow strength-based, self-directed recovery, resiliency, and mind-body whole health:

> They [Certified Peer Specialists] are experts in their own right, but their expertise is different than that of traditional mental health professionals, and their impact is powerful. Peers know what it is like to live through severe depression or a psychotic event. They recognize early warning signs and are familiar with what has worked in the past. They know how to

engage in wellness and are able to share knowledge with others.… Expanding this program nationwide must be a top priority for all who are concerned about improving the quality of care for people struggling with the most serious mental disorders. (p. 154)

Our National Policy on Peer Support Services

The first group to formally promote a national policy in support of peer support services was Mental Health America (MHA), the country's oldest non-profit mental health organization. Mental Health America, a national leader in terms of advocacy, public education, and the delivery of programs and service, formally supported the creation of peer support services through policy change and a national call to action.

In a statement supporting the adoption of peer support services, Mental Health America references a statement from The Center for Medicare & Medicaid Services (CMS) to state Medicaid offices encouraging the use of state certified peer specialists:

> States are increasingly interested in covering peer support providers as a distinct provider type for the delivery of counseling and other support services to Medicaid eligible adults with mental illnesses and/or substance abuse disorders. Peer support services are an evidence-based mental health model of care which consists of a qualified peer support provider who assists individuals with their recovery from mental illness and substance abuse disorders. CMS recognizes that the experiences of peer support providers, as consumers of mental health and substance abuse services, can be an important component in a State's delivery of effective treatment. CMS is reaffirming its commitment to State flexibility, increased innovation, consumer choice, self-direction, recovery, and consumer protection through approval of these services. (Smith, 2007, p. 1)

Recognizing that peer support workers are often paid substantially less than their colleagues, it is important to note that the MHA background statement did not support using peer support services primarily to save funds. Rather, ensuring that peer support workers are qualified for the job requires the assurance that training is relevant and effective. MHA recommended including a certification process that "should be available to all in need, regardless of the financing mechanism" (Mental Health America, 2008).

The MHA Call to Action policy (2008) serves as a blueprint for service design as it highlights critical areas for attention. Peer support is described as "an integral part of mental health and substance abuse service delivery" that should be a priority area for federal and state funding for services, training, and research. Specific areas that would benefit from peer support are listed in the policy statement, including parent partners, adolescent peer services, veterans services, crisis counseling, disaster response, and "whole health recovery to help reduce the 25-year average premature death of those served by public mental health services." Finally, the Call to Action emphasizes that "consumers must be involved at multiple levels of planning and implementation of peer support services, including senior management positions in service programs."

In addition to Mental Health America's Call to Action on behalf of involving and engaging peer support services, the International Association of Peer Specialists was formed to promote the growth of the peer specialist workforce. According to the organization's website (www. inaops.org), iNAPS offers members a quarterly newsletter, discounts on recovery-oriented materials, and access to recovery and peer support information as well as sponsoring an annual conference for peer specialists that brings together peer specialists and supporters of the peer specialist movement to share ideas, strategies, and information about innovative programs that work. The creation of this national organization is an indication of the increasing recognition of the value of the role of peer support.

The Origins of Medicaid Reimbursable Peer Support Services

In 1999, the Georgia state mental health authority created a new service called peer support, which was eligible for Medicaid funding under the federal Psychiatric Rehabilitation Option, enabling a workforce of Certified Peer Specialists able to bill Medicaid for their services. Approval of this new service by the Centers for Medicare and Medicaid Services was bolstered by the landmark Surgeon General's Mental Health Report (USDHHS, 1999) that recognized the role of peers as providers. In Georgia's 1999 revised state plan, peer support services were defined and the role of the Certified Peer Specialist was to provide direct services "designed to assist consumers in regaining control over their own lives and control over their recovery process." The definition went on to say that a Certified Peer Specialist is expected to "model competence and the possibility of recovery" and to "assist consumers in developing the perspective and skills that facilitate recovery" (Sabin & Daniels, 2003, p. 497).

The state of Georgia supported and enhanced its new peer workforce by requiring that Certified Peer Specialists be included in certain rehabilitation services such as Assertive Community Treatment teams, community support teams, and adult peer support programs. If the Certified Peer Specialists were not included in these teams and programs, providers could no longer bill Medicaid. As the new peer support services rolled out, Georgia officials wanted to determine if there were improvements in recovery outcomes for persons participating in those new services. What they discovered cemented Georgia's commitment to funding and expanding the peer workforce.

A research design was created utilizing treatment information housed in the state's external review organization's data system, which included data from the Treatment Request and Integrated Georgia Reporting Survey (TRIGRS) then completed by providers as part of the Medicaid service authorization. The goals of the analysis were to document improvement over time for individuals enrolled in peer supports and to evaluate effectiveness of peer supports by comparing individual-level service outcomes with outcomes produced by other programs. A cohort of persons served by peer supports in state fiscal year 2003 was reviewed with a subsequent reauthorization that included peer supports. The reviewed group was limited to those identified with diagnoses of schizophrenia, bipolar disorder, and/or major depression. The number of persons reviewed was 160 with an average of 260 days between a first TRIGRS submitted and any subsequent TRIGRS. A control group (N=488) with an average of 247 days between TRIGRS composed of those with an enrollment in a generic day supports service during state fiscal year 2002 with a subsequent reauthorization that included the same service was used for comparison. The day supports service was a remnant of the traditional day treatment program that was left operational only for a transition period that ended in state fiscal year 2003. Therefore, it provided an excellent contrast control. Any individuals who were simultaneously or subsequently enrolled in peer supports were excluded from this group. The same diagnostic categories were used for both groups.

Specific items from TRIGRS were used for a non-comparative analysis of outcomes based on initial TRIGRS to subsequent TRIGRS. Grouping of items focused on three areas: (1) current symptoms/behaviors, (2) skill deficits, and (3) available resources/needs. Response items used Likert-type 4- or 5-point scales. Outcomes for purposes of this analysis were changes in scores over time. Overall, people who used peer support showed improvement in each of the three outcomes groups over an average of 260 days between assessments.

When looking at the comparative analysis of peer supports to the day supports service for each of three outcome measures—symptoms/behavior, skills, and needs/resources—the level of improvement for individuals enrolled in peer supports was greater than for those enrolled in day supports, and the difference between the groups was statistically significant (p<0.05). The average annual cost of day treatment services was some $6,400 per person per year while the average cost of peer support services was $1,000 per person per year. The new peer workforce delivering peer support services demonstrated better outcomes and was far more cost effective.

Georgia's state guidelines also promoted that the new peer workforce should gain the Certification of Psychiatric Rehabilitation Practitioners (CPRP) provided by the Psychiatric Rehabilitation Association (PRA), acknowledging the benefit and values of psychiatric rehabilitation to the delivery of peer support services.

Jean Toole, CPRP, the chief executive officer of the award-winning program Community Friendship, Inc. (CFI) in Atlanta, was trained by staff of the Center for Psychiatric Rehabilitation at Boston University. Toole promotes the philosophy of transforming from "what's wrong" to "what's strong," which is also the primary focus of the new Certified Peer Specialist workforce. Toole says, "As psychiatric rehabilitation practitioners, we are taught the values of hope, consumer involvement, treating each person as a unique individual, being respectful, and seeing the person not the illness." Staff at CFI gained new experiences and worked through situations related to peer provider roles and relationships, boundary issues, and relapse on the job. Toole summarizes these experiences this way:

> Overall, I think we deal with issues with our peer providers the same way we deal with other employees, including treating a relapse as we would any other illness. I think accepting and valuing the role of peer providers is easier for psychiatric rehabilitation practitioners than perhaps in some other settings. In some mental health settings, there may be a perceived hierarchy that implies one position is more important or valuable than another. Peers as providers add a depth and understanding that is unique. They can share their stories of tragedy to triumph. They can inspire, encourage, educate and motivate in powerful ways. They can demonstrate "I am the evidence." (personal communication, 2011)

The director of the Centers for Medicare and Medicaid Services (CMS) encouraged all states interested in setting up peer support services under Medicaid programs to adopt the Certified Peer Specialist model implemented in the state of Georgia emphasizing that "peer support services are an evidence-based mental health model of care which consists of a qualified peer support provider who assists individuals with their recovery from mental illness and substance abuse disorders." This statement is also supported by a CMS report on Medicaid-funded peer support (Eiken & Campbell, 2008), which identified positive outcomes in the areas of empowerment and reduced hospitalization.

According to federal guidelines, to be eligible for Medicaid reimbursement, training, continuing education, supervision, and care coordination requirements for peer specialists must be established and met.

Today, the Certified Peer Specialist workforce across the country and around the world is providing a range of services, including support for housing and employment, serving on ACT teams, working in peer support programs including peer respite centers, supporting people in psychiatric inpatient facilities and people moving from inpatient facilities to the community, working in trauma informed and whole health services, and providing support in both group and one-to-one settings.

Peer Support Competencies

Although certification programs for peer support providers vary from state to state, there is common agreement on many competency areas for the peer workforce. These competencies are summarized here under the categories of the peer worker role, empowerment, recovery, building relationship, service delivery, and documentation.

Understanding and fulfilling the peer worker role: These competencies include having an understanding of the job role and the skills needed to do that job; general knowledge related to the meaning and role of peer support and peer support services both broadly and in the local context; specific knowledge related to role and responsibilities of the certified peer specialist (CPS), for people in that role, such as familiarity with both the job description and the CPS Code of Ethics; knowledge of the organizational structure of the state mental health system and how the system provides a context for peer support services; and an understanding of the importance of and have the ability to take care of oneself. Like anyone working in mental health, the CPS must have tools for taking care of him/herself and understand the dynamics of stress and burnout. Using and understanding the common tools of the CPS to help others can also support self-care through the Wellness Recovery Action Plan (WRAP) and peer support whole health and resiliency goals.

Empowerment: From their personal experience and from training, peer workers need to develop competencies in helping the people they serve take personal responsibility for their own health and wellness and to help them advocate for and access the services they want. Knowledge of the meaning and practice of shared decision making is relevant not only for direct service delivery, but for peer workers in a position to influence the practices of other service providers and treatment personnel. Promoting empowerment requires an understanding of the dynamics of power, conflict, and integrity in the workplace and how to work with those dynamics, including understanding the concept and process of seeking common ground.

Recovery: Although the peer worker's personal experience with a mental health condition provides insight into the meaning and process of recovery, peer workers also need knowledge of the five stages in the recovery process, including an understanding of what is helpful and not helpful at each stage and an understanding of the role of peer support at each stage. Understanding of the basic definition and dynamics of recovery includes an awareness of the power of beliefs/values and how they support or work against recovery and knowledge of how recovery is enhanced by an understanding of the basic philosophy and principles of psychiatric rehabilitation.

Building relationships: Peer workers need an understanding about, and the ability to establish, healing relationships. Being able to listen effectively and ask open-ended questions are as important to peers as to other service providers. Telling one's own story, a key competency of peer service providers, includes knowing what has been helpful and not helpful in his/her recovery and when and how much of a recovery story to share. An understanding of the meaning and importance of cultural competency is important for appreciating, valuing, and respecting the diversity found among the people served.

Service delivery: Peer service providers need the general and specific competencies that will enable them to deliver direct services effectively. They need knowledge of the meaning of trauma-informed services; the ability to help people served articulate, set, and accomplish goals, including creating a Peer Support Whole Health and Resiliency goal using person-centered planning, the ability to create and facilitate a variety of group activities that support and strengthen recovery; ability to help a person combat negative self-talk, overcome fears, and solve problems.

Documentation: Peer workers often fulfill professional roles as specialists within the service team. They therefore need competencies to understand the difference between treatment goals and recovery goals and the ability to complete the necessary documentation required by the funding agency.

A Clinician's Perspective on the Peer Workforce

The following section was written by Joseph Handman, a clinician in the Georgia mental health system, who describes his experience in working with peer providers (SAMHSA, 2005):

> I began working in mental health in 1980. At that time, and for a significant time following, the resounding word in the mental health arena was "stabilization," and the key statement was "Keep folks out of the hospital." It wasn't until the late 1990s that the long-awaited new word lifted off the horizon: Recovery. This word has stirred and shifted the mental health paradigm. Our collective goal is no longer to help an individual "remain out of the hospital," "stabilize," or return to "baseline." Our goal is to aid them in their recovery. Although recovery means something a bit different to all, the thread of what has been consistent is the recovery of a life. Things that were previously thought impossible are now achievable. Hopes, dreams, relationships, and activities that brought joy and satisfaction are being reclaimed....
>
> For me personally, it all began in 2001, with the announcement that Day Program managers needed to begin to transfer "traditional staff" out of peer support programs and hire consumers (Certified Peer Specialists) in their place. Initially, many of us "traditional staff" looked at this new directive with suspicion, amazement, and wonder. Our consumers were to be self-governing, without our assistance and leadership? If the medical model was to be thrown out and with it a primary focus on the "problem" or illness, what would we have to talk about with our consumers? How could the "traditional staff" begin the move from identifying the consumer as the patient to joining with them to form a unified "we?"
>
> It has been wonderful to watch Peer Support take off with the leadership of newly hired Peer Specialists. As the bar was raised on Peer Support, energy levels and motivation went up and folks became more engaged in their treatment and recovery.... As consumers are learning to expect more from themselves in a spirit of self-kindness, traditional staff members are learning to expect more and give up our old ways of spoon-feeding and fostering dependence. The glass ceiling continues to lift as evidenced by more of an "I can" attitude. To have increased independence modeled by a peer, to be walked with in partnership, and in concert with the adoption of the 12-step model, the shift in the mental health paradigm has begun. (pp. 44-45).

An Emerging Role: Peer Support Whole Health and Resiliency

Perhaps the most promising new role for Certified Peer Specialists is Peer Support Whole Health and Resiliency (PSWHR) designed to offset premature death of people who are served in public mental health systems and promote mind-body whole health and resiliency that lines up with healthcare reform and the new federal incentives to integrate physical health and mental health.

In 2009, three states—Michigan, Georgia and New Jersey—received Transformation Transfer Initiative (TTI) grants funded by SAMHSA to promote peers working in whole health (Fricks, 2009). The Peer Support Whole Health and Resiliency (PSWHR) curriculum developed with the TTI grant in Georgia has been introduced in ten states since 2009 and is the subject of a federally funded randomized control study by Dr. Judith A. Cook that began in 2012. PSWHR is based on the foundation of self-directed, strength-based recovery. The training includes a person-centered planning process focusing on a person's strengths, interests, and natural supports while emphasizing healthy lifestyle habits that promote self-directed whole health and resiliency.

Peer Support, Wellness, and Respite Centers

The peer specialist workforce has found an expanding role in whole health and resiliency services. An example of that new role is well defined in the operations and outcomes of a peer-operated program called a Peer Support, Wellness, and Respite Center underway at three sites in Georgia. These innovative peer respite centers funded by the state of Georgia and operated by the Georgia Mental Health Consumer Network have a primary outcome of reducing admissions to hospitals and are cost effective. Similar programs are sprouting up across the country.

The first Peer Support, Wellness, and Respite Center opened on January 30, 2008 in Decatur, Georgia, as an alternative to traditional mental health services. In 2011 two new Peer Support, Wellness, and Respite Centers opened in Bartow and White counties. The three peer respite centers are staffed by Certified Peer Specialists 24 hours a day, 7 days a week. The focus of the peer centers is developing mutual relationships, self-direction, and moving toward a life of wellness and whole health, not illness. The peer respite centers have respite beds in private rooms, a 24/7 Warm Line, and daily wellness/whole health activities.

"Respite" is a fairly new service in peer-run programs offering beds in private rooms in quiet residential settings. The respite concept provides peers a place to stay for up to seven nights when they are in serious emotional distress. Respite is most often used as an alternative to psychiatric hospitalization. The absence of clinical staff, locked doors, or coercion encourages individuals to move forward with their recovery in a way that does not interfere with their existing routines.

For example, one respite guest was working part-time, yet needed extra support because of a medication change. *"I needed peace and quiet and peer support,"* she said. *"It really helps to know that the people around me know what I am going through, and I won't be losing my job because I can continue to work while I am staying in respite."* This individual typically goes into a hospital after a med change, but she said the hospital setting caused her to start all over again once she was discharged. *"That was always the setback,"* she said. *"Not the med change. But now I am able to move forward because of respite."* In 2009, an evaluation/feedback form provided to participants at the peer respite center in Decatur indicated that most respondents (83%) reported they had been in a psychiatric hospital at least once prior to coming to the peer respite center, and most (80%) reported they have had no hospitalizations since coming to the peer center. More than half of the respondents (54%) felt that the peer respite center had prevented a hospitalization for them, and another third (32%) felt that it may have.

The peer center staff also uses respite when the stressors of life become overwhelming. "It's so interesting to experience respite from the guests' point of view," says Maureen Mayer, a peer center staff member (personal communication, 2011). "Not only does it help me through rough times, but it also helps me understand what other respite guests' experience."

Respite guests may choose to participate in daily wellness/whole health activities along with daily participants of the peer center. The wellness/whole health activities are holistic in nature, such as managing stress, creative writing, and creating a Wellness Recovery Action Plan (WRAP). Most activities are community integrated. Several downtown organizations and businesses have opened their doors and resources to the peer center while inviting the greater community of Decatur to participate. For example, the Georgia Advocacy Office offers monthly advocacy trainings and free meeting space for weekly wellness/whole health activities, and the Java Monkey coffee house has opened its doors to the peer respite center for weekly art wellness activities. Most wellness/whole health activities are facilitated by the peer center staff, but some are contracted out to participants who have demonstrated expertise and interest in the subject matter.

When wellness/whole health activities are over for the day, daily participants often call the Warm Line for peer support over the phone. The Warm Line, which is an informal, non-crisis phone line, is a statewide service offering a toll-free number to peers seeking peer support at all hours of the day or night. The Warm Line receives an average of 900 calls per month, and many of the routine calls are from peers who cannot make it to the peer respite center due to their locations in other parts of Georgia.

THE PILLARS OF PEER SUPPORT SERVICES SUMMITS

So established is the new peer workforce that in November 2009, representatives of mental health directors from 23 states convened at the Carter Center in Atlanta for the Pillars of Peer Support Services Summit. A second Pillars of Peer Support Services Summit was held in at the Carter Center in October 2010, a third in 2011, and a fourth in 2012.

The goal of the first summit was to publish a report from states that were providing training and certification for their peer support workforce with the intent of nurturing that new workforce (Cook, 2011). At the conclusion of the first summit, the attendees unanimously endorsed a set of 25 best practices called "pillars" for strengthening state peer support services delivered by the peer workforce. Those pillars, summarized at the end of the chapter, included having clear job descriptions, job-related competencies, sustainable funding, continuing education, inclusion of trauma and whole health services, commitment to consumer-run organizations, a culturally diverse workforce, training for supervisors and opportunities for training and advancement (Daniels et al., 2010). Prior to attendance, survey data was collected from those states, most of which are delivering peer support services under Medicaid reimbursement; summary state reports were provided to all attendees. The most significant barriers to building the peer specialist workforce, as identified by state representatives attending the first Pillars of Peer Support Services Summit, were acceptance by other mental health providers and an understanding of their role.

The second Pillars of Peer Support Services Summit held in 2010 was attended by delegates from 24 states and the Navajo Nation that did not, at that time, have an established mechanism to bill Medicaid for peer support services. The report from that Summit provides a summary of the proceedings and resources to help promote the mission of expanding

Medicaid-billable peer support services to all states as well as state responses from a nationwide survey on the use of Medicaid to reimburse for peer support services. The survey focused on three broad categories: the authority to receive Medicaid reimbursement of peer services; the types of services, settings, and payment rates for peer services; and qualifications and training for Peer Specialists (Daniels et al., 2011). State delegates ended the summit by completing action plans to try to implement high quality peer support services and identifying the technical assistance needs of the field.

The 2011 Pillars of Peer Support Services Summit focused on the peer workforce in integrated physical health and behavioral health with presentations on those emerging roles, including early research. The delegates gained unanimous consensus on the following statement:

> Peer Recovery Support Services are evidence-based and have been demonstrated to promote positive health outcomes and control the cost of healthcare. These services are offered by a trained individual with lived experience and recovery from a mental illness, substance use or chronic health conditions. Peer Recovery Support Services minimally include chronic illness self-management, whole health and wellness promotion and engagement, relapse prevention, life skill coaching, and insurance and health systems navigation (Daniels et al., 2012, p. 21).

The 2012 Summit focused on establishing standards of excellence and included panel presentations by leaders in the field on credentialing and on strategies for moving towards a recovery-oriented culture in the mental health and substance abuse service systems.

SUMMARY

Fundamental to the field of psychiatric rehabilitation and recovery from mental illness is cultivating hope and focusing on "what's strong" rather than "what's wrong" to grow self-directed lives of meaning, purpose, whole health, and resiliency. Recovery requires changing deep-rooted beliefs to foster hope and promote strengths and supports rather than symptoms and illness. As a growing body of evidence demonstrates the positive outcomes of peer support services delivered by a peer workforce, the stage is set to expand Medicaid-billable peer support services to all states and the District of Columbia. This rapidly expanding peer workforce is transforming the lives of individuals and entire mental health systems to promote recovery, resiliency, and mind-body whole health and, in so doing, send messages of support and competence, rather than those of lost lives and disability.

The evidence of lived experiences of recovery and competent recovery skills gained from training can also combat negative beliefs that perpetuate societal stigma and a negative self image that can spiral into despair and hopelessness. Certified Peer Specialists are taught in their training that what you believe about mental illness may be more disabling than the illness itself and how important it is to instill in each individual, as soon as possible, a sense of hope and belief that recovery is the expectation, thus promoting the core values of psychiatric rehabilitation.

BEST PRACTICE GUIDELINES FOR PEER SUPPORT SERVICES

1. Develop clear job descriptions and job competencies that define the role and specific duties of the peer worker, including the importance and value of using their recovery and wellness experience to help others recover.

2. Ensure that peer workers (and their colleagues) have adequate knowledge about the prevalence and impact of trauma in the lives of the people they serve and an understanding of how trauma can affect overall health in later life.

3. Support peer workers in getting and maintaining training and certification in skills-based rehabilitation and recovery services, whole health and wellness training, and the values, philosophies, standards, and ethics of peer support and peer specialist services.

4. Provide supervision that is relevant to the peer worker's role and includes opportunities to collaborate, network, and share experiences with other peer workers within the agency, area, and local consumer and advocacy groups.

5. Support professional advancement and leadership development for peer workers.

6. Provide training to all staff on the trained competencies and unique role of Certified Peer Specialists, so they are appreciated as an integral part of the service team.

7. Implement an evaluation to ensure that the peer worker role remains true to the values of peer support and to demonstrate positive outcomes that result from including peer workers in the service system.

ABOUT THE AUTHORS

Larry Fricks serves as the director of the Appalachian Consulting Group. For 13 years he was Georgia's director of the Office of Consumer Relations and Recovery and a founder of the Georgia Mental Health Consumer Network and Georgia's Peer Specialist Training and Certification. He served on the planning board for the Surgeon General's Report on Mental Health and currently serves on the advisory board for the Carter Center Mental Health Journalism Fellowships. Larry has received the World Health Award for significant contributions to improving community mental health and the SAMHSA Lifetime Achievement Voice Award for the development and adoption of multiple innovative, recovery-oriented programs and services.

Sharon Jenkins Tucker is the executive director of the Georgia Mental Health Consumer Network, Inc. She was awarded the 2010 Isaiah Uliss Advocate Award by the Psychiatric Rehabilitation Association and the 2009 Clifford W. Beers Award by Mental Health America. She previously worked for the West Virginia Mental Health Consumers' Association and directed their Mental Health Consumer Network and the West Virginia Office of Consumer Affairs. Prior to that, she was a behavioral health advocate for Legal Aid of West Virginia for nine years. Sherry is a self-identified consumer of mental health services and holds the credential of ITE (I'm the Evidence), I'm the evidence that recovery works. She has extensive experience with the consumer/survivor movement. Sherry has expertise with WRAP facilitation, Leadership Academy training, peer workforce development, advocacy, and mind/body/spirit wellness. She is a Certified Peer Specialist. Sherry's degrees are from West Virginia University, and she holds a Masters and Bachelors of Arts.

REFERENCES

Carter, R. (2010). *Within our reach—Ending the mental health crisis.* Emmaus, PA: Rodale.

Cook, J. A. (2011). Peer-delivered wellness recovery services: From evidence to widespread implementation. *Psychiatric Rehabilitation Journal, 35*(2), 87-89.

Daniels, A. S., Fricks, L., & Tunner, T. P. (Eds). (2011). *Pillars of Peer Support II: Expanding the role of peer support services in mental health systems of care and recovery.* Retrieved from http://www.pillarsofpeersupport.org

Daniels, A., Grant, E., Filson, B., Powell, I., Fricks, L., & Goodale, L. (Eds). (2010). *Pillars of Peer Support: Transforming mental health systems of care through peer support services.* Retrieved from http://www.pillarsofpeersupport.org

Daniels, A. S., Tunner, T. P., Ashenden, P., Bergeson, S., Fricks, L., & Powell, I. (2012). *Pillars of Peer Support III: Whole health peer support services.* Retrieved from http://www.pillarsofpeersupport.org

Davidson, L., Chinman, M., Sells, D., & Rowe, M. (2006). Peer supports among adults with serious mental illness: A report from the field. *Schizophrenia Bulletin, 32,* 443-450.

Eiken, S., & Campbell, J. (2008). *Medicaid coverage of peer support for people with mental illness: Available research and state example.* New York: Thomson Reuters. Retrieved fromre http://cms.hhs.gov/PromisingPractices/downloads/PeerSupport.pdf

Fricks, L. (2009, Winter). Consumers take charge of wellness. *National Council Magazine, 20-21.*

Mental Health America. (2008). *Position statement 37: The role of peer support services in the creation of recovery-oriented mental health systems.* Retrieved from http://www.mentalhealthamerica.net/positions/peer-services

SAMHSA (Substance Abuse and Mental Health Services Administration). (2005). Building a foundation for recovery: A community education guide on establishing Medicaid-funded peer support services and a trained peer workforce [DHHS Pub. No. (SMA) 05-8089]. Rockville, MD: Center for Mental Health Services, Substance Abuse and Mental Health Services Administration.

Sells, D., Davidson, L., Jewell, C., Faizer, P., & Rowe, M. (2006). The treatment relationship in peer-based and regular case management services for clients with severe mental illnesses. *Psychiatric Services, 57*(8), 1179-1184.

Smith, D. (2007). Letter to state Medicaid directors. Baltimore, MD: Department of Health and Human Services Centers for Medicare and Medicaid Services. Retrieved from http://downloads.cms.gov/cmsgov/archived-downloads/SMDL/downloads/SMD081507A.pdf

Solomon, P. (2010). Peer support/peer-provided services: Underlying processes, benefits, and critical ingredients. In M. Swarbrick & L. T. Schmidt, *People in recovery as providers of psychiatric rehabilitation: Building on the wisdom of experience* (pp. 56-69). Linthicum, MD: United States Psychiatric Rehabilitation Association.

U.S. Department of Health and Human Services. (1999). *Mental health: A report of the Surgeon General.* Rockville, MD: U.S. Department of Health and Human Services, Substance Abuse and Mental Health Services Administration, Center for Mental Health Services.

White, W. L. (1998). *Slaying the dragon: The history of addiction treatment and recovery.* Chicago IL: Lighthouse Institute Publications.

MULTICULTURAL COMPETENCE RECOVERY IN CULTURE

Laurene Finley

A B S T R A C T

Multicultural competence is coming of age. Consciousness has been raised at national, state, and local levels; yet cultural disparities persist and will likely increase unless implementation of culture, knowledge, and practice are incorporated into rehabilitation and recovery practices. Novel, cultural, recovery-oriented approaches are required at the practitioner, program, and organizational levels to meaningfully engage and support people from diverse backgrounds. This chapter focuses on three practice applications: (1) strategies that increase the relevance of practices to diverse groups, (2) a multicultural guide for facilitating learning and understanding deeply held cultural beliefs, and (3) three examples of promising practices. Implications for systems, organizations, and practitioners are summarized.

CONSIDERABLE DOCUMENTATION SUPPORTS LONG STANDING MENTAL HEALTH DISPARITIES FOR PEOPLE with diverse cultural backgrounds (New Freedom Commission on Mental Health, 2003; U.S. Department of Health and Human Services, 1999). Yet, inadequate outreach to immigrants or those with varying levels of acculturation to U.S. culture, misdiagnosis, premature termination, and lower levels of quality and access for persons from diverse backgrounds persist (New Freedom Commission, 2003; Vega, 2005). From the perspective of a person in recovery, *"I think that the services are okay, but do they get to the core of the matter about how things truly affect the community we live in? Not even a drop. Not even a drop in the bucket."* (DMHAS, 2009, p. 11).

There are efforts to address these concerns. Professional organizations such as PRA (2008) have developed multicultural principles to guide practitioners in their daily practice. Several states and organizations are systematically addressing these issues in developing culturally specific programming (Whitmore, personal communication, June 25, 2010; Ortiz, personal communication, June 23, 2010). Unfortunately, what is learned is not widely generalized. Many practitioners are still confused about what it means to actually deliver, multiculturally, recovery-oriented practices (Eliminating Disparities in Mental Health Care: Practice Level Interventions, 2009) or how evidence-based practices can be better modified to increase engagement and effectiveness.

IMPORTANCE OF CULTURE FOR RECOVERY

[People] reported feeling quite surprised, even stunned, by their negative experiences (with practitioners) and many discussed a range of responses to the emotions stirred by these experiences, including "stuffing" their feelings, "getting mad," but not showing anger for fear of retaliation, going to their room and "exploding like a balloon," working harder to not be the stereotype (DMHAS, 2009, p. 12).

If progress in addressing the persistence of stigma related to mental illness has been slow (Gill, 2008), for people experiencing *multiple* sources of discrimination as members of one or more socially devalued ethnic or cultural groups, progress in addressing their reality is virtually nonexistent. Corrigan and colleagues (2003) asked almost 2000 people from diverse backgrounds, Latino, Black, gay, lesbian, bisexual, transgendered, and questioning (GLBTQ) communities as well as those with physical disabilities, their perspectives and experiences with discrimination. Over half of the sample reported some experience with a mental illness as only one source of discrimination; race, sexual orientation, and physical disability were others.

IAPSRS (now PRA) distributed a survey developed by its multicultural subcommittee in an open forum at its national conference (2002) to identify the current level and types of discrimination that exist in practice settings. Among the eight themes discussed perceived overt discrimination was ranked as a top priority. Both practitioners and persons in recovery felt that many agencies and practitioners "talk the talk" but do not "walk the walk." In a peer-led program, members were asked to identify why they felt that programs were insensitive to them (Cook, Jonikas, Hamilton, Batteiger, Grey, McNulty, & Guevarra, 2007). Some people mentioned that they were unable to find gay/lesbian groups to meet their needs. Others found it difficult to relate to people outside their own ethnic-cultural groups. Lack of staff training in cultural competence, lack of knowledge about nontraditional healing resources, and overtly racist and arrogant attitudes expressed towards non-whites were several other concerns expressed.

The Office of Multicultural Affairs in the Connecticut Department of Mental Health and Addition Services held 25, day-long, focus group settings over an 18 month period throughout the state. Culturally diverse people (e.g., African-Americans, Latino Americans, European Americans, Asian Americans, youth, GLBTQ), and culturally mixed groups attended. They discussed services they received and the extent to which their cultural beliefs and values were incorporated. Among the eight identified themes, participants perceived ethnic similarity as a factor that facilitated the development of trust. Some respondents felt uncomfortable sharing culture-related concerns. This was particularly true for the African Americans, who consistently reported that they did not discuss race or race-related issues.

Across most groups, respondents reported a number of negative experiences in which they felt stereotyped and disrespected. Some were not surprised by these experiences because they felt the behavioral health care system was a microcosm of the broader society. They felt their expressions of distress were misunderstood; some services were not useful; they were not listened to; or they felt invisible to practitioners (DMHAS, 2009). Language barriers emerged as a prominent theme in all the groups conducted with those of Latino origin. Unable to communicate with practitioners and with increased feelings of isolation, depression, anger, and loneliness, they felt "choked out of the system" (DMHAS, 2009). These themes were consistent with those reported in the broader cultural competence health and mental health literature.

In a study of people who had been with behavioral health practitioners for least a year, cultural competence was not a priority to them (Stanhope, Solomon, Finley, Pernell-Arnold, Bourjolly, & Sands, 2008), and on the whole, they were satisfied with services received. The authors suggest that cultural competence may be more important during the very early engagement phase of services. Those who do prioritize cultural aspects of their care may drop out quickly if these needs are not addressed. Lack of clarity about the meaning of cultural competence may also have influenced their perspectives.

A major role of rehabilitation and recovery is to help people reclaim, or perhaps claim for the first time, their ethno-cultural identities and their community as a part of feeling whole again (Ida, 2007). A person's ethnic or cultural identification involves varying degrees of commitment or attachment to ethno-cultural values and practices that provide a potential source of positive identity. These attachments foster a sense of belonging, safety, preferences for affiliating with members of one's own group(s), and sometimes a level of felt pride that increases a sense of well-being and a level of satisfaction (Kasper & Noh, 2001).

OVERVIEW OF BEST PRACTICES

Practices are more multiculturally competent when they are available, accessible, acceptable, and tailored to accommodate a person's deep cultural beliefs (Barrio, 2000; Pernell-Arnold & Finley, 2000). Linguistic requirements, learning, verbal and non-verbal communication styles, values, and core belief systems are deeply embedded into all practices and supports to maximize the person's "cultural fit" with the agency (Pernell-Arnold & Finley, 2000). Recruiting practitioners from similar racial or ethno-cultural backgrounds or holding a single or annual cultural competency training session does not ensure culturally competent practice.

Humanistic values characteristic of rehabilitation and recovery originated in Western traditions that may conflict with more traditional, "old world view" cultural orientations experienced by different cultural communities (Pernell-Arnold, 1998; PRIME, 2003-2006). Rehabilitation and recovery supports solely based on Westernized approaches may unintentionally bypass multiple concerns faced by persons with world views that may be more deterministic and pessimistic, contributing to subtle, yet profound person-program conflicts and disconnects: *"I never really discuss that with my clinician. I discuss more of how can we get things done as far as my situation, as far as my housing, my social security, bills that need to be paid, how my depression is coming along. These are the things that we talk about. As far as being African-American and race, we never really discuss that"* (DMHAS, 2009, p. 10).

Elements central to recovery, as identified by the Substance Abuse Mental Health Services Administration (SAMHSA, 2006), are listed below to the left each followed by a statement incorporating a multicultural perspective (USPRA, 2008; Finley & Whitmore, 2010).

- *Holistic:* This element encompasses an individuals' whole life, including mind, body, spirit, and community over time, including the past, present, and future.

- *Hope:* Cultural identity is central, not peripheral, to recovery and promotes wholeness. Hopes and dreams are deeply embedded in a unique, historical, cultural context. Having a "lost" identity is a source of *dis*-ease, *dis*-stress, and hopelessness.

- *Self-Direction:* Other world view orientations such as predetermination, interdependence, or strong spiritual beliefs may conflict, contributing to person-program conflicts or disconnects.

- *Individualized and Person-centered:* "Person-in-culture" centered ensures that a person is perceived in ways that maintain connection with his/her multiple group affiliations and available resources for healing and recovery.

- *Empowerment:* This view is fostered by knowledge of self, group history, customs, rituals, and pride. One rests on the shoulders of all those who have come before.

- *Nonlinear:* Other traditional world-view orientations support that everything in the universe is interconnected, including humans, nature, animals, spirits, ancestors, and the creator (Pernell-Arnold, 1998; PRIME, 2002-2005). Life is continuous without barriers between the past, present, and future. A person's ancestors, for example, can also be perceived by some as spiritual support in the present.

- *Strengths-based:* Within each person's cultural context lie resources and strengths for healing, wellness, and recovery. A cultural identity and connection to one's cultural group(s) can promote recovery.

- *Respect:* Daily micro-aggressions because of one's cultural group memberships are recognized as major sources of *dis*-respect and *dis*-crimination. Subtle, they contribute to internalized feelings of self-hate, oppression, trauma, and disempowerment subsequently resulting in psychological or physiological symptoms. Decreased self-efficacy and self-esteem compound one's biological illness (Carter, Forsyth, Mazzula, & Williams, 2005).

- *Peer Support:* Community, group memberships and affiliations, and familial connections, as well as peers, can foster a sense of security, identity, and belonging.

Strategies for Implementing Culturally Competent Practice and Programs

In this section, several approaches are described for implementing multiculturally competent practices in programs. Practices cannot be assumed applicable across all diverse groups (Sue & Zane, 2006; Sue, Zane, Hall, & Berger, 2009) even when they have achieved a standard of being evidence-based. Perspectives of persons with culturally diverse backgrounds have been neglected in evidence-based practices, and little research has been conducted on their value for persons with diverse backgrounds and the conditions under which they might be beneficial (Castro, Barrera, & Martinez, 2004; Constantine, Miville, & Kindaichi, 2008). We are just beginning to understand what makes rehabilitation and recovery practices culturally competent, what works and how.

One strategy is to adapt psychoeducation and practice methods to diverse learning and cultural styles. In educational settings, for example, higher student motivation and educational performance are enhanced when instructional methods complement cultural and learning styles (Vasquez, 1998). Identification of a person's cultural characteristics is challenging. Even if cultural characteristics can be identified, additional challenges are adapting them or incorporating them in the learning process (Vasquez, 1998). PsyR practitioners may well experience similar challenges.

A second strategy to increase cultural relevance of treatment, rehabilitation, and recovery supports (Rogler, Malgady, Constantino, & Blumenthal, 1987) incorporates a continuum of interventions balancing Western-oriented approaches on one hand with culturally sensitive approaches on the other. Concerns or needs related to developing a person's cultural identity, managing immigration, achieving bicultural competence, and learning coping skills to increase adaptation to mainstream culture are examples of recovery supports beneficial to those with diverse backgrounds.

A third strategy is based on the principle that within each culture there may group resources, symbols, or healing practices that can be incorporated to aid a person's recovery process. Native American cultures, for example, pass the "talking stick" in group settings as a cultural symbol signifying it is time to for the person to speak and share thoughts and personal stories. *Cuento* (folktale) is an example of a treatment technique effectively used with Latino children and adolescents. Identity issues and bicultural adjustments are typical themes discussed (Costantino, Malgady, & Ropgler, 1986; Munoz & Mendelson, 2005). Considered a promising culturally specific approach, *Cuento* has been associated with reducing anxiety and increasing self-esteem among Latinos (Costantino, 1986; Munoz & Mendelson, 2005).

A fourth option for maximizing program relevance is the creation of culturally and linguistically specific programs. For example, there are culturally and linguistically, recovery-oriented Southeast Asian and Latino partial programs in local communities throughout the U.S. GLBTQ Alcohol Anonymous self-help groups exist both in communities and inpatient settings where issues of substance abuse, recovery, discrimination, and identity development can be addressed in safe surroundings. There are just not enough of these types of programs available (Whitmore, personal communication, 2010).

There are evidence-based practices that appear universal across groups, such as social skills training or use of cognitive behavioral techniques (Dadlani & Scherer, 2009; Barrio, 2000; Munoz & Mendelson, 2005). A fifth strategy maximizes multicultural practice by culturally modifying one or more of the following while at the same time maintaining the underlying theory, principles, and procedures of the evidence-based practice (Bachrach, 1993): language, translation of materials, delivery and participation styles, types of modalities selected, and/or content.

Some programs, because of their geographical location, may already be well represented by persons from a particular ethno-cultural group. A multicultural training group intervention was developed to impact the self-esteem and job seeking attitudes of homeless men living in a shelter (Finley, 1990). Participants included African-Americans, one Latino, and several European-American participants. They had other social, cultural identities beyond race that contributed to their commonalities, such as gender, homelessness, varying degrees of familiarity with urban culture, dual diagnosis, discrimination, and a desire for better paying jobs. The content or problems that were addressed were applicable across cultures although use of African-American, crossover, popular cultural arts and highly interactive delivery and participant styles was incorporated.

Community Defined Evidence Practices (CDEP)

CDEP achieve "community validity" using cultural or community indices, reaching a level of acceptance and positive results over time. These practices may or may not have been empirically evaluated (Callejas & Martinez, 2009). Cultural community indices include adherence to a particular worldview and taking into account non-Western, indigenous knowledge, historical, and social context. Customs, traditions or rituals, language communication styles, and spiritual and healing practices are also considered. The goals of CDEP are to: (1) engage persons who might otherwise not use mental health services or prematurely terminate; (2) reduce disparities by improving access, quality, availability, and positive outcomes; and (3) create evidence and effectiveness from the ground up to be used for research, evaluation, advocacy, funding, and policy development.

CDEP at the University of South Florida is funded by the Annie E. Casey Foundation and the Substance Abuse and Mental Health Services Administration. A community steering group of family members, recovering persons, and disparities' researchers identifies practices developed or adapted specifically for Latinos using five criteria: (1) knowledge of the population, (2) clear articulation of practice, (3) evidence of practice utilization, (4) potential for demonstrating outcomes, and (5) demonstrated or potential sustainability of practice and related outcomes. Building evidence and effectiveness from the ground up is also being applied to other cultural groups, such as Native American children and youth.

A meta-analysis comparing culturally competent mental health interventions to those typically provided suggests that modified interventions contribute a moderately enhanced positive benefit to outcomes (Griner & Smith, 2006). In the absence of efficacy studies, protocols and guidelines that consider cultural factors and cultural context most likely facilitate engagement of persons and probably enhance outcomes (Miranda, Bernal, Lau, Kohn, Hwang, & La Fromboise, 2005). Culturally adapted cognitive behavioral treatments, for example, demonstrated superiority over those not adapted (Kohn, Oden, Munoz, Robinson & Leavitt, 2002). When certain features were added to a standardized practice, it was more effective than if an entire component of an intervention was replaced (Blakely, Mayer, Gottschalk, Schmitt, Davidson, Roitman, & Emshoff, 1987).

A Multicultural Guide for Learning about Others

Multicultural guides involve identifying cultural factors from a person's unique cultural story and journey. Gathering facts, data, observations, unique features, and ascribed meaning of a person's cultural journey informs the practitioner's understanding of the person, family, and social network strengths and needs. Requirements of various cultural and community settings are also assessed so that people are helped to effectively transition, maximizing their integration into multiple, different, and specific community settings. Through rehabilitation and recovery planning, culturally consistent strategies, interventions, and resources are selected that facilitate and maximize one's community integration.

Barrio (2000) recommends the inclusion of two interrelated types of inquiries: (1) a person's surface and deep cultural beliefs (see USPRA, 2008), practices, and traditions and (2) assessment of how the person and the family are adjusting to the United States. The PRIME Institute (2002-2005) recommends using a systematic multicultural guide as a means of eliciting cultural data to describe a person within his/her unique cultural context from broad-based socio cultural variables to those increasingly interpersonal and intrapersonal variables (Finley, 1995; 2003; Finley & Shake, 2000; PRIME, 2002-2005; Sands & Gellis, 2012). Factors to consider are:

- *Sociocultural and demographic descriptors:* One or more characteristics should be identified that an individual may use to self-identify, such as country of origin, regional locations, race, religion, sexual orientation, language(s), age, gender, and socioeconomic status. Noting that a person is able to speak English may be more complex than it appears. It would not be uncommon, for example, for a person to appear to understand and speak English yet "switch" to his/her native language under circumstances of stress or intense emotional reactions. Expressive skills may differ from receptive language skills. In supported education, one's expressive, receptive, and written English skills may each be at varying levels of proficiency, which affects educational outcomes.

- *Historic and current socio-political context:* Historical and current political forces from a person's country of origin that have influenced and continue to shape a person's individual and group identities are significant. Inquires about individual and/or family trauma experienced in the country of origin or in the immigration process to the U.S. also are valuable.

- *Cultural values, beliefs, and behaviors:* Surface and deeply held attitudes that influence one's approach to the surrounding world need to be identified and understood. These include, for example, notions of time, concepts of what is considered meaningful work, communication and problem-solving styles as well as beliefs about illness and wellness, death and dying, help-seeking, and gender roles. Understanding these attitudes assists practitioners in being more informed about a person's worldview.

- *Family & kinship network:* Exploration should identify both biological and non-biological kinship or support systems as defined by the person.

- *Acculturation and adaptation styles:* It is important to learn more about the quality of how one navigates both mainstream U.S. culture and those other social identity groups to which a person belongs.

- *Developmental life stage:* This is a description of the life cycle, socialization processes, and practices across different cultures, including rules of descent, notions of childhood, adolescence, and adulthood; and one's perceptions of the afterlife. These beliefs govern expectations for individual and group behavior. Celebrations or rituals may symbolize these life transitions.

- *Multicultural identity development:* This includes an identification of cultural groups to which a person belongs and degree of affiliation with each. Attitudes towards members of other groups are clarified as well as attitudes towards members of mainstream U.S. culture. Attitudes towards others from different groups may impact comfortable participation in work, leisure activities, and supervisory relationships.

- *Individual presentation style:* Observation of a person's physical appearance includes any cultural attire, hair styles, piercings, mannerisms, or unique cultural styles, such as eye contact, gait, language, and use of colloquial English expressions. Interpersonal styles with the practitioner, other staff, and peers are observed. Proficiency of receptive and expressive English language skills and preferences for primary and secondary use of languages in different community settings are reviewed.

- *Intrapersonal variables:* Though misunderstood by practitioners, obedience to one's family may be a perceived strength inside a person's particular culture. Selling drugs or an ability to fight for self-protection may involve survival skills at odds with what is acceptable in mainstream U.S. culture. Though selling drugs is illegal, for example, the person may have skills that if redirected might be saleable. Naming, reframing, redirecting, or building on these strengths in other social contexts may be a part of the recovery process for some from diverse backgrounds.

Rack (1982) recommends that practitioners consistently try to discern whether presenting symptoms, behaviors, complaints, attitudes, or feelings (1) could be accurate within the context of the person's cultural background, (2) are shared by others in person's cultural community, (3) are merely a figure of speech or a way of expressing fear or tension and not to be taken literally; or (4) whether the truth lies somewhere in between.

Kleinman (1979), Randall-David (1985), and Westermeyer (1993) offer several examples of open-ended questions that promote inquiry and a respectful entry into another person's worldview. Treatment, rehabilitation, and recovery planning needs to incorporate these factors and their implications:

- What do you, your family and friends call your illness?

- Who do you consider family? Who do you turn to in times of need?

- Which values were most strongly emphasized in your family when you were growing up, e.g., about work, education, religion, people from different cultures?

- What herbs, medicines, or alternative treatments have you tried?

- What language are you most comfortable in speaking? When do you prefer to speak your language, e.g., at home, with doctors, friends, and people at work?

- When reading or writing, which language are you most comfortable using?

- Have you ever had an experience with discrimination? Please describe it. How did it make you feel about yourself and others?

- From each of the following different groups, which is (are) most important to you and why: your race, gender, sexual orientation, people with a mental illness and/or substance abuse, socioeconomic class, relationship status, religion, or something else? In which one(s) do you feel the most pride? The most embarrassment?

• What do you really want to be and do? What hopes does your family have for you? With whom could I speak to learn more about your cultural background? How comfortable would you be?

Practitioners establish rapport by explaining the purpose of culturally cued, open-ended questions and how the information will be used and using a naturally curious, conversational tone. Frequent "check-ins" are to ensure that questions are not perceived as intrusive while also conveying deep respect and understanding. Dialoguing about race and culture demonstrate practitioner comfort with topics typically viewed as "off limits." Every question need not be asked on a single occasion or necessarily in a particular order (Grieger, 2008). Care is taken not to over-pathologize what may seem most unfamiliar from your point of view. Seeing the face of deceased relatives, particularly following a death, may not be a hallucination. Checking in with spiritual leaders, family, or community members may provide multiple perspectives so as to not solely rely on one's personal assumptions. Continual self-appraisals help refine the inquiry and dialogue process.

Applications of the interview guide to scenarios

Scenario: Walt, Chris, JT, and Amir are four urban, 18- to 24-year old African Americans who are in their program's lobby loudly bantering back and forth, "trading" insults with one another. Standing nearby, a staff member observes. Walt says to JT: "Yea, I said it … you don't know what you're talking about!" JT replies: "Man, you know your mother taught you better than that! You better quit messing with me or we'll have to go outside!"

Questions to consider before any actions are taken: What is going on in this situation? Is this a fight about to ensue, or could it be something else? What is the typical relationship of these young men with one another? Do I need to check with other members or staff familiar with the men and their cultural backgrounds? Consider the source of the bantering. What do I know about the cultural or communication styles of young African-American men? Could it be an African-American cultural style, such as "playing the dozens" in which "jostling" or "one upping" one another is often characteristic? They are speaking loudly. How can I intervene?

Possible Action: Speak with the young men in a casual, non-threatening, curious tone and ask them to describe what is going on. Let them know with a touch of humor that their voices are so loud they can be heard in the next county. If they are jostling one another in fun, help them differentiate when cultural styles are effective and under what circumstances they might not be. You may want to follow-up with them about any desire for more constructive, "active" recreational programing in the community where they can let off steam consistent with their cultural styles.

EXAMPLES OF SUCCESSFUL CULTURALLY COMPETENT PROGRAM IMPLEMENTATION

This section describes three programs—one for African American youth, one for Latinos, and a third that could either be specific to people from one culture or could include participants from diverse backgrounds.

Rites of Passage: A Community-Based Model for African-American Youth

A collectivistic, culturally specific model, *Rites of Passage* (ROP; Hill, 1992, 2007), promotes wellness and personal transformation and incorporates spirituality through the use of rituals and ceremonial practices based on or created from historical references. Ritual is central to ROP as it helps operationalize values and beliefs. Across cultures, initiation rites, for example, usher youth into adulthood and represent one of the most important life transitions. To become a "rite" or "privilege," an activity can be established or prescribed by a legitimate authority and performed at a designated time with symbolism (Hill, 2007). African American, delinquent youth focus on their own culture as well as responsibilities to an interdependent, healthy community (Hill, 2007). Programs have been offered in many community and school settings across the United States, and a National Rites of Passage Institute has been created to further promote these programs (Bernstein, 2010).

Temporary, cohesive, groups are developed where youth learn to become "whole" by reclaiming "lost" identity, healing brokenness and avoiding subsequent self-destructive behaviors stemming from both historical assaults and ongoing societal adversities. Predicated on a moral value system of seven principles (known as Nguzo Saba)—unity, self-determination, collective work and responsibility, cooperative economics; purpose, creativity, and faith, personal mastery, and group identity—the program provides a prescription for ensuring cultural continuity over time. These values are also foundation for Kwanza, the week-long family and community celebration enjoyed by many African Americans in late December. In fostering a group identity first, youth learn to acknowledge who they are, their origins, where they're going, and what's needed to get there. Self-discovery, group bonding, team work, completion of assignments, and rituals marking achievements are methods employed.

The original ROP was a year-long program. It has been modified to fit different educational settings, time frames, age, and levels of participant maturity. The original model started with an initiation over a three-day weekend retreat. Isolated from the busy world, youth are able to self-reflect, journal, view historical videos, and participate in bonding exercises in nature, followed by debriefing discussions after each activity. "Unity" circles provide opportunities for brief sharing of awakenings and knowledge at the close of each day. Orientation and training of staff, trainers, volunteers who mentor, as well as elders, parents, and interested supporters, takes place in a workshop format or series of weekend retreats. A curriculum includes basic knowledge (historical overview, books, audio visuals, cultural exercises, and values); survival (nutrition, budgeting, career life planning, wilderness training, and physical fitness); rituals (purpose, achievements, life events, and values); and community development (purpose, promotion, volunteers, and values).

ROP is divided into the three phases of pre-passage, passage, and the passage ceremony. Pre-passage is approximately seven months where cultural history and the development of a cohesive group are emphasized. Passage is a bridging or transformational period of skill acquisition and practice in the community, using assignments promoting community wellness, such as serving meals to the homeless, creating a community garden, or assisting with voter registration. A written log or scrapbook, autobiography, family tree, interview of elders, decision making, and problem solving and special life skills are required. Passage culminates in a festive ceremony conveying readiness for community transition into adult responsibilities. A symbolic welcome to the ancestors, honoring their struggles and past contributions, initiates the celebration. The presence of community participants, family members, and significant others marks the significance of the journey. A feast, drumming, dance, cultural arts and/or poetry are part of the ceremony. Community members bestow gifts upon those about to enter the community-at-large.

Not originally designed as a "mental health" or "recovery" program, ROP's principles parallel those of recovery programs. Principles such as responsibility to self and to one's cultural community are a strong focus as is strength gained through both individual and group identification. Mutual peer support, as well as expected community support, is also emphasized. Many African-American young adult males experience particular alienation in U.S. culture and are frequently stereotyped as aggressive, violent, uncooperative and non-responsive to traditional mental health care. African Americans with a mental illness or co-occurring mental illness and substance abuse could potentially benefit from such a culturally specific program model.

A psycho-educational group offering could be structured or restructured incorporating aforementioned cultural adaptations without expending major, additional financial resources. Steeped in cultural traditions once thought to promote healing and wellness for self and others in the community, these culturally specific approaches are found to particularly engaging, appealing, and adaptable to educational and community organizations. The Connecticut Department of Mental Health and Addiction Services used Rites of Passage as a template for the creation of the "Amistad Project" in operation for three years (Ortiz, personal communication, 2010). It has been discontinued because of budgetary constraints.

Facilitators require advanced preparation or an agency partnership developed with a community organization familiar with ROP, African-American history, and Kwanza philosophy and principles. The gender of the group membership may determine the gender assignment of facilitators. The intervention, for example, would most likely benefit from facilitation of an African-American male facilitator(s) if targeting young adult African American males. Training and consultation provided through the ROP National Institute may also be a useful resource.

There are also implications for the adaptation of this model for other cultural groups consistent with their spirituality, traditions, rites, and communication styles. Intercultural groups with individuals representing different genders and culture could be developed. It is important that a culturally specific model not in any way appear to exclude others. A well-thought out implementation plan is needed to prepare the entire agency for its inclusion. It might be beneficial to speak with those at the Rites of Passage Institute as well as other sites having successfully implemented this model. Empirical evaluation of these types of programs would be helpful to practitioners and their supervisors.

Culturally Competent Engagement and Outreach for Latinos

The Connecticut Department of Mental Health and Substance Abuse tracked data on Latino access and service use throughout their six regional behavioral health system. Substance abuse had been increasing, and traditionally, Latinos did not self-refer. Individuals were difficult to reach and engage in treatment and recovery programs. Lack of trust and faith in institutions, shame, and stigma of illness in the Latino community posed barriers to service access.

Proyecto Nueva Vida (PNV) or Project New Life was implemented in 1997 and continues as of the date of this publication. A five-year pilot program was created, providing Latinos with culturally specific services and developing measurement criteria to be able to discover what actually works with Latinos. Outreach workers were hired to find people requiring behavioral health services in both traditional and non-traditional settings such as homes, abandoned buildings, social clubs, and shooting galleries. Occasionally, one outreach contact generated additional family members requiring similar behavioral health supports. People are identified who currently aren't receiving help or are at risk of having problems for which they would not likely seek treatment.

Continuity with people is maintained throughout the entire treatment and recovery process. Education and training of individuals, family members, and practitioners are implemented to increase access to services and reduce the number of Latinos who leave services against medical advice. In-service trainings also convey ways practitioners could assist in preventing discouragement or relapse and help create support and wrap around services.

Admissions increased by 29% and 32% in two successive years of the project's implementation (Ortiz, personal communication, 2010). PNV has operated for 13 years and can be replicated with other cultural groups. Initially, unprepared for the influx of Latinos, there were inadequate bi-lingual, bi-cultural staffing, too few inpatient hospital beds, and difficulties accessing recovery programs. Leadership was initially concerned for staff safety because of their participation in non-traditional work roles, settings, and responsibilities. Many staff members, already familiar with the high risk community settings, were highly optimistic, motivated, and committed. Ideas, approaches, successes, and failures are shared at monthly meetings of regional Latino initiatives for coordination and future planning activities. In Bridgeport, CT, PNV demonstrates a model of collaboration between three agencies—the Co-op Center of the Council of Churches of Greater Bridgeport, which offers job training; CASA Inc., which provides outpatient and inpatient treatment; and Optimus Health Care, which offers medical and HIV treatment. Intake is centralized, an open door policy is maintained, and staff availability occurs outside of scheduled office hours. Social gatherings are also provided, such as monthly family forums, picnics, sober dances, and concerts.

"Latinos bond with people, not with institutions" (Ortiz, personal communication, 2010). By including staff and mentors, the treatment and recovery system recreates the strengths of the Puerto Rican kinship system. One PNV program participant, drug free for four years, reports feeling that she's been with staff for so long that they feel like family, and she feels "at home" both professionally and personally supported. PNV is one of six national programs meeting the University of South Florida's Community Defined Evidence Project criteria.

Adapting a Universal, Evidence-Based Intervention for Discrimination Management

Negative psychological and physiological effects on a person's psychological well-being and health associated with racial, cultural, or ethnic discrimination are well documented (Carter, Forsyth, Mazzula, & Williams, 2005). Effects are similar to those who have experienced psychological trauma and stress associated with physical or psychological abuse or emotional and verbal assault. The internalization of negative societal messages that impart feelings of inferiority is a major threat to a person's identity, self-esteem, and recovery. These historical messages continue to stifle and negatively impact the hopes and dreams of people from diverse cultural backgrounds.

Inoculation Against Discrimination (IAD; Finley & Pernell-Arnold, 2005) is a cultural adaptation of Meichenbaum's flexible, evidence-based Stress Inoculation Training (SIT). "Inoculation" is analogous to the concept of medical immunization where one builds psychological antibodies or coping skills to resist the toxicity of stress (Meichenbaum, 1996). SIT emerged as an integration of cognitive behavior modification and the role of cognitive and affective factors in coping with stress (Meichenbaum, 2007). It has been used in two ways: as treatment to help individuals cope with the aftermath of exposure to stressful events and as a preventive model to "inoculate" individuals against ongoing or future stressors. The goals are to enhance individuals' coping repertoires and empower them to use their skills. On some occasions, SIT extends beyond individual and group interventions to adopt a community-based focus. It has been used with people receiving mental health services in both hospital and community settings.

In SIT, there is a recognition that the underpinnings of personal stress often emanate from societal and institutional forces that are unavoidable. However, environmental stressors are also open to alteration, whenever possible. SIT has also been used to foster personal adjustment to cross-cultural interactions in new cultural milieus. Interventions can range from 20 minutes to a series of one hour weekly or bi-weekly sessions (Langer, Janis, & Wolfor, 1975). Booster or follow-up sessions are built into the training model and occur over an additional three- to twelve-month frame as people experiment with new behaviors.

IAD is an intentional, planned, intervention aimed at resisting the internalization of accumulated, daily, micro-aggressions. The purpose is to strengthen or build up one's resistance against potential discriminatory experiences in various employment, neighborhood, educational, and social settings. Expected outcomes are stress reduction and enhancement of one's personal repertoire of resources for coping and problem-solving skills so as to more effectively manage cross-cultural encounters.

A 14-week, three-phase structure, similar to the SIT framework, is used with a follow-up session completed one month after the program is completed. Participants receive an illustrated workbook; there is also a companion facilitator's manual. Sessions are two hours in length. In Phase 1, people learn more about themselves as cultural beings and what discrimination is and its psychological and physiological impact. During this phase, the term "discrimination" is introduced, reframed as "nibbles", i.e., daily micro-aggressions or insults diminishing one's self-esteem. Micro-aggressions also exacerbate a person's symptoms or produce stressful symptoms that may be quite similar to symptoms of one's mental illness. In Phase 2, skills are taught to help manage stress arousal in the face of perceived discrimination. Based on SIT's theoretical framework and phase structure, IAD teaches similar skills, such as rehearsal (reframed as practicing discrimination stories), problem-solving, imagery (reframed as "use your imagination"), self-soothing (reframed as "creating a safe place"), identification of social and community supports (my "go to" people or "who do I turn to?") so as to be more "user friendly." Assertiveness skills are reframed as "tools to interrupt and manage nibbles." "Comebacks," or playing-the-dozens, are a culturally accepted form of bantering between individuals. They are presented as another assertiveness tool, "self-talk" used to preserve one's dignity. Proactively, positive messages are internalized rather than the negative when it would be inappropriate to express oneself verbally in a given situation or with a person in authority. When, where, and with whom bantering is appropriate is also discussed.

Participants are also taught to recognize and articulate examples of negative messages they have learned and internalized, later reframing them so that they are less toxic. Throughout primary and secondary school, for example, a person from a culturally devalued group may have heard and internalized from a teacher or counselor, "You shouldn't go to college; you'll never make it! You should go to a trade school instead." An alternative message a person might give herself is, "I come from a rich cultural history where this has been said to many from my cultural group. It didn't stop them from succeeding; it doesn't have to stop me."

An important component of Phase 2 are interpersonal role plays adapted from Pederson's (1997) "triadic" role play model originally used to train counselors in becoming more multiculturally effective. Personal examples of residual, unresolved, challenging, discriminatory experiences are identified, and within a small group, participants demonstrate the subtle, discriminatory messages with an opportunity to apply a newly acquired skill followed by peer feedback. Reactions to both the scenario and intervention are discussed with the entire group. Phase 3 provides a booster session as well as reports of successes and challenges and culminates in a closing celebration.

Inoculation has been developed over a 20-year period and has been presented to training groups of multiculturally diverse practitioners and persons in recovery. It currently has been implemented as a randomized control trial for African Americans with psychiatric disabilities or co-occurring disorders and is funded through the Rehabilitation Research and Training Center, Temple University Collaborative on Community Integration. Reduction in symptoms and culture-related stress, an increase in skills for coping with discrimination, an increase in their social networks, and community integration with fewer inappropriate drop-outs are expected outcomes. Research data and results are being compiled.

IMPLICATIONS FOR PRACTICE

First, there are implications for systems/organizations in which practitioners practice that include multicultural organizational development and training that addresses reduction in disparities. A summary and general best practice guidelines conclude the chapter.

Multicultural Systems and Organizations

Multiculturally competent, recovery-oriented practices are best provided in systems and organizations that make "culture" operational in their mission, goals, values, and performance appraisals as well as explicit in policies and practices. Multicultural organizational audits (assessments) can be used as a tool to identify organizational strengths and needs in addressing diversity issues. Some organizations and state systems may create in-house multicultural advisory committees with representative members from diverse groups to help identify and examine key demographics, service needs, and barriers across different community groups using mental health services. Organizations and systems dedicated to becoming multicultural organizations consider all the data and will develop multicultural strategic plans charting a course for change. SAMHSA, as well several states, has developed cultural competence standards, including recommended performance indicators and outcomes as guides for delivering culturally competent services (SAMHSA, 2000).

Multicultural Training

Training occurs within organizations working to support the long-range strategic plan to increase cultural competence. Training, alone, can rarely address the complex service issues that are to be addressed. Comprehensive, integrated training approaches are needed at multiple organizational levels. Unfortunately, multicultural competence training has had little credibility, appears unscientific, takes time and resources, and is perceived as exotic (Vega, 2005). It is also perceived as burdensome and increasing demands on practitioners already over taxed. As a result, it is not well integrated into wellness, treatment, recovery, and rehabilitation practices.

Multicultural training typically provides practitioners with awareness, information, and knowledge in a limited time format. Findings from training programs limited to only a few hours with no planned follow-up are likely be ineffective in helping practitioners in developing the confidence and comfort with acquired skills for the next generation of cultural competence (Vega, 2005). Even though countless provider cultural competence trainings have been implemented across multiple settings and in different formats, there has been little discernible impact on provider achievement of cultural competence (Dougherty, 2004). Much of multicultural training over emphasizes cognitive learning rather than achieving a balance with affective, attitudinal and skill-based learning.

A more effective use of resources is to use trainers with organizational development skills to assist in the effective implementation of agency policies and the promotion of transformative, organizational change. They can help to make "culture" operational throughout the organizational structure. Many organizations have not yet recognized the link between disparities, multicultural competence training, organizational development, and change (Pernell-Arnold, 2009).

Partners Reaching to Improve Multicultural Effectiveness (PRIME), a promising model, is one of four projects funded by the Substance Abuse Mental Health Services Administration in collaboration with three academic organizations and a state office of mental health. It is a developmental, multimodal, multicultural training program promoting different participant skill sets. Goals were to increase knowledge, challenge attitudes, and cultivate new skills with coaching for agency application. Participants completed an assignment to identify and implement an agency project that enhances services for persons not served or underserved and were further supported by facilitators' technical assistance.

Quantitative results using a modified version of the Multicultural Awareness/Knowledge/ Skills Survey—MAKSS (D'Andrea, Daniels, and Heck, 1991) and the Cross-Cultural Adaptability Inventory (CCAI) (Kelley and Meyers, 1992) and the Organizational Scale on Cultural Competence (OSCC) designed for the training program were used. Significant improvements demonstrated increased awareness, knowledge, and the ability to understand the impact of discrimination on persons receiving mental health services. No overall improvement was found on the CCAI though closer analysis found changes in individual scores from pre to post test. Three subgroups were identified: those who increased their scores (42%); those who stayed the same (24 %), or decreased their scores (34%). Further analysis suggested that number of years of behavioral health employment and racial-ethnic group membership may have effected improvement. Curriculum fidelity was assessed to ensure consistency and standardization. The Milton Bennett Developmental Model of Intercultural Sensitivity (Hammer, Bennett, & Wiseman, 2003) was used to assess different orders of change as one's potential competence in intercultural relations increases. The model was combined with extensive field observations and detailed notes to further understand the process of becoming culturally competent. The process occurs in a non-linear fashion for both individuals and at the group level. Time is apparently required for practitioners to learn, practice, integrate, and implement new skills with coaching support (Bourjolly, Sands, Solomon, Stanhope, Pernell-Arnold, & Finley, 2005). Furthermore, for the majority of participants, there were fundamental changes in worldview perspectives suggesting that a transformation or second order learning had occurred (Pernell-Arnold, Finley, Sands,

Bourjolly, & Stanhope, 2012). Awareness and knowledge, while necessary, will not be sufficient for the present and future challenges practitioners face working with increasingly diverse people. Consensus on training goals and theoretical framework and emphasis on perspective or second-order change as well as expected outcomes, skills, methods and types of models (length and time frame) may all be required if the elimination of decades old disparities is seriously expected.

SUMMARY

We are entering the next generation of cultural competence. Though there are emerging new directions and knowledge, the information remains fragmented and not well disseminated. Practitioners might benefit from a compendium of both evidence-based and community-defined evidence practices across disciplines, cultures, and age groups. Increasing the application and generalizing of learning, removing institutional barriers encountered by practitioners as well as increasing organizational cultural competence are new frontiers. Adaptation or modification of evidence-based practices to different cultural identity groups will be increasingly required as will challenges posed for trainers to better manage affective learning and applied approaches.

BEST PRACTICE GUIDELINES FOR THE NEXT GENERATION OF CULTURAL COMPETENCE

• Focus on developing and applying skills and their application to move PsyR and recovery beyond consciousness-raising.

• Identify specific skills that promote genuine, respectful (as defined by the culture), cross cultural conversations with recovering persons, families, and members of their social network.

• Identify what questions to ask and when and how to ask them in ways that elicit a person's and family's surface, deep cultural beliefs and personalized meanings without being perceived as intrusive.

• Incorporate and use cultural, familial, community strengths, and resources throughout rehabilitation and recovery plans to facilitate a person's recovery.

• Raise questions, even when there are no definitive answers, about whether observations or information received may possibly be cultural, secondary to one's illness, or perhaps a combination of the two.

• Develop a multicultural assessment guide and illustrative case examples that facilitate cross cultural interviewing and communication.

• Implement novel practices that meet criteria for community defined evidence.

• Standardize methods in a "lesson plan" or facilitator's manual when designing community defined practices so that others within a program or across practice settings can replicate the intervention. This can pave the way for future research.

• Modify, adapt, or tailor evidence-based practices so that they better accommodate a person's cultural traits and characteristics.

- Increase access to behavioral health and recovery services for those marginalized through development of culturally adapted outreach strategies.

- Inquire about effects of discrimination due to both the illness(es) and/or memberships in other culturally, socially devalued groups by targeting self-management and advocacy skills.

- Upgrade and standardize PSR cultural competency training so that it better addresses current and future needs for practitioner skill acquisition and implementation.

ABOUT THE AUTHOR

Laurene Finley is a licensed psychologist who provides organizational consultation, training, and education to behavioral healthcare settings. She is a faculty member of the PRIME Institute (Partners Reaching to Improve Multicultural Effectiveness) at Drexel University, College of Medicine, Division of Behavioral Healthcare. Dr. Finley has received special recognition from the Pennsylvania Association of Psychosocial Rehabilitation Services for "an outstanding state contribution" to the development of cultural competence in psychiatric rehabilitation and the distinguished career award. She has also served on the editorial board of the *Psychiatric Rehabilitation Journal* and has been a member of the Psychiatric Rehabilitation Association Certification Committee.

REFERENCES

Bachrach, L. (1993). Continuity of care and approaches to case management for long-term mentally ill patients. *Hospital and Community Psychiatry, 44*(5), 465-468.

Barrio, C. (2000). Cultural relevance of community support programs, *Psychiatric Services, 51*(7), 879-884.

Berstein, M. (2010, May 12). Cleveland-based National Rites of Passage Institute reaches a milestone. *Cleveland Plain Dealer.* Retrieved from http://blog.cleveland.com/metro/2010/05/national_rites_of_passage_inst.html

Blakely, C. H., Mayer, J. P., Gottschalk, R. G., Schmitt, N., Davidson, W. S., Roitman, D. B., & Emshoff, J. G. (1987). The fidelity-adaptation debate: Implications for the implementation of public sector social programs. *American Journal of Community Psychology, 15,* 253-268.

Bourjolly, J., Sands, R. G., Solomon, P., Stanhope, V., Pernell-Arnold, A., & Finley, L. (2005). The journey toward intercultural sensitivity: A non-linear process. *Journal of Ethnic & Cultural Diversity in Social Work, 14,* 41-62.

Callejas, L., & Martinez, K. (2009, October 15). Community-defined evidence: Research from the ground up. *National Network to Eliminate Disparities in Behavioral Health.* Forum conducted online.

Carter, R., Forsyth, J., Mazzula, S., & Williams, B. (2005). Racial discrimination & race-based traumatic stress: An exploratory investigation. In R. Carter (Ed.), *Handbook of racial-cultural psychology and counseling: Vol. 2, training and practice* (pp. 447-475). Hoboken, NJ: Wiley and Sons.

Castro, F., Barera, M., & Martinex, C. (2004). The cultural adaptation of prevention interventions: Resolving tensions between fidelity and fit. *Prevention Science, 5,* 41-45.

Constantino, G., Malgady, R., & Ropgler, L. (1986). Cuento therapy: A culturally sensitive modality for Puerto Rican children. *Journal of Consulting and Clinical Psychology, 54,* 639-645.

Cook, J., Kiosk, S., Jonikas, J., Hamilton, M., Batteiger, D., Grey, D., McNulty, J., Guevarra, R. (2007). Cultural competency in peer-led programs: A web survey & program assessment tool. Chicago, IL: UIC/STAR Center.

Corrigan, P., Thompson, V., Lambert, D., Sangster, Y., Noel, J., Campbell, J. (2003). Perception of discrimination among persons with serious mental illness. *Psychiatric Services, 54*(8), 1105-1110.

Constantine, M., Miville, M., Kindaichi, M. (2008). Multicultural competence in counseling psychology practice and training. In S. Brown & R. Lent (Eds.), *Handbook of counseling psychology* (pp. 141-158). Hoboken, NJ: Wiley.

Dadlani, M., & Scherer, D. (2009). Culture in psychotherapy, practice, research: awareness, knowledge, and skills. Retrieved from http://www.divisionofpsychotherapy.org/dadlani-and-scherer-2009

DMHAS. (2009). Culture and behavioral health service delivery: An analysis of focus group findings. Hartford, CT: Connecticut Department of Mental Health and Addiction Services, Office of Multicultural Affairs. Retrieved from http://www.ct.gov/dmhas/lib/dmhas/publications/Disparitiesreport.pdf

Dougherty, R. (2004). Reducing disparity in behavioral health services: A report from the American college of mental health administration. *Administration and Policy in Mental Health, 31*(3), 253-263.

Eliminating disparities in mental health care: Practice-level interventions (2009, December). *Data Matters: Interactive Electronic Newsletter.* Washington, DC: Georgetown University Center for Child and Human Development National Technical Assistance Center for Children's Mental Health. Retrieved from http://www.gucchdgeorgetown.net/data/issues/2009/1209_article.html

Finley, L. (1990). Workshops sponsored by the Office of Services to the homeless adults presented at the Ridge Avenue Shelter, 5/90-6/90.

Finley, L. (2003). When cultures meet (rev). MCP/EPPI, Philadelphia, PA.

Finley, L., & Shake, M. (2000). Cross cultural diagnosis and assessment. Connecticut Department of Mental Health and Hospitals, Hartford, CT.

Finley, L., & Pernell-Arnold, A. (2005). *Inoculation against discrimination: A skills training cognitive-behavioral model.* Workshop presentation at Columbia University, Teacher's College Roundtable, New York, NY.

Finley, L., & Whitmore, C. (October, 2010). Workshop presented at Mental Health Recovery: Practice, Services, and Research, Silver School of Social Work, New York University, New York, NY.

Gill, K. (2008). The persistence of stigma and discrimination. *Psychiatric Rehabilitation Journal, 31*(3), 183-184.

Grieger, I. (2008). A cultural assessment framework and interview protocol. In L. A. Suzuki & J. G. Ponterotto, *Handbook of multicultural assessment, clinical, psychological, and educational perspectives* (pp. 132-161). San Francisco, CA: Wiley & Sons.

Griner, D., & Smith, T. (2006). Culturally adapted mental health interventions: A meta-analytic review. *Psychotherapy: Theory, Research, Practice, Training, 43,* 531-548.

Hammer, M. R., Bennett, M. J., & Wiseman, R. (2003). Measuring intercultural sensitivity: The intercultural development inventory. *International Journal of Intercultural Relations, 27*(4), 421-443.

Hill, P. (1992). *Coming of age: African-American male rites of passage.* Chicago, IL: African-American Images.

Hill, P. (2007), retrieved June 5, 2007 from http://www.ritesofpassage.org/df99-articles/harvest

Ida, D. (2007). Cultural competency and recovery within diverse populations. *Psychiatric Rehabilitation Journal, 31*(1), 49-53.

IAPSRS (2002). Discrimination survey. Mullticultural Subcommittee. Unpublished.

Kasper, V., & Noh, S. (2001). *Discrimination and identity: An overview of theoretical and empirical research.* Commissioned by the Department of Canadian Heritage for the Ethnocultural, Racial, Religious, and Linguistic Diversity and Identity Seminar, Halifax, Nova Scotia.

Kleinman, A. (1979). Sickness as cultural semantics: Issues for anthropological medicine and psychiatry. In P. Ahmed and G. Coelho (Eds.), *Toward new definitions of health psychosocial dimension* (pp. 53-66). New York: Plenum Press.

Kohn, L. P., Oden, T. M., Muñoz, R. F., Leavitt, D., Robinson, A. (2002). Adapted cognitive-behavioral group therapy for depressed low-income, African-American women. *Community Mental Health, 38,* 497-504.

Langer, T., Janis, I., & Wolor, J. (1975). Reduction of psychological stress in surgical patients. *Journal of Experiential Social Psychology, 11,* 155-165.

Meichenbaum, D. (1996). Stress inoculation training for coping with stressors. *The Clinical Psychologist, 49,* 4-7.

Meichenbaum, D. (2007). Stress inoculation training: A preventative and treatment approach. Retrieved December 1, 2010 from http://www.melissainstitute.org/documents/stress_inoculation.pdf

Miranda, J., Bernal, G., Lau, A., Kohn, L., Kwang, W. C., & La Fromboise, T. (2005). State of the science in psychosocial interventions for ethnic minorities. *Annual Review of Clinical Psychology, 67,* 734-745.

Munoz, R., & Mendelson, T. (2005). Toward evidence-based interventions for diverse populations: The San Francisco General Hospital prevention and treatment manuals. *Journal of Consulting and Clinical Psychology, 78*(5), 790-799.

Partners Reaching to Improve Multicultural Effectiveness [PRIME]. (2003-2005). Workforce training curriculum to reduce racial and ethnic disparities 2002-2005. Funded by the Substance Abuse and Mental Health Services Administration (SAMHSA), Philadelphia, PA: Drexel University.

Partners Reaching to Improve Multicultural Effectiveness [PRIME]. (2006). *Evaluation of the PRIME training: Final report,* submitted to the Substance Abuse and Mental Health Services Administration. Philadelphia, PA: University of Pennsylvania School of Social Policy & Practice.

Pedersen, P. (1997). *Culture-centered counseling interventions: Striving for accuracy.* Thousand Oaks, CA: Sage.

Pernell-Arnold, A. (1998). Curriculum: Cross-cultural communication in counseling. PEL Program, Eckerd College, St. Petersburg, FL.

Pernell-Arnold, A., & Finley, L. (2000). Integrating multicultural competence in psychosocial rehabilitation. In R. Hughes, D. Weinstein (Eds.) *Best practices in psychosocial rehabilitation* (pp. 213-244). Columbia, MD: IASPRS.

Pernell-Arnold, A. (2009). *Introduction to PRIME Institute: Multicultural clinical behavioral health curriculum.* Unpublished document.

Pernell-Arnold, A., Finley, L., Sands, R. G., Bourjolly, J., Stanhope, V. (2012). Training mental health providers in cultural competence: A transformative learning process. *American Journal of Psychiatric Rehabilitation, 15*(4), 334-356.

PRA (2008). *Multicultural principles.* McLean, VA: Psychiatric Rehabilitation Association.

President's New Freedom Commission on Mental Health. (2003). *Achieving the promise: Transforming mental health care in America, final report.* No. Pub. No. SMA-03-3832. Rockville, MD: U.S. Department of Health and Human Services.

Rack, P. (1982). *Race, culture and mental disorder.* London: Tavistock Publications.

Randall-David, E. (1989). *Strategies for working with culturally different communities & clients.* Washington, DC: Association for the Care of Children's Health.

Rogler, L. H., Malgady, R. G., Costantino, G., & Blumenthal, R. (1987). What do culturally sensitive mental health services mean? The case of Hispanics. *American Psychologist, 42,* 565-570.

Sands, R. G., & Gellis, Z. (2012). *Clinical social work practice in behavioral mental health: Toward evidence-based practice* (3rd ed.). Boston, MA: Allyn & Bacon.

Stanhope, V., Solomon, P., Finley, L., Pernell-Arnold, A., Bourjolly, J., & Sands, B. (2008). Evaluating the impact of cultural competency trainings from the perspective of people in recovery. *American Journal of Psychiatric Rehabilitation, 11*(4), 356-372.

Sue, S., & Zane, N. (2006). Ethnic minority populations have been neglected by evidence-based practices. In J. C. Norcross, L. E. Beutler, & R. F. Levant (Eds.), *Evidence-based practices in mental health: Debate and dialogue on the fundamental questions* (pp. 329-337, 359-361). Washington, DC: American Psychological Association.

Sue, S., Zane, N., Hall, G., & Berger, L. (2009). The case for cultural competence in psychotherapeutic interventions. *Annual Review Psychology, 60,* 525-548.

U.S. Department of Health and Human Services. (2000). *Cultural competence standards in managed health care services.* Washington, DC: Substance Abuse and Mental Health Services Administration, Center for Mental Health Services.

U.S. Department of Health & Human Services. (2006). *National consensus statement on mental health recovery.* Washington, DC: Substance Abuse and Mental Health Services Administration, Center for Mental Health Services. Retrieved from http://www.mentalhealth.samhsa.gov/publications/allpubs/sma05-4129

U.S. Department of Health & Human Services. (1999). *Mental health: A report of the Surgeon General.* Rockville, MD: US Department of Health and Human Services.

U.S. Department of Health and Human Services (2001). *Mental health: Culture, race, and ethnicity—A supplement to Mental Health: A report of the Surgeon General.* Rockville, MD: U.S. Department of Health and Human Services, Substance Abuse and Human Services.

U.S. Department of Health and Human Services. (2006). *National consensus statement on mental health recovery.* Rockville MD: Center for Mental Health Services.

Vasquez, J. (1998). Distinctive traits of Hispanic students. *The Prevention Researcher, 4*(1), 1-4.

Vega, W. (2005). Higher stakes ahead for cultural competence. *General Hospital Psychiatry, 27,* 446-450.

Westermeyer, J. (1993). Cross-cultural psychiatric assessment. In A. C. Gaw (Ed.), *Culture, ethnicity, and mental illness* (pp. 125-144). Washington, DC: American Psychiatric Press.

CHAPTER 10

HOUSING

Priscilla Ridgway
Sam Tsemberis

ABSTRACT

This chapter reviews the development of supported housing and describes
the practice of Pathways Housing First (PHF) that provides permanent
social-integrated housing and flexible support services to people with
severe psychiatric problems. The approach is a hybrid blend of psychiatric
rehabilitation, intensive case management, harm reduction, and other
recovery-oriented services. The authors describe the evidence base and core
practices of PHF that helps people select, acquire, and maintain the housing
of their choice and succeed at community living.

AN UNMET NEED FOR HOUSING FOR PEOPLE WITH SEVERE PSYCHIATRIC DISABILITIES HAS EXISTED IN THE U.S. since the advent of de-institutionalization in the 1970s. Tens of thousands of people were discharged from institutions into communities that lacked decent low-income housing without sufficient planning or follow-up. Many were merely transinstitutionalized into large nursing homes, board-and-care settings, and adult homes that did not support integration into community life. Many others found their way to urban center cities where they resided in substandard housing, often without support services.

In the 1980s, the erosion of federal safety net programs coupled with a real estate boom resulted in the demolition or conversion of most single-room occupancy hotels (SROs) and other affordable housing. Public policy and housing market forces coalesced to devastating effect: People on low fixed incomes such as Supplemental Security Income (SSI) were priced out of the housing market, resulting in widespread homelessness. Shelters provided short periods of relief, but the number of shelter beds was insufficient. Ironically, shelters opened in the vacated wards of closed mental institutions or in church basements and armories. As shelters filled to capacity, many people were turned away. Crowding and structured rules of shelter living often intimidated people with psychiatric disabilities, many of whom opted to risk spending their nights on the streets or in other public spaces.

The primary model of residential services during the early 1980s was "the residential continuum." The continuum included a range of settings: community residences (some called halfway or quarterway houses), cooperative apartment programs, and social model housing designed for people with special needs. Later shelters, safe havens, and other transitional housing options were added to the array of programs. In a continuum, people were to be placed in the setting assessed as meeting their level of functioning. They were to move through settings as they learned daily living skills and earned privileges. As they moved, the level of staff supervision lessened until they achieved self-sufficiency or independent living. Service packages were included that met the needs of a prototypical resident.

Unfortunately, insufficient arrays of residential services were developed. Due to bureaucratic bottlenecks and long waiting lists, the continuum model failed even where a number of programs existed. Some people were stuck at a point on the continuum while others were placed anywhere an opening existed. People with intense needs were often screened out of residential programs altogether because their problems were viewed as too severe, their behavior too disruptive, or group living environment too emotionally challenging for them.

Residential programs with onsite staff were costly; yet staff members were often entry level workers with little training who struggled to work effectively with groups of people with complex needs. The final step on the continuum—independent living—remained out of reach for most people on a disability entitlement income; no housing market in America was affordable for people on an SSI income (Cooper & O'Hara, 2002), and many needed ongoing supportive services to succeed. Those who "failed" often experienced revolving-door admissions to inpatient facilities and were discharged either to the streets or to substandard housing where they were vulnerable (for a more in-depth historical review, see Ridgway, 1997).

Intensive case management models were linked to housing subsidies to meet these needs in demonstration programs in the 1980s. A formal model of service called "supported housing" was designed at the Boston University Center for Psychiatric Rehabilitation during that era (Carling & Ridgway, 1987; Ridgway & Zipple, 1990). The model held that people should be housed in the environment of their choice and have ready access to intensive, flexible personalized support services that would help them to succeed in their living environment. A needs assessment format was designed to capture consumer housing and support preferences (Ridgway & Carling, 1987). A synthesis of findings (Tanzman, 1993) revealed that almost all consumers wanted mainstream housing that was socially integrated. They did not want to live in settings where people with psychiatric disabilities were the sole tenants. They wanted flexible personalized supports rather than a prepackaged bundle of services embedded within their housing or staff members on site.

Despite initial skepticism, over time, research demonstrated supported housing programs to be at least as effective as other residential services, but much more satisfying to people in recovery (Livingston, Gordon, King, & Srebnick, 1991; Nelson, & Smith, 1997; Rog, 2004; Shern, Felton, Hough, Lehman, Goldfinger, Valencia, Dennis, Straw, & Wood, 1997). Costs were much less for flexible programs with individualized and loosely linked support services attached to housing rather than single-site facilities with staff on site around the clock (Culhane, Metraux, & Hadley, 2002; Gulcur, Stefancic, Shinn, Tsemberis, & Fischer, 2003; Perlman, & Parvensky, 2006).

Throughout the late 1980s and 1990s, many forms of supportive housing were developed, depending on the resources available and the philosophy and approach of the host agency. Some offered clustered housing that housed only people with psychiatric disabilities or people who were homeless; some used scattered-site mainstream housing units made affordable through rent subsidies. People in scattered-site supported housing were found to achieve more social integration and have better recovery outcomes. For example, they were more likely to work and formed more social connections beyond their immediate peer group (Yanos, Felton, Tsemberis, & Frye, 2007). While many areas incorporated subsidized apartments with off-site services in their continuum, many did not fully embrace the psychiatric rehabilitation, flexible services, or the person-driven philosophy that formed the foundation of the initial supported housing model. They offered supportive housing only after people completed transitional programs, demonstrated compliance with psychiatric treatment, and were clean and sober.

THE PATHWAYS HOUSING FIRST MODEL

In the early 1990s, the problem of chronic homelessness became a national concern. In 1992, Pathways to Housing, an agency founded on the principles of psychiatric rehabilitation and consumer involvement in the agency's governance, developed the *Housing First* model (Tsemberis & Eisenberg, 2000; Padgett, Gulcur, & Tsemberis, 2006; Tsemberis, 2010). This model works especially well for people with severe psychiatric disabilities with co-occurring disorders who have been chronically homeless. Pathways to Housing First (PHF) offers people what they want most—an apartment of their own—without requiring readiness, treatment, or sobriety as preconditions for getting into housing. Pathways Housing First is based on the premise that housing is a basic human right, not something that people must earn or prove they deserve by complying with treatment.

Pathways moved permanent supported housing from the end of a long process of transitional steps along the continuum, to the very beginning of the engagement process. People are offered permanent supported housing when they are literally on the street—without demanding compliance with treatment or sobriety. Thus "Housing First" reverses the approach of most continuum of care that demands treatment and sobriety first. The first in "Housing First" refers to this change. When potential participants understand the basis of the program, they often say, "Oh, I get it. You're doing it backwards. You're giving me the housing first." More importantly, housing first refers to individuals' expressed choice about what problem they want to deal with first when they are struggling with homelessness, mental illness, and alcoholism and/or addiction. Pathways' Housing First has many of the elements of the original vision of the supported housing model in its philosophy and operation (Ridgway & Rapp, 1997).

Pathways Housing First is in accord with contemporary social policy. In 1999, the *Olmstead v. L.C and E. W.* Supreme Court decision demanded the elimination of unnecessary social exclusion for people with mental disabilities. The ruling demands the development of socially inclusive programs that provides them the same access to social and cultural possibilities as the rest of the population. It specifies that they have the opportunity to live in the "least restrictive" environment possible. This decision has helped reduce the use of institutions and congregate-care facilities in favor of more socially inclusive and socially integrated housing options. An apartment of one's own in a normal building within the larger social community is ideally suited to satisfy the requirements of the Olmstead decision.

During the last decade, many local mental health systems have included permanent supported housing as one component of a recovery-oriented system of care. On a national level, in 2010, the U.S. Department of Housing and Urban Development began emphasizing the requirement for having permanent supported housing within the local continuum of care plan. HUD's goal is to transform existing systems so that the bulk of services are provided in the form of permanent supportive housing. Thus, policy and funding are moving away from an emphasis on emergency shelters, transitional housing, and other readiness programs that are costly and generally ineffective in eliminating chronic homelessness (Hopper, Jost, Hay, et. al., 1997).

Overview of the Practice of Pathways Housing First

Pathways' Housing First serves people who are homeless or unnecessarily institutionalized and people exiting incarceration or diverted from jail by a mental health court. Participants have severe psychiatric disabilities; many have co-occurring alcohol or addiction problems. Staff help participants chose, attain, and maintain affordable, decent, secure, permanent housing. Housing is linked to continuous helping relationships provided through multidisciplinary intensive treatment teams. Staff members deliver a comprehensive set of personalized support services with flexible intensity to meet the needs of each individual. High intensity support services are provided by Assertive Community Treatment teams that include a primary care provider while medium intensity services employ enhanced case management teams with 24-7 on-call response. The program serves people on an ongoing basis; the housing subsidies and support services are not time-limited (For complete program fidelity criteria, see Tsemberis, 2010).

The program's person-directed services and supports are delivered in their homes, neighborhoods, or other natural community settings rather than being office-based. Services include counseling, practical help with managing an apartment, teaching of community living skills, guidance regarding wellness, and other services and supports desired by the individual. Team members with specialized expertise provide a fully integrated array of services, including healthcare, psychiatric and addiction services, supported employment, and supported education. Staff link participants to additional formal and informal supports and services as needed, including dual diagnosis drug and alcohol support groups, educational institutions, and other community resources.

Housing and clinical operations are functionally separated within the agency. Housing search, management, lease signing and renewal, landlord issues, apartment repairs, and other housing issues are delivered by one arm of the program. Meanwhile, either an Assertive Community Treatment (ACT) Team or intensive case management (ICM) team delivers ongoing support and clinical services. The separation of housing and service functions avoids the problem of difficult or unethical dual relationships, such as a service provider acting to evict his or her client.

Pathways Housing First (PHF) has proven to be effective in multiple formal program evaluations across a variety of sites (For a complete review of the evaluation research, see Tsemberis, 2010; Greenwood, Schaefer-McDaniel, Winkel, & Tsemberis, 2006; Siegal, Samuels, Tang, Berg, Jones, & Hopper, 2006; Stefanic & Tsemberis, 2007). In 2007, the federal Substance Abuse and Mental Health Services Administration (SAMHSA) reviewed the research on Housing First programs and placed the program on the National Registry of Evidence-based and Promising Practices (NREPP) and in 2010, produced an Evidence-Based Practice Toolkit on Permanent Supportive Housing based on the Pathways model.

In general, Housing First's success rate for maintaining people in stable housing is more than 85% over a five-year period. These outcomes are impressive, but are remarkable given that the program does not screen people out based on typical criteria that many other residential programs use to select participants (clean and sober, asymptomatic, compliant with treatment, high degree of readiness, etc.). Instead, PHF purposefully seeks out those who have been homeless for a long time and have multiple diagnoses. Most PHF participants would never be accepted into traditional residential programs.

People are accepted based on their stated interest in having an apartment. They have only to agree to pay a portion of their income in rent and express a willingness to be visited by program staff a few times a month. Based on their stated preferences, they are then housed in scattered-site, open-market rental housing units that are fully socially integrated. Unless the person wants to disclose, his or her psychiatric history is never revealed to fellow tenants or neighbors.

Tasks and Phases of Pathways Housing First Supported Housing

Values based services

Pathways Housing First is strongly values-based. The core values of Pathways are: (1) All people have a right to housing; (2) People with psychiatric disabilities should not have to prove they are "housing ready" nor "earn the right to housing" by complying with psychiatric treatment or attaining sobriety; (3) Strengths are appreciated, and each person's potential for creativity, growth, and recovery is acknowledged, honored, and encouraged; (4) Respect, hope, and creating possibilities are the foundations of helping; and (5) People have the power of choice, and their life choices are honored and upheld.

Engagement and relationship building

Workers in PHF programs are encouraged to consistently demonstrate their concern and interest in each person. They may approach a person many times as they strive to develop a positive helping relationship. They don't give up, even if the person repeatedly expresses that s/he has no interest in the help offered. Workers are trained to assume a practical, helpful, encouraging, but generally humble stance; they don't take the refusal of services personally. They continue to offer assistance and services but do not impose them; all support services are voluntary (although periodic home visits are required).

The core of PHF is the therapeutic alliance between staff and participants. They develop positive helping relationships in which participants know that staff genuinely and authentically cares for and about them. People are not referred to by their diagnosis or by any other label or category; they are never slotted into a subgroup based on their perceived needs; they are not treated according to an abstract system such as a level-of-care determination, and *nobody* in the program is ever described by terms such as "low functioning."

Staff members work to create relationships that are free of prejudice and grow from trust rather than mistrust. They refrain from judging participants based upon their life circumstances, life choices, or past histories. Each person is accepted and honored just as s/he is, and is treated with dignity and warmth. Staff do not try to put on a neutral "professional" mask or assume a dispassionate stance when serving people; rather, they are open, friendly, actively concerned, enthusiastic, and authentically engaged. They are not afraid to laugh; humor is common in the program although never at the expense of an individual. All people in the program, service providers and service users alike, are viewed as having their own unique personality quirks and needs and are respected as who they are—complex individuals.

The program rejects an atmosphere in which there are two classes of people—providers and recipients. They strive to create a culture in which everyone works together. The work of the peer specialists is essential to creating a positive recovery culture; they were once program participants themselves, and now they work as full-time employees on each team. Day in and day out, staff members express their genuine interest in each person's hopes, dreams, beliefs, and self-perceived needs.

Working with people who have drug and alcohol problems

Because drug and alcohol use often co-occurs with histories of trauma and abuse, staff members are trained in trauma-informed care, motivational interviewing, and harm reduction to encourage dual recovery or less frequent use of drugs and alcohol over time. By using a harm-reduction approach, the motivation to change behavior remains, as it should, with the participant. As noted, people are not required to become clean and sober in order to get into housing, receive services, or stay in their apartments. Staff members refrain from manipulating or coercing participants to make choices in alignment with social norms or adhere to a treatment regime. Rather, the motivation to change comes from within the participant, borne from a growing understanding about how drug and/or alcohol use interferes with or creates serious problems in his or her life.

Staff encourages and supports changes that the individual wants to make in drug and alcohol use. Using techniques such as the decisional balance, they help participants explore the pros and cons of change. Through open and honest dialogue, staff and participant explore why the person is using drugs or alcohol. Such dialogue is an on-going process, and many decisions are made along the way. Relapse is a frequent occurrence. By using an empathic approach, with the goal of understanding and analyzing behavior, the work creates a collaborative and trusting therapeutic alliance in which problems of addiction can be fully explored and healed. Although empathic, PHF staff never condone illegal drug use, nor do they provide drug paraphernalia.

Most supportive housing programs provide a person with housing only when they are drug-free and sober, underestimating how difficult it is to abstain from drugs or alcohol while homeless. Pathways Housing First has found that once people are housed, they like their living situation so much that they become highly motivated to get their drug and alcohol use under control in order to keep their apartments. This motivation is powerful. Decent housing and privacy seem to help many people recover from drug and alcohol use or to significantly cut back their use. Over time, we find harm reduction, offers of treatment, access to alcohol- and drug-free social and educational activities, housing, and support services are just as effective in helping people achieve drug and alcohol recovery as is the demand that sobriety be achieved prior to obtaining housing.

Determining Housing Preferences and Choosing Housing

Choice is a central tenet of the PHF approach, pervading many of the day-to-day operations of the program. For example, choice informs the program's efforts to reach out to people living on the streets, in shelters, or in institutions (It should be noted that some outreach efforts are undertaken by sister agencies.). During outreach, staff actively engage with potential participants and inform them that the program provides housing and support services based on their personal goals and preferences. Often, potential participants cannot believe that housing is being offered without strings attached. Sometimes they are reluctant to accept any form of help due to their experiences with involuntary services, coercive care, or other restrictive and rule-bound residential options. Engagement is sometimes a prolonged process.

The program removes as many barriers as possible. The admission process is simple. Most potential participants have already been categorized as being chronically homeless and having a severe and persistent psychiatric disability and drug and alcohol problems. They don't need to undergo another formal assessment; their condition and status is already known to the outreach worker. There is little paperwork and no testing. The lack of intrusive measures, assessments, waiting periods, and formal questioning makes entry into the program easy and quick. If the person expresses interest, s/he is admitted to the program. It's that simple.

Once people choose to work with Pathways, they are offered assistance with whatever they believe is most urgent. Almost everyone chooses to work on getting into permanent housing as the first goal. Housing First seeks to get people into permanent housing as soon as possible, ideally within a period of two to four weeks. The search for permanent housing usually begins within a matter of a few days. The program offers rapid access to decent rental housing; an apartment may even be available the day an individual joins the program. If not, the program offers newly enrolled participants a place to stay at a local hotel, the Y, or other short term accommodation until a suitable apartment is found.

Staff members involved in the housing search encourage new participants to express their housing preferences and make choices about where they want to live. Some things they take into consideration are neighborhood location and characteristics, such as proximity to transportation and support services, the floor an apartment is on, and if there is an elevator, affordability, and requirements and limits of the available housing subsidy. Even when limited options are available, staff members demonstrate that they take the person's housing preferences into account by showing a few units from which s/he can choose. Involvement in the process of finding housing improves the person's investment in the apartment, increases satisfaction with the place, and reduces the likelihood that s/he will soon want to move (See Srebnick, Livingston, Gordon, & King, 1995, on the importance of choice). Most participants choose to live as the sole occupant in a studio or one-bedroom apartment. Participants say such options increase their personal sense of security, privacy, freedom, and control over their living situation; reduce their stress; and improve their self-image.

Apartments are almost always found through community landlords operating within the open housing market; they are "mainstream" rental units. In some instances, units are found in public housing. Over time, Pathways housing staff develop good working relationships with a network of landlords who offer housing suitable for rental subsidy and who understand and value the benefits of the support services provided to their tenants. Some Pathways programs employ their own maintenance staff who makes any necessary repairs and quickly ready units to ensure they meet the formal quality standards as defined by regulatory agencies and make needed repairs when relocation is needed to ensure apartments are left in good shape.

Housing First respects the person's choice to live in a regular apartment and therefore does not rent more than 15% of the units in any given building (Stefanic & Tsemberis, 2007). Services are not located in the apartment buildings; the service teams rent office space in the community and make home visits. Thus, PHF programs can enter a community and be fully operational, and very few people know that the program exists. The program is so integrated that it is virtually invisible, thus avoiding NIMBY (not in my back yard) battles.

The program works to integrate people into their neighborhoods, thereby avoiding prejudice and negative attitudes. Landlords are given only general information about their tenants, and the number of a housing specialist who can be called at any time if concerns arise. Landlords and building managers are never given personal, clinical, or historical information about the tenant; the details they receive are only facts anyone must provide to lease an apartment. In some PHF programs, depending on local housing market factors or landlord concerns, leases are held by the housing arm of the agency, but everyone who does not hold the lease has a formal sublease with the agency that offers the same provisions, rights, and safeguards as a standard lease. In other cities, participants more often hold their own leases.

Most participants have very low incomes, and some come into the program without any income or benefits. In such cases, staff members help them get onto entitlement programs or into benefits counseling. Small loans are made to tenants, if needed, with reasonable repayment plans. Staff members help people learn to budget if needed. Some PHF programs manage funds for their participants and sometimes serve as their fiduciary agent, directly paying all major monthly bills, such as rent and utilities. In other PHF programs, almost all participants manage their income and monthly bills themselves.

Moving in: Making Housing a Home and Creating a Healthy, Settled Lifestyle

The work of creating a home is very important for many people. It helps them establish a space that reflects their personal identity and develop a sense of ownership and pride. Making a housing unit into one's home is a major undertaking. PHF ensures that each person has all the necessities to furnish his or her home, including a sofa, bed, bureau, television, a table and chairs, basic kitchenware, and a telephone (land line or mobile). Program participants are offered choices that help them personalize their apartments, such as in furnishing style and upholstery material that reflects their taste. Because workers are admitted to participants' homes based on their positive supportive relationship, they are careful to respect each person's rights of tenancy and sense of privacy. Workers do not treat a person's apartment as program space and never make unannounced home visits.

The initial weeks or months in housing can be difficult for people, especially if they have been institutionalized or homeless for some time. Some people feel uncomfortable, isolated, and alone, or bored and restless. It is very important for staff to offer additional support during this adjustment period. This may include frequent home visits and outings, such as a trip to the grocery store or a walk in the neighborhood. During the adjustment period, it is vital that the person sees that there are things to do and places to go, so he or she does not feel at a loss and lonely. Staff facilitate this by helping each person establish a positive daily routine, a personalized set of activities and natural supports, such as by volunteering, working, taking a course, attending program activities, or cultivating new interests, hobbies, and talents.

The shift in cultural expectations from street dwelling to apartment living and neighboring is a learning experience for many people. Some need a great deal of coaching about their role and expected behavior as tenants. For example, people learn to share what little they have with others living on the street. However, they can find themselves in trouble if they try to share their apartment with someone who is not on their lease. On the street, it is wise to expend all of one's resources every day, to avoid being beaten or robbed. However, once housed, it is much wiser to hold back resources for daily needs so that one's meager resources extend as far as possible throughout the month.

The provision of ongoing supportive services

In PHF, services are offered by modified Assertive Community Treatment teams or modified Intensive Case Management teams (For a full description of staffing configurations, see Tsemberis, 2010). The program is person-centered and supports are individually tailored. Team members encourage each person to set at least one important goal that will guide their initial work together. This goal is written down, remembered, and reinforced by all team members. That way, it is clear that the person's own goals are guiding the work together. Goals are wide-ranging. A goal can be anything—initially, however, it most often relates to getting and keeping an apartment or staying off the street or out of the hospital.

Participants are encouraged to choose the timing and frequency of staff visits (over and above the periodic visits required by the program). They are encouraged to express what they want or need help with and to call if they have any needs, problems, or concerns between visits. They have 24-hour access to staff via telephone in case an issue arises after hours. On-call services are essential to the program; people feel comfortable as they know they are not facing lives without support. It further establishes that staff are not imposing services upon them; services are individually driven based on participants' choices and self-perceived needs.

The home visit is the core service of the program. During the home visit, the staff member builds upon the therapeutic relationship and gets to know the person better. While a formal functional assessment is not undertaken, the staff person unobtrusively assesses the situation by scanning the living environment and noticing any concerns or problems. The visit often begins with the staff member offering to provide practical help to address any concern the participant may be having. Staff may offer to help with the work of keeping the person's apartment in order or getting to know the neighborhood. Staff teach any skills the person may need to learn to function well in the living environment, such as budgeting, cooking, cleaning, shopping, interpersonal skills, community exploration, and assistance with transportation. Supports offered during the home visit are wide ranging and extend beyond the living environment to encompass wellness and self-management of one's mental and physical health conditions as well as citizenship and community participation.

In PHF, staff members help people connect with others. While most people want to live alone and enjoy a sense of security, control, and peacefulness, too much social isolation can be detrimental to their long-term success. It's important to offer help and encouragement to participants who are forming new relationships and facing loneliness. Some common forms of support include peer support, self-help, substance-use recovery meetings, volunteer opportunities, employment, taking classes, dating, and finding a spiritual community. All of these things, and more, can broaden and deepen an individual's ties to his or her community and lessen the tendency some people have to withdraw or isolate.

Staff help participants navigate within the community by exploring the area and accompanying them to community events or appointments with other agencies. Staff members try to stay informed about community assets and opportunities, so they can offer the widest range of options and suggestions to participants based upon their individual interests. Referrals to out-of-agency resources are made based upon each person's unique needs and preferences.

Many people in integrated housing connect well with other members of the community, and some choose not to disclose their status as former or current mental health clients. Interpersonal issues do sometimes arise, including conflicts with other tenants or neighbors, especially if people have severe symptoms or do not blend in with other tenants in terms of age or lifestyle. Sometimes issues arise with intimate partners or when someone tries to form an exploitive relationship with a person who appears vulnerable. The program is equipped to assist the participant with such issues by offering support while, at the same time, giving the participant room to make decisions, even if those decisions do not seem to be the most prudent ones. On a more positive note, after settling into their apartments, people often work to heal relationships and reconnect with family members. Over time, as participants gain the ability and confidence to do more things themselves, they rely less and less on staff to do things for or with them.

PHF programs offer opportunities and choices of becoming involved in a variety of groups and activities conducted by the agency. For example, Pathways to Housing in New York City has a photography course, a painting studio where participants can express their creativity, a computer lab, and meeting rooms where groups are held on topics such as current events, spirituality, cooking and nutrition, and mental health and substance use recovery. Support groups, harm reduction groups, social and cultural activities, alcohol-free celebrations, and other projects and activities the program offers are all designed with participant input. People can choose to participate in, or choose not to attend, any of the groups or celebrations the program offers.

Clinical services are fully integrated within the Housing First program. People are initially connected to the psychiatric services provided by the Assertive Community Treatment team, and when they no longer need intensive services, they are introduced to community providers. PHF psychiatrists often offer psychiatric medications, but participants can choose whether or not to take them. Some initially refuse medication; however, after a period that may extend to months or years, they may decide to try meds. Others go off medication entirely.

Wellness is encouraged, but participants are not forced to follow any specific health regimen. The importance of healthcare, however, cannot be overemphasized. Many people in the program have multiple chronic health conditions, such as diabetes and heart disease, and they may need assistance with foot care or a special diet. To identify and accommodate these needs, PHF has a physician or a nurse practitioner on staff.

Avoiding Crises and Setbacks

Housing First workers know that the recovery process is nonlinear. Setbacks are a common part of the process. To keep a setback from turning into a major crisis, staff work proactively to spot problems in their early stages and act to prevent a situation from deteriorating further. Home visits are excellent opportunities for early detection of problems. By intervening early, it is often possible to keep a person from losing his or her housing or requiring intensive out-of-home treatment. In situations where imminent danger is apparent, emergency hospitalization is undertaken.

Even in a full-blown crisis, staff members do not abandon or give up on people; they keep working on the therapeutic relationship. Even when people are struggling and not doing well, they are held in positive regard. Participants are not written off if they make choices that don't serve them well, if they have to move, or they continue to use drugs or alcohol. Staff members understand that people make decisions all the time, some positive, some negative; they do not see themselves as being responsible for actively controlling people or their personal behavior. Rather, they see the person in recovery as being empowered to make his or her own decisions in life.

By using motivational interviewing, staff members help the person align their choices with their long-term goals and desires and actively engage people in problem solving to clarify situations. When they see problems arising such as hoarding or increased drug or alcohol use, they express their concern. When a person makes a decision that brings grief to him or her, that feeling is shared by staff; staff members do not tell the person that they must experience "logical consequences," nor do they assume a superior "I told you so" attitude. They do not introduce sanctions or restrictions, nor do they threaten to discharge the person from the program. Setbacks are treated not as failures, but as meaningful learning experiences.

The organization covers the rent if people need short term detoxification, intensive residential drug treatment, or hospitalization. Staff may visit people in such settings and keep in touch. If the person's apartment is lost, either through eviction or because the program cannot keep it any longer, personal belongings are stored, and another living situation is obtained when the person is released. Occasionally, staff may encourage a participant to move before s/he is evicted. That way, any problems with the unit can be taken care of by the agency, and a positive working relationship can be maintained with the landlord.

Helping People Move Forward in Recovery

Permanent supported housing often serves as a springboard into mental health and substance use recovery and opens opportunities for a fuller, healthier life. Once settled, people often become much less stressed; they begin to become more hopeful and able to see more options for the future. It becomes easier for them to set goals and achieve them. In fact, research shows that people in permanent supported housing are more likely to make community connections and are more likely to be self-employed or to find employment in the open job market than are those in congregate programs (Yanos, Felton, Tsemberis, & Frye, 2007).

A specialist on each service team provides supported employment. People are helped to go to work as soon as they express an interest and feel ready to work. Their interests are taken into account in a job search; they are not "placed" in a job they do not want simply to gain work experience. Some participants are hired by the Pathways to Housing agency. They work on the service teams as peer specialists, as maintenance workers, as accountants, and in other positions, thereby becoming role models for their peers and serving to remind other staff of how much each participant can achieve.

Over time, as people become more settled, more connected, and better able to undertake the tasks of caring for their homes and participating in their communities, agency-provided support services are provided with less intensity. Contacts and relationships are still cordially maintained, and people can call on their teams for help at any time. As people take on new challenges, they may find they need more intensive supports for a period of time, and the program has the flexibility to serve people based on their expressed needs. The helping relationship offered by the team is ongoing; people are not terminated or forgotten, even when their need for support services lessens. Sometimes their need for support services ends, and they can remain in their apartments and take over the leases if they desire, and the staff move on to serve other people.

The Experience of Supported Housing from the Participants' Perspective

Most people who participate in permanent supported housing programs express gratitude for the opportunity to have decent permanent housing. Some feel isolated initially, so it is important to ensure people have the opportunity to connect with others, to get busy with activities, or to have a pet. People frequently report that Housing First makes them feel happier and more optimistic, improves their well-being, and reduces their symptoms or drug/alcohol use. They feel empowered and more able to actively begin the process of mental health or dual recovery. The deep sense of security that comes from having control over one's living situation is palpable: People come to view their housing as their *home*.

A few sample letters from Pathways participants illustrate the many changes that happen when people are housed and provided with the supports they need:

> *I apologize for not having written sooner. I don't know where to start. Thank you for saving my life. Thank you for allowing me to be a father to my children and for having a place for them to come and visit me. Thank you for the longest period without going to the hospital since I can remember. Thank you for my sobriety. Thank you for having a place to shower, a stove to cook on, a bed to sleep in, a warm place to go when it's cold. Thank you for not having to take my possessions everywhere I go. Thank you for my home.*
>
> *Sincerely,*
>
> *M*

> *My name is J. I have been in Pathways since March 3, 2006. My life has changed drastically. I was on the streets for 6 years. Not taking my medications, being abused, using drugs, going into dangerous places. Now my life is so different, thanks to Pathways. I am so grateful. I have my own apartment. I have an ongoing relationship with my children again (smile).*
>
> *I'm grateful. I love you Pathways.*

IMPLEMENTATION ISSUES

Not surprisingly, the effectiveness of Pathways Housing First has encouraged many areas of the country to replicate the program. Today, the Pathways Housing First model is being widely implemented in the United States, Canada, and parts of Europe. In June of 2010, the federal Interagency Council on the Homeless endorsed Housing First as one of the five cornerstones strategies for reducing and ending homelessness in America.

There are at least two ways that PHF program comes into a community. The first is through a ground-floor, consensus-building approach where key stakeholders (i.e., representatives from agencies providing services to people who are homeless and who have psychiatric disabilities) gather to determine if there is a need for such a program often as part of developing or planning the local continuum of care. The second way is when a mayor or county executive is persuaded that there is a need for the PHF program and decides to implement such a program. The second approach is often quicker, but the first is the more common way replication occurs. In both cases, the key questions to be answered in determining the local need are:

- Are there people in our community who are experiencing homelessness as well as psychiatric disabilities and co-occurring disorders?

- Have these people remained homeless and without proper services for a significant length of time?

- Are these people well known to existing social service agencies?

- Do these people use the resources of shelters, emergency rooms, and the police, yet still remain homeless and without treatment?

If the answer to these questions is "yes," there is need for a Housing First program, because it very effectively houses and supports such individuals.

Some key steps must be undertaken between identifying the need and gathering together the people and resources that bring such a program to life. A local champion should be identified who initiates the process of change in a community or an agency who spurs the program on. The local champion engages key stakeholders, identifies sources of funding, coordinates grant applications, and generally oversees implementation. S/he reaches out for the technical assistance and works closely and collaboratively with all parties to ensure the program's smooth and efficient implementation.

When implementing a PHF program in an existing agency, there often must be a culture shift from treatment-as-usual to the Housing First approach. Leadership of the agency, the executive director, and the board of directors must be educated and enthusiastically support adopting the Housing First model. Staff must come to see the Housing First program as a solution for a group of people who are currently not well served. Leadership and staff must embrace the core value that housing is a basic right, and not a privilege that must be earned by demonstrating compliance with treatment or program rules. Leadership and staff must embrace the psychiatric rehabilitation consumer-choice philosophy. They must commit to adopt a harm-reduction model that includes motivational interviewing when working with people with co-occurring disorders. Ideally, new funding is identified to implement the program.

There is always some period of adjustment when a new program model is implemented, especially one that differs in value-orientation and practice from existing programs. However, once the program has been operating for a few months, people in the agency typically begin to appreciate that it engages and houses people who have been homeless for years. Soon, other providers begin to accept the approach.

One challenge when starting up a program is that funding for the housing component and for the support services often comes from different sources. Regardless of the sources of funding, program leaders must always remember that this is a permanent supported housing program. The funding obtained for both housing and support services must be secure for a long period of time, because program participants housed by the program will need help, especially with paying rent, for many years.

Once funding is secured, the program can be brought into being rapidly. One of the big advantages of implementing a Housing First program is the remarkably quick start-up time; on average a program can begin about three to four months from the time funding is received. Program implementation and the first year of operation are by far the busiest times in a Housing First program. Everyone is on a steep learning curve—staff, participants, landlords, and funders. It is a year with multiple tasks that require exceptional organizational skills. It is also an emotional phases in the life of the program; everyone is by turns jubilant, festive, confused, and stressed. No one knows how a new participant will respond to a new apartment or how that early adjustment period will turn out. There are many ups and downs, and every day is different. A great deal of good is done, and good will abounds as participant after participant—homeless, exhausted, and in a mild state of disbelief—enters into a newly furnished apartment and sits down on his or her own bed for the first time in years. If the program is implemented with fidelity to both principles and practices, more than 85% of them will still be successfully housed five years down the road.

SUMMARY

Pathways Housing First has grown from a single innovative New York-based program (Pathways to Housing, Inc.) to an approach that is literally serving thousands of people in hundreds of communities throughout the U.S., Canada, and parts of Europe. The innovative approaches have solidified into a program model with formal fidelity criteria (Tsemberis, 2010) and extensive training and technical assistance. Considerable research demonstrates the program is a highly effective evidence-based practice. Many cities have made Housing First the cornerstone of their 10-year plan to end homelessness. Staff in well-run Housing First programs have the satisfaction of working within a person-centered psychiatric rehabilitation approach that employs strong, well-supervised multidisciplinary teams of supportive professionals and peers. Such programs are dynamic, and the work is ever changing.

The program is especially satisfying because it literally transforms people's lives. It offers dignity through decent housing and ongoing person-directed supports, engenders and upholds mental health and dual disorder recovery, improves the quality of life of the individual and the entire community, and achieves the important goal of social integration by embracing and serving people with severe psychiatric disabilities, who have for too long been forced to live on the margins of society.

BEST PRACTICE GUIDELINES FOR PERMANENT SUPPORTED HOUSING

- Recognize that all people have a right to housing.

- Eliminate eligibility criteria that create unnecessary and unreasonable barriers to entry. There should be no need to prove "housing readiness," no requirement for sobriety, and no contingency demands, such as medication compliance.

- Appreciate strengths and value each person's potential for creativity, growth, and recovery.

- Offer choices, including varied housing options, and honor the decisions people make in response to those offers.

- Develop positive helping relationships, recognizing that success will depend on building an alliance with each program participant.

- Use harm reduction and motivational interviewing approaches to encourage (rather than mandate) recovery from drug and alcohol problems.

- Locate and support "normal" non-segregated housing and help people develop connections and interests that will promote community integration.

- Provide long-term and flexible supports that build skills and independence while avoiding crises and setbacks.

ABOUT THE AUTHORS

Priscilla Ridgway, MSW, Ph.D. worked, most recently, at the Center for Community Support and Research at Wichita State University. Ridgway's career in the mental health field includes direct service, advocacy, program development and administration, policy, planning, training, consultation and research. Ridgway has an MSW from the University of Connecticut and a Ph.D. from the University of Kansas. Dr. Ridgway designed and ran an innovative supported housing program in the 1970s, devised the innovation of permanent supported housing, and did nationwide research and technical assistance on residential programs in the 1980s while at Boston University Center for Psychiatric Rehabilitation. She has served as a researcher in three rounds of supportive housing research, was part of the team that developed the SAMSHA supportive housing best practice toolkit, and continues to consult and develop curriculum about permanent supported housing. She has personal experience with mental health recovery and has been involved in the consumer movement since the 1970s.

Dr. Sam Tsemberis is a clinical-community psychologist and the CEO of Pathways to Housing, an organization he founded in 1992. Dr. Tsemberis is the originator of Housing First, an evidence-based model for effectively ending homelessness for people with psychiatric disabilities. The model is partly based on the principles of psychiatric rehabilitation. Pathways currently operates programs in New York City, Washington D.C., Philadelphia, and Vermont and provides consultation and technical assistance to housing first programs in Canada, Europe, and Australia. Dr. Tsemberis serves as principal investigator for several federally funded multi-site studies of homelessness, mental illness, and addiction, and has published a book, numerous articles, and book chapters on these topics. In 2006, Dr. Tsemberis was the recipient of the prestigious Macy Award for individual achievement in the battle to end homelessness from the National Alliance to End Homelessness. Dr. Tsemberis is currently working with the Mental Health Commission of Canada in a national five-city implementation of Housing First. Dr. Tsemberis holds a Ph.D. in clinical psychology from New York University and currently serves on the faculty of the Department of Psychiatry of the Columbia University Medical Center and at the University of Toronto.

REFERENCES

Carling, P. J., & Ridgway, P. (1989). A psychiatric rehabilitation approach to housing. In W. A. Anthony & M. D. Farkas (Eds.). *Psychiatric rehabilitation: Putting theory into practice* (pp. 28-33, 69-80). Baltimore, MD: Johns Hopkins University Press.

Cooper, E., & O'Hara, A. (2002). *Priced out in 2002: Housing crisis worsens for people with psychiatric disabilities.* Boston, MA: Technical Assistance Collaborative.

Culhane, D., Metraux, S., & Hadley, T. (2002). Public service reductions associated with placement of homeless persons with severe mental illness in supportive housing. *Housing Policy Debate, 13*(1):107-163.

Greenwood, R., Schaefer-McDaniel, N., Winkel, G., & Tsemberis, S. (2006). Decreasing psychiatric symptoms by increasing choice in services for adults with histories of homelessness. *American Journal of Community Psychology, 36*(3/4), 223-238.

Gulcur, L., Stefancic, A., Shinn, S., Tsemberis, S., & Fischer, S. N. (2003). Housing, hospitalization, and cost outcomes for homeless individuals with psychiatric disabilities participating in continuum of care and housing first programs. *Journal of Community & Applied Social Psychology, 13*(2), 171-186.

Hopper, K., Jost, J., Hay, T., Welber, S., & Haugland, G. (1997). Homelessness, severe mental illness and the institutional circuit. *Psychiatric Services, 48*(5), 659-665.

Livingston, J. A., Gordon, L. R., King, D. A., & Srebnick, D. S. (1991). *Implementing the supported housing approach: A national evaluation of NIMH supported housing demonstration projects.* Burlington, VT: Trinity College, Center for Community Change through Housing & Support.

Nelson, G., & Smith F. H. (1997). Housing for the chronically mentally disabled, part II: Process and outcome. *Canadian Journal of Mental Health, 6*(2), 79-91.

Padgett, D. K., Gulcur, L., & Tsemberis, S. (2006). Housing First services for people who are homeless with co-occurring serious mental illness and substance abuse. *Research on Social Work Practice, 16*(1), 74-83.

Perlman, J., & Parvensky, J. (2006) *Denver Housing Frst collaborative cost benefit analysis and program outcomes report.* Denver, CO: Coalition for the Homeless.

Ridgway, P. (1997). From asylums to communities: A historical perspective on changing environments of care. In A. Tasman & J. Kay (Eds) *Psychiatry* (Vol. 2, pp. 1751-1769). Philadelphia, PA: Saunders Press.

Ridgway, P., & Caring, P. J. (1987). *A user's guide to needs assessment in community residential rehabilitation.* Monograph. Boston, MA: Boston University, Center for Psychiatric Rehabilitation.

Ridgway, P. A., & Rapp, C. A. (1997). *The active ingredients of effective supported housing: A research synthesis.* Lawrence, KS: University of Kansas, School of Social Welfare.

Ridgway, P. A., & Zipple, A. M. (1990). The paradigm shift in residential services: From the linear continuum to supported housing. *Psychosocial Rehabilitation Journal, 13*(4), 11-31.

Rog, D. J. (2004). The evidence on supported housing. *Psychiatric Rehabilitation Journal, 27*(4), 334-344.

Shern, D. L., Felton, C. J., Hough, R. L., Lehman, A. F., Goldfinger, S., Valencia, E., Dennis, D., Straw, R., & Wood, P. A. (1997). Housing outcomes for homeless adults with mental illness: Results from the second-round McKinney Program. *Psychiatric Services, 48*(2), 239-241.

Siegal, C., Samuels, J., Tang, D., Berg, I., Jones, K., & Hopper, K. (2006). Tenant outcomes in supported housing and community residences in New York City. *Psychiatric Services, 57*(7), 982-991.

Srebnick, D. S., Livingston, J., Gordon, L., & King, D. (1995). Housing choice and community success for individuals with and persistent mental illness. *Community Mental Health Journal, 3,* 139-152.

Stefancic, A., & Tsemberis, S. (2007). Housing First for long-term shelter dwellers with psychiatric disabilities in a suburban county: A four-year study of housing access and retention. *The Journal of Primary Prevention, 28*(3), 265-279.

Tanzman, B. (1993). An overview of surveys of mental health consumers' preferences for housing and support services. *Hospital and Community Psychiatry, 44,* 450-455.

Tsemberis, S. (2010). *Housing First: The pathways model to end homelessness for people with mental illness and addiction.* Center City, MN: Hazelden.

Tsemberis, S., & Eisenberg, R. (2000). Pathways to housing: Supported housing for street-dwelling homeless individuals with psychiatric disabilities, *Psychiatric Services, 51*(4), 487-493.

Tsemberis, S., Gulcur, L., & Nakae, M. (2004). Housing First, consumer choice, and harm reduction for homeless individuals with a dual diagnosis. *American Journal of Public Health, 94*(4), 651-656.

Yanos, P. T., Felton, B., Tsemberis, S., & Frye, V. A. (2007). Exploring the role of housing type, neighborhood characteristics, and lifestyle factors in the community integration of formerly homeless persons diagnosed with mental illness. *Journal of Mental Health, 16*(6), 703-717.

WORK

Richard C. Baron
Arlene Solomon
George H. Brice, Jr.
Timothy Connors

A B S T R A C T

Any best practice of psychiatric rehabilitation must have at the center of its approach programs and practices that help people to attain and maintain competitive employment, for people with psychiatric disabilities are very interested in working. This chapter reviews the importance of competitive employment in the lives of those with psychiatric disabilities and identifies four generations of program models and rehabilitation practices that have focused on returning people return to work with an emphasis on the principles and practices of Supported Employment. The employment programs of Horizon House—one of the oldest psychiatric rehabilitation programs in the nation—are discussed, and two service recipients discuss the role of work in their lives. The chapter ends with a review of challenges for the future.

AT THE CORE OF PSYCHIATRIC REHABILITATION PRACTICE IS—OR OUGHT TO BE—A COMMITMENT TO assist every interested person in succeeding in the competitive labor market. Despite the inaccurate, but still prevalent, conviction among clinicians, psychiatric rehabilitation practitioners, and even people using services that people with psychiatric disabilities are either unready, unmotivated, or unable to work, there is no best practice of psychiatric rehabilitation (PsyR) that does not place helping people reach their competitive employment goals at the center of its approach. Indeed, the PsyR field must make competitive employment a reachable goal for substantially more consumers or risk dooming another generation of those with psychiatric disabilities to a lifetime of thwarted ambitions, numbing poverty, and limited community inclusion.

Working, after all, is one of the things that recovery is for. Avoiding inpatient stays, feeling positively about oneself, and living with hope—key aspects of the recovery journey—are also the pre-requisites for greater participation in community life, and one critical component of community life is the ability to work at a real job for real pay—meeting work's demands and reaping its varied rewards.

Nonetheless, the hard reality is that very few people with a serious psychiatric disability work in the competitive labor market. Despite the pronounced increase in the amount of lip service paid to competitive employment goals, from the Report from the President's New Freedom Commission (DHHS, 2003) to state mental health planning documents (Pennsylvania Recovery & Resiliency, 2008) and agency mission statements, unemployment continues at a staggering 85% rate among those with serious psychiatric disabilities (Anthony & Blanch, 1987; Cook & Razzano, 2000; Trupin, Sebesta, Yelin, & LaPlante, 1997).

People with many years of experience using mental health systems frequently report that no one has ever seriously discussed competitive work with them (Baron, 2002) despite the PsyR field's identification over the past twenty years of a number of best practices to help people succeed at work. The field has not only built a strong evidentiary base for program models that return people to work, it has also identified a range of rehabilitation practices that lead to competitive work and real careers.

DEFINITIONS OF EMPLOYMENT AND THE IMPORTANCE OF COMPETITIVE WORK

First, it is useful to define more specifically what we mean by "competitive work." The term, as used here, refers to jobs that (a) are available to anyone, disabled or not disabled, in the nation's workforce, (b) offer wages and benefits that are comparable to industry standards, and (c) provide opportunities for work alongside non-disabled co-workers (SAMHSA, 2009). Such a definition excludes some of the types of jobs that PsyR programs are tempted to classify as successful work outcomes, including steady work in an agency-based workshop or work crew, volunteer work in the community, or long-term jobs in an agency-sponsored business.

However, this narrow definition of competitive work nonetheless allows for wide variation in patterns of competitive work. Most Americans work full-time, but a substantial number work part-time. Everyone wants that first job to be a perfect fit, but most young people move in and out of first jobs (and second and third jobs) fairly rapidly. We cherish an ideal of working for the same company for a lifetime; yet increasingly Americans hold six to eight jobs over the course of their careers. While no one wants to lose a job, most of us have been fired or furloughed more than once (or twice). We should expect those with psychiatric disabilities to establish similarly varied and normative patterns of work. This variety of normative work patterns suggests that competitive work goals are attainable not just for those consumers with the most obvious work potential, physical/emotional stamina, encouraging work history, and motivation, but for just about everyone who turns to a psychiatric rehabilitation program for support.

Focusing on normative definitions of competitive work also suggests the need to embrace a wider range of types of jobs. While about 35-40% of Americans today work in entry-level, low-skill positions, about 50% of us work at middle-skill jobs (truck drivers and beauticians, medical billing staff and personal care attendants, plumbing assistants and data entry personnel) that do not require a college degree but do require specific training and state licensing, and 10-15% of us work in professional positions or at executive levels within business and industry and the human services (Holzer & Lerman, 2007). All of these jobs, if done honestly and well, have the inherent dignity that comes with hard work and a decent paycheck, and the PsyR field should assist people with psychiatric disabilities in finding jobs across this broad spectrum rather than rest easy with the current emphasis on entry-level work outcomes.

Nonetheless, helping people with psychiatric disabilities toward competitive work, as defined above, has proved challenging. Many of those PsyR agencies serve do not work competitively at all, and the patterns of employment and the types of jobs for those who do work have been far less varied than a normative model would suggest. We need to do better. Indeed, at the heart of best practices in employment services is the conviction that people with psychiatric disabilities, like everyone else, should work, would work, and could work.

Should work: There is mounting evidence that work, despite the fears of many, does not commonly exacerbate symptoms and foment psychiatric crises. Rather, work has a demonstrated ability to provide structure to the day, build self-esteem, hold symptoms in abeyance, and improve levels of functioning in community settings (Bond, et. al., 2001; Harding, 1987; Marrone & Golowka, 1999; Rutman, 1994).

Would work: Despite the frequent assertion that few people with psychiatric disabilities are motivated to work, they repeatedly reveal in surveys that their three major goals are "a decent place to live, a few close friends, and a good job." Indeed, in the early years of their psychiatric disability, people return to competitive work whenever they can as a way to assert their emotional health and re-establish their role in community life (McQuilken et al., 2003; Mueser, 2001; Rogers et al., 1991).

Could work: The field's most exacting research has demonstrated that work is eminently possible. A psychiatric rehabilitation agency must be willing to challenge institutional barriers to work and provide the supports needed to help build new identities—normative identities—as part of the nation's competitive labor market (Bond et al., 2001; Bond, Drake, Mueser, & Becker, 1997; Ridgway, 1998).

The Importance of Work

Two of our coauthors can attest first-hand to the important role that work plays in recovery.

> *I was diagnosed as having schizophrenia in 1997, but managed to graduate from college in 1999 before being diagnosed with a schizoaffective disorder in 2001. I always wanted to work, but it took time for my recovery and medications to progress enough to be able to return to*

work. Work is an important part of recovery, offering meaningful activity, financial gain, and personal responsibility—and lessens the stigma of mental illness that you feel when you do not fully participate in such a common activity. (Timothy Connors)

During the fourteen years I relied upon Social Security's pseudo-benefits, I endured the significant burden of insecurity, guilt and shame ... and could not find mental health professionals who would help me develop a Social Security "exit plan." I succumbed to learned helplessness and hopelessness, but then created my own exit plan and found a full-time job, and that allowed me to flex my resilience muscles, assume personal responsibility, and feel like a citizen of the world. I have a degree of economic security and feel fiscally empowered. Work has fostered improvements in my self-esteem and my social and family relationships and has been the catalyst for my recovery. (George T. Brice, Jr.)

Reshaping programs and practices to help people return to work isn't easy. The barriers to work, including the distractions of the illness itself, the discouragement of staff and families, the persistence of financial disincentives, the limited educational and training qualifications of many job seekers, and the current dismal job market, make the challenge particularly daunting (Baron & Salzer, 2002). Nonetheless, the PsyR field has begun to define a set of best practices that offer staff and consumers the opportunity to meet those challenges.

OVERVIEW OF BEST PRACTICES IN PROMOTING COMPETITIVE EMPLOYMENT

The best practice program models and rehabilitation approaches reviewed here need to be understood as part of an evolving process. There has been a gradual 30-year evolution in what is considered to be a best practice. What were once seen as progressive, effective initiatives were later challenged by more robust approaches. Today's best practices need to be understood in the same light. The policies and programs that are proving most effective at the moment will likely yield to adaptations and improvements and entirely new approaches as the years go by. We talk here, then, about a first, second, and third generation of employment best practices and suggest as well what a future fourth generation of best practices will need to consider.

First Generation Programs and Approaches

Part of what we know about what does and doesn't work (or doesn't work very well or for very many people) has been learned from the disappointing results of first generation employment programs. What seemed like good notions at the time, when the majority of people with psychiatric disabilities spent years in psychiatric hospitals and the notion of competitive work was at odds with the concept of "chronic" mental illness, may in fact have held the field back and closed doors of opportunity for many.

Sheltered work programs

The field was dominated for generations by the once-progressive notion that people with psychiatric disabilities could be helped back to competitive employment by starting off in a sheltered work setting, which provided a safe and supportive environment where individuals could learn or relearn the fundamentals of employment. The soft skills of interpersonal relations, the on-the-job behaviors needed in any position, and the technical skills associated with particular tasks would be a stepping stone to competitive work. Psychiatric hospitals employed patients in their kitchens and on their landscaping crews; the early psychiatric rehabilitation programs ran packaging and printing workshops in-house; and community mental health agencies developed in-house thrift shops, snack bars, maintenance crews, and greenhouses.

Two persistent problems with sheltered work emerged over the years. First, although most forms of sheltered work verbally established competitive employment goals, over time sheltered work became, for both service providers and service users, the goal itself. Sheltered workers found themselves reluctant to move on, fearful of the demands of genuinely competitive work, and unsure of the supports they would receive beyond the workshop (Condeluci, 1991; Cook, et al., 1992; Rubin, 1994; Stroul, 1986). Staff not only shared those fears, but also increasingly relied on the most productive consumers for the smooth and profitable functioning of the workshop. Second, sheltered work often proved to be a poor preparation for the actual demands of the competitive job environment where the pressures for consistent production were high and the tolerance for differences was low. Long-term sheltered work became the default solution for many, ultimately and unintentionally limiting rather than expanding their work potential.

Step-wise practices

The field once highly valued a linear step-wise approach to the vocational rehabilitation process. Counselors would begin talking about work only when someone was clinically stabile and ready for the challenges of a job, initial work assignments would be in a sheltered setting with the worker needing to prove his/her competency in a variety of tasks, and only then would they be ready to be placed in entry-level roles in competitive jobs. Beginning in the most basic jobs in the competitive labor force, similarly, would be a useful grounding, it was thought, for a person who wanted to move later on to more demanding and better paying jobs.

Much of this turned out not to be as helpful as hoped. Waiting for clinical stability, rather than just the abatement of the most acute symptoms, proved counter-productive. Clinical stability turned out to be less a prerequisite for the demands of work than it was a side-product of the opportunity to work (Bond, Dietzen, McGrew, et al., 1995; Bond & Dincin, 1986; Newman, 1970). Further, many people found that they could hold their symptoms at a distance when they were called upon to focus on work tasks. While some job seekers were appropriately placed in entry-level roles and were happy to remain there, others were bored and unmotivated to continue or somewhat affronted by the reluctance of staff to help them move to more demanding roles. As with the rest of the national labor force, getting stuck at the entry level was a common experience (The Workforce Alliance, 2002).

While sheltered work and step-wise practices are not always bad ideas, they proved useful avenues to competitive work for only a very few. In time, new approaches emerged.

Second Generation Programs and Approaches

A second generation of work programs sought to establish rehabilitation programs in real work settings and develop new ways to assist people in finding work for themselves.

Community-based employment programs

To help move consumers beyond sheltered workshops and work crews, psychiatric rehabilitation agencies have developed three types of programs that provide consumers an opportunity to go to work in the community, but with a range of assistance and support.

The most prominent of the second generation programs is *Transitional Employment* (TE), pioneered by Fountain House (in New York City) and still a central service component in clubhouses nationwide. In TE, program participants have available an array of community-based job placements arranged for them by their agency—often half-time, entry-level work in hospitals, banks, or restaurants (Beard, 1978; Picone, 1998). These jobs are reserved for the agency, and each worker spends up to six months in his/her TE position before moving either to another TE setting or to fully competitive employment or to a Supported Employment program (described later).

Other agencies used enclaves, in which a small group of individuals work together within an existing community business, for example, operating a mailroom or working in a stockroom. These jobs are not only reserved for workers from the agency, but workers in the enclave are provided with on-the-job supervision from agency staff. Enclaves offer exposure to the real demands of work life and more contact with other workers or customers, but at the same time, offer the support of staff and the reassurance of peers with disabilities who work alongside them as they prepare for more independent jobs.

Agency-operated businesses

Agency-based businesses, such as a restaurant in a town or a landscaping crew working under contracts with community agencies and businesses, have also been popular. In them, the agency seeks to build a self-sustaining economic venture, while providing both employment income and training opportunities for the people they serve, along with relatively normalized contact with customers. While few agency-operated businesses have been able to generate significant income for their agencies, most do manage to show enough profit to meet their workers' salaries (Granger, 1990).

These second generation programs are effective for some and an appropriate starting point for others, but reprise the concerns raised by more sheltered programs. Although widely used by psychiatric rehabilitation agencies, these programs may become ends in themselves for workers who are uncomfortable in moving toward competitive work and may not offer the most realistic preparatory training they will need for moving to "real jobs for real pay."

Placement practices

With or without the benefit of a formal program model, many direct service staff in psychiatric rehabilitation agencies do help the people they serve find jobs in the competitive labor market.

Perhaps the oldest of these practices is the *Job Club*—a formal regular opportunity for people to meet together to develop job-finding skills, share job leads, and celebrate their successes when they land jobs. Job clubs can be useful in helping develop resumes, practicing job interview techniques, identifying job openings through newspapers and personal contacts, and providing ongoing group support for people who are working (Azrin, 1979).

Many agencies offer more intensive career counseling where, in either individual or group settings, job seekers assess their own interests and skills. Then, they explore, through research and visits to worksites, what the jobs they are interested in are really like (and what qualifications they require); develop short-term job-finding skills; and plot longer-term career development plans, which may include further technical education.

Most psychiatric rehabilitation programs also provide employer education. Many agencies develop a cadre of cooperating employers who are willing to interview and hire people the agency serves. Some establish employer advisory boards to acquaint them with emerging labor market trends, help shape the agency's training agenda, and spread the word to other employers. Other agencies sponsor media campaigns targeting employers and their hiring practices.

Job clubs, career counseling practices, and employer education initiatives have all proven valuable in advancing the employment agenda. While there is not compelling evidence that on their own they significantly increase competitive employment outcomes (Vandergoot, 1987), they have often proven to be a critical link to competitive employment.

Third Generation Programs and Practices: Supported Employment

A third generation of employment programs and practices, centered on Supported Employment (SE), has emerged over the past thirty years. SE has its origins in the developmental disabilities field where the preponderant use of sheltered workshops in community settings proved unsuccessful in helping more than a handful of workers move to competitive employment. Broad scale public policy changes and encouraging research into SE outcomes for people with developmental disabilities led to a firestorm of change in the 1980s when sheltered workshops were closed or converted and Supported Employment became the new service delivery standard (Newman, 1970; Wehman, 1986). Although sheltered workshops remain a staple of the developmental disabilities field today, in many states, SE programs offer a significant challenge.

The programs and practices that constitute the SE approach have also made significant inroads in the mental health arena (Mellen & Danley, 1987), although perhaps no more than 5% of people with psychiatric disabilities who could benefit from SE services can find SE programs in their communities. Nevertheless, the SE model continues to expand its influence in national and state policies. Growing numbers of PsyR agencies either have added SE programming to their existing array of vocational supports or have converted their entire work programs to the SE model. A significant body of compelling research studies have long established the efficacy of the SE approach (Mellen & Danley, 1987), and it is now widely considered to be one of the field's most successful best practices (SAMHSA, 2009).

Supported Employment Principles

The principles presented here are a mix of the elements that framed the initial approach serving people with developmental disabilities and additional elements found especially helpful in serving people with psychiatric disabilities (Bond, 2004). Because each of the program elements below is considered critical in improving competitive employment outcomes, there are now fidelity measures to help local programs assess whether they are indeed offering consumers a best practice SE program effectively (SAMHSA, 2009). The core principles guiding SE best practices follow.

SE programs are focused only on assisting consumers in gaining and maintaining competitive employment. In contrast to many of the programs discussed above, where long-term participation in a sheltered workshop, a volunteer job, or an agency-operated business are acceptable end goals, SE programs establish competitive employment as the only successful outcome for consumers receiving services. The focus is on regular jobs in mainstream businesses or agencies that could be held by anyone without a disability ("real work for real pay"), jobs that pay wages and offer benefits commensurate with local industry standards and jobs in which the consumer is neither surrounded by other workers with psychiatric disabilities nor isolated from co-workers or the public.

SE programs move consumers into competitive jobs quickly. In contrast to programs with an explicit "train-then-place" model, SE services move consumers into competitive jobs rapidly using a "place-then-train" model that relies upon the ability of the worker, with appropriate on-the-job supports as needed, to master a new job through on-the-job experience. No element of the SE model has proven more radical, or more successful, than the decision to abandon a major investment in "readiness" (at both clinical and vocational levels) as a pre requisite for placement. SE programs rely, instead, on both on-the-job and off-the-job support from job coaches to help workers succeed.

SE programs rely on the job seekers' preferences and choice. Choice is implemented in several ways. First, the job placement process begins as soon as an individual expresses his/ her interest in working. Second, SE programs search for job opportunities that match each person's talents and vocational goals rather than fitting the person into existing opportunities. Third, the decision of whether to disclose a psychiatric disability to an employer is also a matter of individual choice, involving who disclose to and when and how to manage both supervisory and co-worker responses to disclosure.

SE programs provide continuous and long-term supports to workers. People who require intensive support during their initial days or weeks on new jobs have the support of job coaches, with an expectation that job coaching services will fade, but not vanish, as the workers grow more comfortable on their jobs. Continuous long-term support (and many SE programs currently report one to two contacts a month for a year or two) plays an important role in helping sustain the initial placement and find a new job if the worker is either fired or seeks to find a more interesting, better paying, or simply more convenient job elsewhere (Bond & Kukla, 2009).

SE programs are closely linked to clinical treatment. Supported Employment programs ensure close linkages between job specialists and the clinical team, making it far less likely that clinical changes (e.g., in appointment times or medications) will undermine vocational success and far more likely that the worker will receive consistent and coordinated clinical and rehabilitation support in pursuing a competitive job. This helps to make competitive employment a major and significant activity for everyone the worker relies upon for support and speeds clinical attention to behaviors that might otherwise limit success on the job.

SE programs provide extensive and ongoing benefits counseling. One of the most significant barriers to employment has been confusion over the financial impact of employment on SSA income and medical benefits (for service users, service providers, family members, and other caregivers). The SSA Work Incentives program provides a variety of mechanisms "to make work pay," and the additional ability of states to offer low-cost Medicaid to workers, who would otherwise no longer be eligible for Medicaid coverage, makes competitive employment more feasible (NJ DHS, 2009). Benefits issues are often complicated, however, and SE programs need to ensure that job seekers have access to benefits expertise, both at the beginning of engagement in work and throughout the person's career. While local training and online guidelines are available, skilled personal counseling is critical to effectively ease fears about loss of benefits.

SE programs are distinctive in their singular commitment to competitive employment outcomes, their rapid placement into competitive jobs without extensive preparatory activity, and their delivery of continuous post-placement supports. Supported Employment is our current best practice because there is now ample evidence that SE moves people with psychiatric disabilities into competitive employment more rapidly with at least modest increases in both monthly income and sustained employment (Cook et al., 2005).

Implementation Issues

It is also useful to note that SE programs are not a universal panacea: Many people in SE either do not succeed at all in obtaining jobs or do not continue in competitive employment beyond their first placement, and earnings gains are modest. For the field to continue to evolve, the principles described above will be expanded upon to address a few new implementation issues that SE practitioners and researchers have identified.

System re-orientation. Success in Supported Employment may depend upon more than the combination of motivation, job coach activity, and clinical involvement. Because SE offers such a distinctly different approach, it is often necessary to work toward a comprehensive system reorientation in which family members, residential staff, case managers, and others supporters are aware of and enthusiastic about the SE program.

Employer education. While media campaigns targeted to employers remain a useful approach to confronting employer prejudices, many psychiatric rehabilitation agencies find more success in working with employers one-to-one, particularly in instances when someone is comfortable revealing his/her psychiatric history. Cooperating employers who have hired people with psychiatric disabilities and who have had positive experiences can be invaluable in spreading the word in an employer-to-employer campaign about the value of the SE approach.

Peer support. The growth of the peer support movement has transformed many mental health settings as people with personal experience with a mental illness play increasingly central roles in service delivery. There is a growing interest both in hiring peers as job coaches and in using specialized Certified Peer Specialists to assist job coaches in providing support, whether at the initial stages of the SE process or in the delivery of long-term support, and giving workers and job seekers successful models and in-the-trenches advice about competitive work.

Rehabilitation Services

Supports can be critical to employment success:

> Within the mental health system, there were two kinds of supports. The first were the encouragement I received from mental health staff who believed in my recovery journey. The second were the employment programs I used, including evaluation by the local Office of Vocational Rehabilitation and the OVR referral to the workforce reentry program. Recovery evolved by moving through a gradual process of accepting increasing levels of responsibility at work. Aside from the mental health challenges, one of the difficulties I had was the rapid turnover of frontline staff in the mental health system, which was disappointing and slowed my progress. (Timothy Connors)

> I had two kinds of rehabilitation experiences. The first was while I was attending a day program but worked with a job coach who encouraged me to volunteer at the agency's community thrift shop. I feared both internal (self) and external (public) stigma, but I valued my social role as a worker performing tasks, such as cashiering, straightening clothes, and interacting with customers. The second was the financial support I received from the local Office of Vocational Rehabilitation toward a Bachelor's Degree in Social Work, which I was able to earn over five years despite repeating 14 courses before I could graduate. Although OVR wouldn't then support

me in my pursuit for full-time work, by 2002—after submitting 15 applications and going through six interviews, I finally landed a job as a Case Manager, got off Social Security (paying off a $13,000 overpayment), and continue to work full-time and support myself. (George H. Brice, Jr.)

IMPLEMENTING SUPPORTED EMPLOYMENT

Implementing a Supported Employment program can be a challenge to a PsyR agency, and we review here some of the issues that have emerged over several years of developing SE services within one of the nation's oldest and largest psychiatric rehabilitation agencies. Horizon House, Inc., based in Philadelphia, offers psychiatric rehabilitation, education, employment, substance abuse, outpatient, and residential services to individuals who have a variety of challenges, including mental illnesses, developmental disabilities, substance abuse, and homelessness.

Horizon House (HH) has long recognized the importance of employment in the lives of people with psychiatric disabilities. Over twenty years ago, HH began a sheltered workshop focusing on assembly line work, in-house training programs, and federal set-aside contracts for individuals with psychiatric disabilities. As the field of vocational rehabilitation evolved, so did Horizon House, which closed its sheltered workshop in 1994 to shift to Supported Employment. With this approach, there also came several significant changes and challenges to business as usual.

Identifying Job Opportunities

HH quickly realized that dramatic changes were needed in how to assist people in identifying competitive jobs. First, the agency changed its orientation from one in which staff "placed" people in jobs to one in which more responsibility for obtaining employment shifted to the job seeker, which required increased staff time for teaching job finding skills. HH established a resource center with computers, posted job leads, and began teaching people how to use the Internet for job searches. Second, because SE argues for a "no reject" policy (the only criterion for acceptance is a desire to work), a substantial number of individuals said they were ready to work, but who were only willing, initially, to try non-paying positions. HH helped them get volunteer and internship positions and found that volunteer and internship first-steps made it easier to serve people with a wide range of education levels ranging from college education to minimal literacy.

HH also has added an intensive career exploration component. Too often, individuals base their choice of employment upon the opinion of a case manager, residential staff, or family member rather than on their own preferences, experiences, or knowledge. Because many people who come to HH did not have opportunities for typical career exploration activities in late adolescence due to the onset of symptoms, and jobs held after the onset of their illnesses were often chosen out of financial necessity, the HH approach has been to help people choose a career rather than just a job.

Improving Education

Because many job seekers face real academic and technical challenges in obtaining and succeeding in the jobs they desire, HH has developed an array of educational programs that provide preparation for better paying and more interesting jobs than someone might otherwise obtain. HH quickly conducts an assessment of academic skills, worker traits, learning styles, and interests using various WorkKeys tests along with Win for WorkKeys (WIN WorkKeys Assessment System, 2009), allowing job seekers to explore hundreds of jobs and critical information about their essential functions, salaries, and availability by location, which makes it more likely that job seekers will choose careers beyond the series of entry-level jobs that characterize their work histories (Cook et al., 2005). Win for WorkKeys also includes self-directed exercises for improving academic skills that can lead to earning a National Career Readiness Certificate, which is recognized by employers in over 40 states as an assurance that applicants have the foundation skills necessary to learn and to perform their jobs. Finally, HH uses functional assessments at work sites in the community that allow participants to both try out their skills in an area of interest and get a realistic picture of employer expectations. By using this assessment process, participants often are surprised to learn the depth and range of their marketable skills.

In a departure from many other Supported Employment initiatives, but in keeping with the HH emphasis on career building, the agency encourages interested individuals to increase their qualifications for jobs at all levels of the workforce continuum. Some are encouraged to improve their basic literacy or to complete their GED. Others are supported as they enroll in a community college or four-year degree program. If they have the prerequisite academic standing, this will afford them opportunities beyond entry-level employment. If someone is interested in working at one of the 50% of U.S. jobs that pay markedly better than entry-level work, but do not require a four-year college degree, HH provides assistance in securing financial aid for career-specific training. HH offers support for post-secondary academic programs through its Education Plus Program, a mobile supported education program that assists students throughout their academic experiences at schools in the Philadelphia region.

Post-Employment Supports

Continuous long-term supports are an essential component in Supported Employment and range from weekly phone calls and visits at job sites to hands-on job coaching. The type of activity and the frequency of the contact are determined by individuals and their employment specialists, and although there is no time limit on services, HH teaches participants a problem-solving approach they can use independently to reduce the supports the agency directly offers them over time. Because an individual's ability to function on the job can change in unpredictable ways, perhaps due to shifts in job responsibilities, personal crises, new medications, or local economic circumstances, long-term supports cannot be time-limited. Workers know that they may contact the agency at any time to help solve a problem, to negotiate reasonable accommodations, to apply for a promotion, or to begin seeking another job.

Long-term supports are also needed when individuals who have found jobs on their own without disclosing their disabilities now require reasonable accommodations under the Americans with Disability Act (ADA, 2009). The decision to disclose weeks, months, or years after being hired sometimes is difficult, and people may avoid asking for reasonable accommodations when they need them most. On the one hand, participants who do not disclose may feel more independent, less stigmatized, and in charge of their lives by not disclosing, but they may not be skilled at asking for help when they need it. If someone requests help, HH's employment specialists will reach out to employers, many of whom will then call the ES when they need help figuring out a strategy to keep another troubled employee on the job.

Customized Employment

HH has begun to make greater use of customized employment approaches where Employment Specialists work directly with employers to shape a new job specifically for a new employee, taking into account his or her particular strengths and challenges and the employer's specific needs. This means that staff members need to learn as much as possible about specific job requirements as well as how to help an employer meet his/her workforce needs. By using techniques such as job carving (creating a job that fits a workers' unique abilities), HH not only helps the employer be more efficient, but also creates a better match for the participant, increasing the chances for success. This shift requires additional staff training and time to make a placement successful.

Building Quality Services

HH faces the challenge of continuing to provide quality services that meet participants' employment goals in a changing workforce. Several years ago, HH used a database to track employment outcomes with information about the name of the employer and title of the job, length of employment, whether the job is full- or part-time, and the salary. The data provide clear evidence that fewer people are getting jobs and it is taking much longer for participants to find employment, creating frustration for both job seekers and the staff supporting them. Staff work together to identify the key factors affecting outcomes and what could be done differently. The database, one part of a continuous quality improvement approach that involves program participants, allows the agency to address emerging issues, refine plans, and set new program goals. Finally, Horizon House continues to search for stable and flexible funding for its SE programs with support currently cobbled together from various sources (e.g., the Social Security Administration's Ticket-to Work program, which has become one approach to providing long-term supports that often have no clear funding base).

Building Careers

For many people, having just any job is not enough—building a meaningful career enriches work life.

> Work now plays several roles in my life. The social component of working with other people has improved my social skills; I am now financially responsible for myself and I have finally become independent of the community mental health system. Employment also lessens my internal stigmatization and has increased my own integration into social communities of my own choosing. I'm not sure where my career will take me, but I have the comfort of hope—based on where I am in my career now. (Timothy Connors)

> Over the next decade or so I expect my career to be very promising, as I learn to better deal with adversity and live a healthy lifestyle, leaving the many years of isolation, shame, guilt, and feelings of inadequacy behind me. I want to wake each morning to a daily routine, feel a sense of self-worth that counteracts the past of disappointment and deferred dreams, and be able to better cope with the daily life stressors and triggers that threaten my career. My future vocational success is predicated on my ability to maximize my skills, talents, self-worth and wellness, health, and self-discovery. (George H. Brice, Jr.)

A FUTURE FOR FOURTH GENERATION SERVICES: CHALLENGES AHEAD

Although the Supported Employment approach is well-defined and its success is well-demonstrated, it is likely to be adapted and adjusted in the years ahead as we learn more about how to help people with psychiatric disabilities return to competitive work. Several challenges exist.

Responding to the Needs of Youth

Psychiatric rehabilitation agencies often report difficulty engaging younger people in services. Younger men and women remain reluctant to join the subculture of psychiatric disability that seems to place so little emphasis on the importance of competitive work. Older people in the service system often have been discouraged from seeking competitive employment and have been offered few supports to assist them in developing a long-term attachment to the competitive labor market. Consequently, they have been more likely to accept workshops and work crews, in-house assignments, and specialized community-based employment rather than challenging themselves and their agencies to focus on real work for real pay. Supported Employment offers a partial answer to this challenge by moving work-motivated individuals onto jobs quickly, but more needs to be done to ensure that younger people entering the system are encouraged to work from their very first engagement with a PsyR agency to help them build real careers beyond entry-level positions. Competitive work remains a core goal for most people with psychiatric disabilities, but it is central to the aspirations of teens and young adults. The more effectively the field responds to this normative ambition, the better it can avoid building lifestyles of idleness, poverty, and social isolation.

Supporting Educational Achievement

Most of the jobs found by graduates of PsyR agencies, whether through SE programs or not, are entry-level positions with the low pay, limited benefits, and short-term guarantees that characterize such jobs. This is so, in part, because so many are educationally unqualified for more demanding jobs (Baron & Salzer, 2002). Those without basic educational skills often could benefit from literacy programs or high school diploma classes and should be supported in pursuing them. For those who are interested in the "middle-skill" jobs that often require specialized training, certifications by mainstream educational institutions and licensing by local or state agencies, service providers need to help people find these educational programs, apply for needed financial aid, and pull together any educational support and practical assistance needed for them to succeed. For people seeking professional or executive careers, help in returning to and succeeding in college will need to be integrated through emerging Supported Education programs if they are to reach their career potential.

Guaranteeing Long-Term Supports

Although one of the important principles of Supported Employment is the availability of long-term supports, the field knows very little about the types of supports needed, nor has it found the required long-term funding. People with psychiatric disabilities may require varied types of assistance beyond the early weeks and months of a job placement; some on-the-job problems (with co-workers or supervisors, for instance) may emerge long after placement. Someone may have difficulty negotiating a reasonable accommodation for an unexpected onslaught of symptoms; others may struggle with a range of practical off-the-job problems, such as transportation, child care, or a family crisis. Still others may need to find new jobs, either because they have been laid off or let go or because they are ready to move forward in accepting new work challenges. These are, the practitioner needs to keep in mind, the kinds of normative problems many workers without disabilities face, but well-funded long-term support for people with psychiatric disabilities can be the key factor in helping them define and maintain themselves as workers (Bond & Kukla, 2009).

Developing Entrepreneurial Skills

For some, the goal is less a "job" and more a "business." Establishing and operating a small business is often demanding but also exhilarating, and people who want to own their own businesses are increasingly finding the support they need within SE programs. Job placement assistance is often replaced with help in putting together a business plan, finding the funding needed to get started, and developing the entrepreneurial skills that will be required. A number of programs in community settings specialize in training in this area—these are not resources and competencies job coaches themselves need to develop—and can provide the budding entrepreneurs with the savvy needed to work for themselves successfully (Revell et al., 2009).

SUMMARY

The startlingly high unemployment rate among people who use psychiatric rehabilitation services and the continuing unavailability of best practice employment programs in many communities suggest that meeting the demands of service users for a role in the competitive labor market will involve vast changes. PsyR agencies can play an important part in drawing attention to the need, experimenting with new approaches, and demonstrating success.

At the most immediate level, more will need to be done to re-orient mental health systems around the proposition that every person with a psychiatric disabilities should, would, and could work if provided the supports and services needed. Competitive employment is not a specialized goal for an especially motivated or experienced group, but a reachable goal for nearly everyone. This suggests leaving behind the failed clinical programs and short-sighted initiatives that have kept people from realizing their career goals.

Second, it would be naïve not to recognize that moving in the direction of establishing competitive employment goals for nearly everyone will entail a significant shift of resources from other programs. This will be a challenge in the years ahead. There is an array of responsibilities that employment programs and practitioners must address if people using services are to be successful in becoming workers, which will require both skilled staff (and a lot of them) as well as the resources to support them.

Third, writing at a time of economic troubles and stubbornly high general unemployment rates means reasserting that employment for people with psychiatric disabilities is not simply an option but a right. They do not have to wait until everyone else is gainfully employed to demand the psychiatric rehabilitation programs and employment opportunities that can make real work a reality. The alternative is to wait forever.

Best practices in employment, it follows, include recognition of the paramount importance of competitive employment in the lives of people with psychiatric disabilities, the acceptance of the need to move funding in this direction, and a commitment to help assert the rights of people with psychiatric disabilities to work alongside everyone else. It is a simple enough proposition to state, but it will take everything we have, and all of us working together, to move forward.

BEST PRACTICE GUIDELINES FOR SUPPORTED EMPLOYMENT

- Focus on helping people get and keep competitive employment ("real jobs for real pay").
- Move job seekers into competitive jobs quickly.
- Offer choice, and build employment services around the preferences and interests of the job seeker.
- Provide continuous and long-term supports.
- Link services to clinical treatment to coordinate services in a way that supports, rather than impedes, employment.
- Provide extensive and ongoing benefits counseling.

ABOUT THE AUTHORS

Richard C. Baron is the director of knowledge translation for the Temple University Collaborative on Community Inclusion of Individuals with Psychiatric Disabilities and has been a leading researcher, trainer, and policy analyst on the issues surrounding competitive employment for people with mental health conditions for over 40 years, including two NIDRR Switzer Fellowship publications on employment issues.

Arlene Solomon, CPRP, CRC is director of employment and education services at Horizon House, Inc. and coordinator of knowledge translation for the Temple University Collaborative on Community Inclusion. She has provided technical assistance and training nationally on community integration, employment, and supported education, and she has served on the board of directors of PRA's Pennsylvania chapter.

George H. Brice, Jr. is an instructor and trainer for the Integrated Employment Institute at the University of Medicine and Dentistry's Department of Psychiatric Rehabilitation and Counseling Professions. He is also currently teaching a wellness and recovery course and in a peer wellness coaching/mentoring/training project in New Jersey and co-chairs the state's Governor's Council on Mental Health Stigma.

Timothy Connors is employed at Magellan Behavioral Health as a peer specialist and has worked as a recovery coach for an innovative self-directed care program for the Mental Health Association of Southeastern Pennsylvania. He has been a respected advocate for over ten years, serving on mental health advisory committees for Delaware County (PA), the Southeastern Pennsylvania region, and the Commonwealth of Pennsylvania.

REFERENCES

ADA. (2009). EOC enforcement guidance on the Americans with Disabilities Act and psychiatric disabilities. Retrieved from http://www.eeoc.gov/policy/docs/psych.html

Anthony, W. A., & Blanch, A. (1987). Supported employment for persons with psychiatric disabilities: A historical and conceptual perspective. *Psychosocial Rehabilitation Journal, 11*(2), 5-23.

Azrin, N. H., & Phillip, R.A. (1979). The job club method for the job handicapped: A comparative outcome study. *Rehabilitation Counseling Bulletin, 23*(2), 144-155.

Baron, R. C. (2002). *People at work: The past and future career patterns of people with serious mental illness.* Tinley Park, IL: Recovery Press.

Baron, R. C., & Salzer, M. S. (2002). Accounting for unemployment among people with mental illness. *Behavioral Sciences & the Law, 20*(6), 585-599.

Beard, J. H. (1978). The rehabilitation services of Fountain House. In L. Stein & M. A. Test, *Alternatives to mental hospital treatment* (pp. 201-208). New York: Plenum.

Bilby, R. (1992). A response to the criticisms of transitional employment. *Psychosocial Rehabilitation Journal, 16*(2), 69-82.

Bond, G. R. (2004). Supported employment: Evidence for an evidence-based practice. *Psychiatric Rehabilitation Journal, 27*(4), 345-359.

Bond, G. R., Becker, D. R., Drake, R. E., Rapp, C. A., Meisler, N., Lehman, A. F., et al. (2001). Implementing supported employment as an evidence-based practice. *Psychiatry Services, 52*(3), 313-322.

Bond, G. R., Dietzen, L. L., McGrew, J. H., et.al. (1995). Accelerating entry into supported employment for persons with severe psychiatric disabilities. *Rehabilitation Psychology, 40,* 91-111.

Bond, G. R., & Dincin, J. (1986). Accelerating entry into transitional employment in a psychosocial rehabilitation agency. *Rehabilitation Psychology, 31*(3), 143-155.

Bond, G. R., Drake, R. E., Mueser, K. T., & Becker, D. R. (1997). An update on supported employment for people with severe mental illness. *Psychiatric Services, 48*(3), 335-346.

Bond, G. R., et. al. (2001). Implementing supported employment as an evidence-based practice. *Psychiatric Services, 52*(3), 313-322.

Bond, G. R. Kukla, M. (2009). *Service intensity and job tenure in supported employment: A final report.* Indianapolis, IN: Indiana University Purdue University Indianapolis, Department of Psychiatry.

Condeluci, A. (1991). *Interdependence: The route to community.* Orlando, FL: Paul M. Deutsch Press.

Cook, J. A., & Razzano, L. (2000). Vocational rehabilitation for persons with schizophrenia: Recent research and implications for practice. *Schizophrenia Bulletin, 26,* 87-103.

Cook, J. A., Jonikas, J. A., & Solomon, M. L. (1992). Models of vocational rehabilitation for youths and adults with severe mental illness. *American Rehabilitation, 18*(3), 6-11.

Cook, J. A., Lehman, A. F., Drake, R., McFarlane, W. R., Gold, P. B., Leff, H. S., et al. (2005). Integration of psychiatric and vocational services: A multisite randomized, controlled trial of supported employment. *American Journal of Psychiatry, 162*(10), 1948-1956.

Granger, B. (1990). *Agency sponsored entrepreneurial business employing individuals with long-term mental illness: Findings from a national survey.* Philadelphia, PA: Matrix Research Institute.

Harding, C. M. (1987). Work and mental illness I: Toward an integration of the rehabilitation process. *The Journal of Nervous and Mental Disease, 175*(6), 317-326.

Holzer, H. J., & Lerman, R. I. (2007). America's forgotten middle-skill jobs: Education and training requirements in the next decade and beyond. Retrieved from http://www.urban.org/publications/411633.html

Marrone, J., & Golowka, E. (1999). If work makes people with mental illness sick, what do unemployment, poverty, and social isolation cause? *Psychiatric Rehabilitation Journal, 23*(2), 187-193.

McQuilken, M., Zahniser, J. H., Novak, J., Starks, R. D., Olmos, A., & Bond, G. R. (2003). The work project survey: Consumer perspectives on work. *Journal of Vocational Rehabilitation, 18,* 59-68.

Mellen, V., & Danley, K. (1987). Special issue: Supported employment for persons with severe mental illness. *Psychosocial Rehabilitation Journal, 9*(2), 1-102.

Mueser, K. T., Becker, D. R., & Wolfe, R. S. (2001). Supported employment, job preferences, job tenure, and satisfaction. *Journal of Mental Health Administration, 10*, 411-417.

New Jersey Department of Human Services. (2009). New Jersey Work Ability: Helping people with disabilities increase their income, without reducing their benefits. Retrieved from http://www.state. nj.us/humanservices/dds/projects/discoverability

Newman, L. (1970). Instant placement: A new model for providing rehabilitation services within a community mental health program. *Community Mental Health Journal, 6*(5), 401-410.

Picone, J., Drake, R. E., Becker, D. (1998). *A survey of clubhouse programs.* Indianapolis, IN, Indiana University Purdue University Indianapolis, Department of Psychiatry.

Pennsylvania Recovery & Resiliency. (2008). A call for change: Employment—A key to recovery. Retrieved from http://www.parecovery.org/services_employment.shtml

President's New Freedom Commission on Mental Health. (2003). *Achieving the promise: Transforming mental health care in America, final report.* No. Pub. No. SMA-03-3832. Rockville, MD: U.S. Department of Health and Human Services.

Revell, G., Smith, F., & Inge, K. (2009). An analysis of self-employment outcomes within the federal/state vocational rehabilitation system. *Journal of Vocational Rehabilitation, 31*, 11-18.

Ridgway, P., & Rapp, C. (1998). *The active ingredients in achieving competitive employment for people with psychiatric disabilities: A research synthesis.* Lawrence, KS: University of Kansas.

Rogers, E. S., Walsh, D., Masotta, L., & Danley, K. (1991). Massachusetts survey of client preferences for community support services (final report). Boston, MA: Center for Psychiatric Rehabilitation.

Rubin, H. (1994). Andrew and fellowship: Response to disaster in a psychological rehabilitation program: A hurricane tolerance test of structure, philosophy, and methodology. In Publication Committee of the International Association of Psychosocial Rehabilitation Services (Eds.), *An introduction to psychiatric rehabilitation* (pp. 281-293). Columbia, MD: The International Association of Psychosocial Rehabilitation Series.

Rutman, I. D. (1994). How psychiatric disability expresses itself as a barrier to employment. *Psychosocial Rehabilitation Journal, 17*(3), 15.

SAMHSA. (2009). *Evidence-based practices: Shaping mental health services toward recovery.* DHHS. Retrieved from http://store.samhsa.gov/product/ Family-Psychoeducation-Evidence-Based-Practices-EBP-KIT/SMA09-4423

Stroul, B. A. (1986). *Models of community support services: Approaches to helping persons with long-term mental illness.* Boston, MA: Boston University Center for Psychiatric Rehabilitation.

The Workforce Alliance. (2002). Workforce development policies: Background and current issues. Retrieved from www.nationalskillscoalition.org

Trupin, L., Sebesta, D. S., Yelin, E., & LaPlante, M. P. (1997). *Trends in labor force participation among persons with disabilities, 1983-1994.* Washington, DC: U.S. Department of Education, National Institute on Disability and Rehabilitation Research.

Vandergoot, D. (1987). Review of placement research literature: Implications for research and practice. *Rehabilitation Counseling Bulletin, 30*(4), 243-272.

Wehman, P. (1986). Supported competitive employment for persons with severe disabilities. *Journal of Applied Rehabilitation Counseling, 17*(4), 24-29.

WIN WorkKeys assessment system. (2009). Retrieved from http://www.w-win.com

SUPPORTED EDUCATION

Anne Sullivan-Soydan

A B S T R A C T

The pursuit of education for people in recovery offers both the risk and promise of real world achievement. Best practices in educational support integrate the effective practices of vocational rehabilitation with key psychiatric rehabilitation principles and provide them within the context of recovery. This chapter provides an overview of these current best practices and raises the bar for the new decade with new research evidence from the first multi-site study of educational supports. Lessons learned from the explosion of new programs over the last 30 years identify key factors that facilitate success. Examples from programs that have effectively dealt with obstacles, key issues related to funding, legislation, the training and supervision of providers, and challenges and opportunities created by new technology are discussed.

AN EXPLORATION OF THE SPECIFIC BEST PRACTICES IN EDUCATIONAL SUPPORT BOTH ILLUSTRATES AND underscores the importance of educational achievement and support within the context of recovery for people with psychiatric disability who want to return to school. While good research evidence is still needed, we have much that demonstrates what can help and what can hurt. This chapter highlights the key factors that facilitate success and identifies those that can hinder even the most determined student, while providing some examples of how educational support can work in the real world to enhance and support the process of recovery. Recovery from the experience of a psychiatric disorder involves moving beyond the impact of the experience of a psychiatric disorder, but most importantly, it means achieving a full and satisfying life. Educational attainment has an enormous impact on economic well-being and quality of life.

Thirteen years into the new millennium, the U.S. unemployment rate hovers at about 8% for the general population. Unemployment for people with psychiatric conditions ranges between 85% and 95% (Bertram & Howard, 2006; Salkever, Karakus, Slade et al., 2007). In today's economy, the broad base of skills and knowledge employers require necessitates the acquisition of higher education. A postsecondary degree can mean the difference between earning a living wage and poverty, between job security and unemployment, especially. Individuals with the least amount of education have the highest rates of unemployment (U.S. Bureau of Labor Statistics, 2013). The higher the education level attained, the greater the immunity to economic trends. For people with psychiatric conditions, education has repeatedly been demonstrated to predict vocational outcomes. A postsecondary degree offers access into the primary labor force where pay is higher (Baron & Salzer, 2002) and promotes economic self-sufficiency, independence, community integration, and a boost to the personal journey of recovery (Murphy, Mullen, & Spagnolo, 2005).

The onset of psychiatric disorders frequently hits between the ages of 18-25 when young people are making career choices and pursuing an education or vocational training (Kessler, Berglund, Demler, et al., 2005). Despite the disability, and perhaps because of it, they retain a strong interest in the pursuit of higher education (Stein, 2005). Two thirds of people with a psychiatric disability want to attend college (Corrigan, 2008), and their post-secondary enrollment is increasing (Eisenberg, Golberstein, & Gollust, 2007). Yet returning to school is a daunting task at the best of times and is especially challenging with a psychiatric disability.

Whether it is a temporary "stop-out" or a more permanent "dropout," data from the recent two decades indicate that 86% of students with mental illnesses withdraw from college prior to completing their degrees (Kessler, Foster, Saunders, & Stang, 1995) compared to a 45% withdrawal rate for the general student population (Kuh, Kinzie, Buckley, Bridges, & Hayek, 2006). Kessler et al. estimated that in 1990 an additional 4.3 million people would have obtained a college degree if they had not experienced psychiatric symptoms. Typical reasons for dropout are problems caused from psychiatric symptoms and their impact on concentration, motivation, social interactions, and attendance. Exacerbating these are a lack of academic support and accommodations as well as social barriers such as stigma and lack of supportive peer relationships (Megivern, Pellerito, & Mowbray, 2003; Salzer, 2011; Warwick, Maxwell, Statham, Aggleton, & Simon, 2008). Support is essential, but often difficult to find and fund. Recent research suggests that less than half the students with mental illnesses on campuses seek out mental health services (Oliver, Reed, & Smith, 1998). Suffice it to say that the students with psychiatric disabilities, as well as the faculty and administrators on campuses across the country, are struggling with how to address the unique needs caused by psychiatric disabilities in an academic setting (Gallagher, 2007; Collins & Mowbray, 2005), and this together with the recent violence and campus shootings, have created a "campus mental health crisis" (Kadison & Diggeronimo, 2004).

So that leads us to the question of "what works?" How can we improve these outcomes? We now have some good evidence that suggests that individuals with significant psychiatric disabilities can successfully pursue educational opportunities (Collins, Bybee, & Mowbray, 1998; Mowbray & Collins, 2002; DRRK, 2010). Supported Education (SEd) was developed to assist individuals with severe psychiatric disabilities in developing and achieving post-secondary educational goals. Using an application of the recovery-oriented psychiatric rehabilitation approach, SEd programs began in the 1980s as a way to assist individuals with psychiatric disabilities who wanted to pursue postsecondary education in campus settings.

PROGRAM MODELS

Since its inception in 1984, the supported education approach has been documented, replicated, adapted, and widely disseminated (Unger, 1993; Mowbray, Collins, & Bybee, 1999; Mowbray, Strauch-Brown, Furlong-Norman, & Sullivan-Soydan, 2002), and supported education programs have evolved across the country and internationally. Programs used group- or individual-based services to increase the access to, retention in, and completion of post-secondary education by adults who have had difficulties in higher education because of psychiatric disabilities. Unger (1990) first documented and described the three early models of SEd, delineating them by the settings and services delivered: (1) self-contained classroom, (2) mobile support, and (3) on-site model.

In the self-contained classroom model, all students have a psychiatric disability and are instructed by a provider of mental health or rehabilitation services. The curriculum concentrates on vocational preparation, such as career exploration and vocational goal setting, and is not for academic credit. The mobile support model offers individualized SEd services that can be provided to individuals on college campuses, in the community, or in any setting of the person's choosing. The on-site support model assists students on college campuses and links them to existing resources. The on-site model mandates that the office of disability services for the academic institution must have at least one specialized service or staff person for students with psychiatric disabilities.

These three models were a helpful place to start, but were outmoded quickly as SEd services proliferated across the country. By 2003, the results of a nationwide survey revealed there were over 140 SEd programs across the United States (Mowbray, Megivern & Holter, 2003), and they could be more efficiently categorized by (1) types of services delivered and (2) the settings in which they were offered. Service-based models included mobile support, classroom support, group support, individual support, and on-site support. While these service-based models are often used as descriptors, they held little utility to fully describe the type of interventions or services provided. Setting-based models were summarized into the following four classifications of service: (1) the clubhouse approach "full" model, (2) the clubhouse approach "partial" model, (3) the on-site model, and (4) the freestanding model (Mowbray et al., 2003). Three of these four categories are based within or funded by mental health agencies, such as a psychosocial clubhouse. Some of these models are described in the discussion of program examples, but even this configuration of models is now largely irrelevant. There is such a broad array of supported education services being offered that the service elements become much more worthy of note than where, how, and by whom services are provided.

RESEARCH EVIDENCE

There is a general shortage of good quantitative research in SEd; most of the literature documenting the development and effectiveness of SEd is descriptive. A systematic review of all literature related to supported education for individuals with severe psychiatric disabilities (DRRK, 2010) verifies this lack of robust evidence. The review suggests that "there are a very few well-controlled studies of supported education and numerous studies with minimal evaluation data and less rigorous designs, and therefore concludes that there are limited effectiveness data for supported education programs" (p. 1). Some broad conclusions of the report claim sufficient evidence to suggest that individuals with psychiatric disabilities, when compared to the general population, have a lower rate of postsecondary degree completion and that those who are enrolled in supported education programs are younger, more highly educated, and less functionally impaired when compared to individuals with psychiatric disabilities in general (p. 2).

The most valuable contribution of the DRRK systematic review was an in-depth analysis of any and all published studies from 1989-2009, measuring the effectiveness of supported education, its correlates, and relationship to other relevant variables. This review builds on and clarifies the first review of SEd published seven years earlier by Mowbray and Collins (2002) in which they synthesized a total of eleven "evaluations" of supported education done from 1996-2002. The findings from these, as well as more recent studies, are included throughout this chapter, and research evidence on the effectiveness of SEd is summarized in order to provide an updated snapshot of what we know works.

Effectiveness of Supported Education

Measuring supported education is a complex task because it involves studying both educational processes and outcomes. In their examinations of the supported education literature, both Mowbray and Collins (2002) and Rogers and her colleagues (DRRK, 2010) discovered some confusion about process versus outcomes measures in supported education. For example, is enrollment in school a process measure or an outcome measure? Rogers' group (DRRK) used the following categories to differentiate the variables: educational engagement (how many enroll and attend), educational attainment (how many complete courses and/or graduate), employment (hours worked and wages), productive activity (either educational or employment activity), self-perception (self-esteem or school self-efficacy), quality of life (including number of return hospital admissions), and satisfaction with the supported education intervention.

A point worth noting about the supported education literature is that to date, there are few research studies in SEd that truly focus on effectiveness questions. Rogers' group found only two trials that could be considered rigorous in design. They also add a second note of concern, which is that the majority of publications in the field are based on one dataset, the Michigan Supported Education Research Project study (MSERP) conducted by Mowbray, Collins, and their colleagues in the 1990s. This has led to some skewed emphasis on the MSREP models in the literature. Taken together with some methodological problems in this study, "the findings from this study, in its different iterations and presentations, [are] difficult to interpret with confidence" (DRRK, 2009, p. 12).

True experimental designs using a control or comparison group yield the most convincing evidence of effectiveness, and there is not yet any evidence from a randomized trial or well controlled quasi-experimental trial demonstrating that participation in a supported education intervention results in significantly greater educational engagement or enrollment (Mowbray et al., 1999). At follow up in the MSERP study, there were no significant differences in the employment of individuals participating in a supported education intervention versus those not participating (Mowbray et al., 1999). Several studies using experimental designs without control groups have suggested that as a result of participation in a supported education intervention, students improved in their level of employment and educational status (Unger et al., 1991; Hoffman & Mastrianni, 1993; Unger & Pardee, 2002; Best, Still, & Cameron, 2008; Cook & Solomon, 1993), and were able to complete courses and achieve a satisfactory grade point average (Unger, Pardee, & Shaefer, 2000; Unger & Pardee, 2002; Cook & Solomon, 1993; Best et al., 2008). Taken together, the lack of conclusive evidence for the effectiveness of supported education in any model underscores the need for more rigorous research to document the validity of the supported education approach. One such study is currently underway in New Jersey: a randomized control study of SEd, funded by the Temple University Center for Community Collaboration and being conducted by psychiatric rehabilitation faculty researchers at the University of Medicine and Dentistry of New Jersey (UMDNJ; Mullen & Gill, in preparation). This study, with some preliminary results, described in more detail below, offers excellent promise for some good evidence about the effectiveness of supported education.

The UMDNJ multi-site randomized control study on the effectiveness of educational supports (Mullen & Gill, 2012) seeks to evaluate the effectiveness of SEd in improving academic performance. Baseline data show that of the college students participating, 30% are on their first attempt, 21% on their second, 36% are either attempting college for the third or fourth time, and perhaps the most staggering, 13% have attempted school five to seven times prior to their current attempt (n=68). Forty percent of student participating have been diagnosed with bipolar disorder, 35.5% with depression, 16% with schizoaffective, 3.2% with schizophrenia, and 4.8% with other diagnoses. The experimental group is participating in "enhanced SEd supports and activities," while the control group is receiving some basic resources and information and no enhanced support. Preliminary results suggest a significant difference in process and achievement measures outcomes as well as satisfaction with services.

So what can we glean about best practices in supported education so far? Clearly we need more research, but we have learned a lot about specific barriers and supports that help people with psychiatric disabilities to succeed at school. The next section is a discussion of the risk factors and barriers that interfere with participation in school as well as the supports and protective factors that can ameliorate the impact on a person's functioning and well-being.

Lessons Learned and Key Factors

There are three levels of facilitators and barriers: those that affect the individual, those created and facilitated by the institution, and those encountered and addressed by the service provider. Several studies have provided data and support for the facilitators and barriers on all three levels. Hartley (2010) suggests using the concept of resilience to help explain the differential impact of these barriers. Resilience has been used to help us understand how individuals behave adaptively under great stress (Masten, 2001). A resilience framework is strengths-based and so supports the process of recovery and can be applied to all three levels of barriers and facilitators. Hartley suggests that individuals can achieve college success by using protective factors, which he refers to as the individual's personal qualities or contexts that predict positive outcomes under high-risk conditions (p. 296).

Individual barriers and facilitators

Individual level barriers are those obstacles that originate with the person and the individual impact of the academic experience as well as his or her experience of psychiatric symptoms. The primary barrier of students with psychiatric disabilities to accessing services was overwhelmingly reported as a fear of disclosure, which of course speaks to the biggest barrier of all, that of stigma. A survey of 350 college students at the University of South Florida found that 54% believed their campus paid little to no attention to mental illnesses (Becker, Martin, Wajeeh, Ward, & Shern, 2002). Students with psychiatric disabilities have reported that when they disclosed their disability, faculty and peers either had little to no accurate information about mental illnesses (Brockelman, Chadsey, & Loeb, 2006; Weiner & Wiener, 1996), and many were advised to discontinue their studies (Blacklock et al., 2003). Clearly, stigma remains a risk factor. Other common barriers to service access included a lack of knowledge about services, a lack of specific services, and students not perceiving themselves as having a disability.

Psychiatric symptoms can interfere with cognitive abilities, especially depression and anxiety (Svanum & Zody, 2001; Hembree, 1988). Possible effects include deficits in short-term memory, critical thinking, elaboration, and planning, organizing, and regulating learning (Brackney & Karabenick, 1995; Dobson & Kendall, 1993; Heiligenstein, Guenther, Hsu, & Herman, 1996). The side effects of psychotropic medications can impact attention, energy level, concentration, and stamina (Weiner & Wiener, 1996), making it difficult to pay attention in class and complete assignments on time (Collins & Mowbray, 2005; Knis-Matthews et al., 2007; Sullivan-Soydan, 1997). Collins and Mowbray provide a lengthy list of barriers, including general coping with school, issues related to obtaining accommodations and supports, attendance issues, specific issues related to the person's diagnosis, general anxiety, low self-esteem, test anxiety, social skills, personal issues, memory and concentration troubles, and conflicts with faculty. Lack of confidence, sometimes from internalized stigma (Megivern et al., 2003), and a lack of skill and practice in an academic setting can further exacerbate these barriers. College students in the UMDNJ study (Mullen & Gill, 2012) rated the skills with which they had the greatest difficulty; the top five were concentration (85%), time management (77%), stamina (75%), organization (71%), and prioritizing tasks (70%). In addition to these, the majority of the respondents stated they had difficulty memorizing information, managing psychiatric symptoms, studying for exams, taking exams, preparing for class, writing papers, taking notes, researching information, and meeting deadlines (M. Mullen, personal communication, April 26, 2012).

From Hartley's (2010) resilience perspective, SEd service providers can address some of these barriers using protective factors, including active coping, peer support, counseling and psychosocial support, academic support, and academic accommodations. Active coping is closely connected to self-efficacy, and there is increasing evidence of its importance in the success of college students. Use of positive coping strategies, such as problem solving strategies, helped later functioning (Collins et al., 1999). Research on coping strategies suggests that it is possible to identify potential stressors encountered in an education setting and prepare students to be able to handle them, which in turn, can influence later outcomes (Collins et al., 1999). In a study of the effects of psychiatric symptoms on college learning, Brockelman (2009) found that active coping was a significant predictor of cumulative GPA.

Support of peers and counselors is a critical facilitator. Research shows that students with psychiatric disabilities who have encouraging peers are more likely to remain in college (Blacklock et al., 2003; Knis-Matthews et al., 2007; Weiner & Wiener, 1997) and that a peer network is critical to combat feelings of isolation and increase resilience for students with psychiatric disabilities (Hefner & Eisenberg, 2009). On a more individualized level, they needed help with substance abuse issues, stress management, and personal support as well as help coordinating mental health and educational services (Corrigan et al., 2008).

Academic support is another protective key to resilience in college. Knis-Matthews et al. (2007) found that faculty meeting with students with psychiatric disabilities outside of class reduced drop out. When supports are available and accessible, students with disabilities succeed at levels commensurate with their abilities and to the same degree as other students (Salzer, Wick, & Rogers, 2008; Dalke, 1993), and awareness of this increases use among all students with disabilities (Tagayun, Stodden, & Chang, 2005). Hope is, as ever, an essential ingredient in recovery, and in school especially; it also helps to be surrounded by people who believe one can succeed (Collins, Mowbray, & Bybee, 2000).

Institutional barriers

The increased presence of students with psychiatric disabilities creates programmatic and administrative pressures on institutions of higher education. Ignorance and lack of knowledge about legislation and accommodations, how to separate behavior issues from disability issues, and how to be flexible without diluting the essential requirements of the academic environment challenge all levels of administration. Disability services staff, faculty, and student affairs personnel spend hours working with students to address multiple, complex problems. In the past, these problems were often addressed in isolation with little or no communication between academic departments and service offices, often to protect confidentiality. These gaps in coordination, labeled "silos of service," combined with the persistent and pervasive negative effects of stigma, created a multitude of negative outcomes: academic failure, social isolation, loss of insurance benefits, withdrawal, and even expulsion. In the past ten years, the problem of isolation has increased drastically, primarily because of the several suicide/homicide shootings that have occurred on campuses and in the community, such as those at Virginia Tech and Northern Illinois University. If there were a "mental health crisis on campus" before, these shootings just make it more pronounced. Elaborate systems of alerts using mobile phones and e-communication are now in place on most campuses, and information is shared much more freely in the interest of creating a safe environment.

Still, the issue underscores one of the biggest barriers of all: stigma. Even before these tragedies, stigma and prejudice were by far the most significant barriers students with psychiatric disorders faced. "Whenever there is a tragedy, we shudder" were the words of Harvey Rosenthal of the NY Association of Psychiatric Rehabilitation Services after the 2013 Newtown, CT, elementary school gun slaughter. The label of "mental patient" is daunting in its impact on rehabilitation and recovery (Corrigan & Lundin, 2001; Surgeon General, 1999), creating insidious discrimination against people with psychiatric disabilities in all areas of life (Byrne, 2000; Link et al., 1987). In 1994, Unger cited the stigma of mental illness as a primary obstacle to equal access to educational programs for people with psychiatric disabilities, and it remains so two decades later.

Facilitators

We need innovative strategies for working more effectively with students with psychiatric disabilities. A campus-wide system has long been recommended that uses the expertise and resources of multiple campus providers—from the dean of students to the counseling offices to residence hall advisors and individual faculty members (Blacklock et al., 2003; Mowbray et al., 2006; Nolan et al., 2005). Academic support, a well-documented protective factor, can be provided for in more organized, publicized ways, such as making study and computer rooms available into the later evening hours. Supplemental instruction by qualified advanced students, regular faculty office hours, and education about warning signs and where to get help as well as having that help easily accessible, free, available, and relevant are essential.

Regarding stigma reduction, education about, exposure to, and personal contact with people with psychiatric disabilities is one of the best ways to combat negative public attitudes. The behavioral health service at Boston University (2012) has an award-winning website with an array of the faces of actual students who have experienced one or more major psychiatric disorders. Clicking on the face elicits a two- to three-minute personal story about the student's experience with the disability. Finally, the policy of "no wrong door" is a protective measure against the gaps; wherever someone presents for help should be the right place, either for service or immediate referral.

Service provider barriers

Many disability services staff members still do not feel adequately trained to address the needs of individuals with psychiatric disabilities. The most common concerns raised by faculty or staff at postsecondary schools working with individuals with a psychiatric disability are how to deal with general behavior problems in the classroom, address attendance problems, and field questions about whether the student can handle the workload or should be enrolled in school (Collins & Mowbray, 2005). Having someone in a student disability office with supported education expertise who can address these concerns is important and shows a commitment to helping such students with aid, transportation, and study skills (Corrigan et al., 2008).

What helps overcome these challenges? Are there predictors of success or proven strategies to address some of these barriers? In terms of predicting whether students with psychiatric disabilities will be served in postsecondary educational settings, size of school may be important because of the resources available at larger institutions. Two-year public schools play an important role in providing access to higher education for individuals with psychiatric disabilities. Other factors that make a difference in serving individuals with psychiatric disabilities include having an outreach/recruitment policy for students, conveying a perception that the environment is supportive, having a larger disability office, and increasing the number of staff members with training and experience with psychiatric disabilities (Collins & Mowbray, 2005).

Blacklock and her colleagues (2003) advocate four strategies: (a) implementing universal instructional design strategies to improve the learning experiences for all students, including those with psychiatric disabilities, (b) creating sub-communities to foster social connections for students with psychiatric disabilities, (c) improving clarity, coordination, and communication with all key stakeholders, including inter-organizational and community-based service providers, and (d) promoting access to resources for all key stakeholders through information sharing and training efforts.

SUCCESSFUL PROGRAMS

There are several hundred supported education programs offered in clubhouse, community mental health centers, VA centers, psychiatric rehabilitation centers, on campuses, in disability service offices, in research and training centers, in private counseling, and through vocational rehabilitation. The next section summarizes one of these to underscore the essential components of the educational support that is offered and highlight why this is a model program.

Bridgeway Rehabilitation Services based in Elizabeth, NJ, is a psychiatric rehabilitation (PsyR) service agency that offers a range of PsyR services, including several ACT teams, a justice-involved program, supported housing and homeless outreach, and career services. Bridgeway's Career Services has two programs that work together to support people in any and all aspects of their career development. All individuals entering into the program must have a long-term vocational goal of employment. Individuals may come into the program with an educational goal and later transition into employment or an educational goal may be cultivated if individuals are dissatisfied with their employment options. For consistency, most individuals remain with the same counselor, regardless of the short-term goal. Bi-monthly staff training and the philosophy of the director keep the environment potentiated for optimal growth. The PsyR values and expertise are a job requirement as are job and role shifts to respond to participant needs. The training keeps the environment fertile for learning, and personal and professional growth and development is valued and rewarded, which minimizes burnout and staff turnover with its consequent negative impact on participants. All staff members are cross-trained in both supported education and employment approaches, services, and interventions, which means minimal stress and transition as participants progress or shift goal environments.

The Bridgeway SEd program is an innovative approach to combining educational supports within the larger context of vocational development. For individuals expressing interest in education, the staff members provide a full continuum of services from developing readiness for school to employment transitioning upon graduation. Participants take courses for credit in integrated settings for a credential that will increase employability. Service components include goal setting and planning, decision making, and tailored skills and supports for choosing and matriculating in a course or a program of study. SEd counselors are mobile, often working from their cars or campus cafeterias and other public spaces. Available by phone for both check-in calls and emergencies, they work with participants for as long as needed and support all aspects of the enrollment and retention process. Supervision is regular and ongoing, and caseloads are kept low to allow maximum contact hours with students.

A recent satisfaction survey (Corey Storch, personal communication, September 12, 2012) of twelve SEd respondents at Bridgeway revealed a mean score of 3.3 out of 4, showing a consistently high level of satisfaction from the participants. Comments were overwhelmingly positive:

- *CO is there to coach and guide me; she's there whenever I need her for help.*

- *Bridgeway has given me the opportunity to relate with people that share my needs. The counselor's support has influenced my outlook about my future.*

- *My counselor is an amazing person who has helped me greatly I would not be where I am if not for her assistance. I am grateful.*

- *This program has played an important part in assisting in my mental health recovery and in working to achieve my goals. I am very appreciative of all the opportunities you have made possible and of all of the efforts of my case manager, who made them happen for me.*

Bridgeway continues to strengthen its leadership role in the mental health system and is a leader in New Jersey in several areas of PsyR services. Their strategic plan places a major emphasis on wellness and integrated physical and mental health services. The SEd program is beginning to see people graduate from two-year colleges and move on to new career goals. They have served 122 people over the last three quarters with 63 people currently enrolled in school. Seven students graduated from several four-year and community colleges in May 2012.

Supported Education Fidelity Scale

As noted by Rogers and her colleagues (DRRK, 2010), supported education is a promising practice that continues to gather empirical support but does not yet have sufficient research foundation to make it an evidence-based practice. A critical element of this process is to continue to investigate supported education interventions, to compile the findings, and to slowly build a foundation of empirical support. Diane McDiarmid and her colleagues at the University of Kansas (KU) developed a Supported Education fidelity scale (McDiarmid, Rapp, Holter, Dykes & Ratzlaff, 2006) that is now in its third iteration (Manthey, Coffman, Goscha, Bond, Mabry, Carlson, Davis, & Rapp, 2012). A version of this scale has been recognized and adopted by SAMHSA as a model for use in assessing and implementing supported education programming and services (SAMHSA, 2012). The rationale for using fidelity scales to guide practice is to standardize delivery and to facilitate outcomes research to determine whether programs that are higher in fidelity will have better outcomes.

Diane McDiarmid, the primary architect of the KU Scale, developed the measure using principles based upon years of experience delivering supported education services as well as input from community mental health centers, college staff, students, and others who received mental health services. Individual and group interviews were used to elicit information about facilitators and barriers of the supported education process. Program staff were intensively trained and supervised in supported education best practices using group supervision weekly. A comprehensive review of all available program data outcomes helped to refine the final fidelity scale. With input from all on specific strategies and practices to improve, the fidelity scale rating was repeated every six months for two years. The most recent version of the KU SEd Fidelity Scale includes twenty-one supported education best practice items, each with several indicators that operationalize the element and each rated on a 1-5 scale according to presence of each. Fidelity scales such as these provide a useful tool for program assessment and evaluation of key elements of supported education. The scale has been modified twice, most recently in 2012 (see Manthey, Coffman, Goscha, et al., 2012), and the original constructs (McDiarmid et al., 2006) are summarized in the best practice guidelines list at the end of the chapter.

Key Issues

Implementing programs in PsyR is, by nature, a complex process, and putting SEd into operation is no exception. A range of challenges has been described in the literature, some revealed by way of intentional investigation of the barriers, others by program evaluation, and still others more informally by observation and tracking of anecdotal evidence. The most frequently cited challenges include lack of funding, lack of coordination between service agencies and providers, lack of commitment from the educational institutions, and providers' lack of knowledge.

Funding

A singular lack of adequate funding for SEd programs and services has long presented an insidious barrier to implementation on every level. Federal mental health funding sources perceived SEd to be an educational intervention and therefore the responsibility of higher education or disability services funding sources. In contrast, educational funders classified SEd as a mental health program. This diffuse identity relegated SEd to an unfundable crevice that prevented any sort of well-organized implementation. On a state level, SEd services remained a hot potato, tossed between offices of vocational rehabilitation (VR) offices, disability services (DS), and mental health centers regarding payment and support roles.

These and related implementation barriers were documented in a joint study of SEd in the Netherlands and in Michigan (Mowbray, Korevaar, & Bellamy, 2002). In both locations, there were major barriers attributed to governmental bureaucracies. In Rotterdam, the Social Security system had insufficient flexibility to approve and pay for eligible students' courses in a timely manner. In Michigan, the state VR agency was often an impediment. Their polices typically discouraged funding for postsecondary classes in general courses such as liberal arts or basic academic preparation despite the fact that many of these courses were a prerequisite for the more skills-based or paraprofessional training courses (Mowbray et al., 2002).

As supported education has become more recognized, and the population (and visibility) of students with mental health needs has increased, the concomitant demand for more intensive services is being placed on disability services personnel daily. Consequently, colleges and universities are allocating more funding and resources to meet the increased needs, frequently through campus wide initiatives such as suicide prevention grants and programs that increase the mental health services for all students on campus.

Legislation

The advent of disability legislation such as the Rehabilitation Act of 1973, the 1990 Americans with Disabilities Act and their subsequent amendments ensure equal access for all aspects of academic life. The ADA mandates that places of public accommodation must provide protection from discrimination for and access to reasonable accommodations for otherwise qualified individuals with disabilities There are a number of technical terms associated with these laws, but essentially legislation mandates protection from discrimination and provision for reasonable disability accommodations (e.g., sign language interpreters, e-books, extended time on tests, or a proctored exam in a non-distracting environment). Campus accommodations for physical impairments provide a normalized blueprint for the adjustments needed to minimize the often invisible yet all-encompassing impairments created by psychiatric disorders. These accommodations are critical factors for students whose impairments have a disabling effect on academic functioning and have emerged as a key facilitator for success for many students with psychiatric disabilities on campus.

Accommodations require a formal request by the student backed by medical documentation on file with the campus disability services office. Academic accommodations for students with psychiatric disabilities include, for example, allowing beverages in class, extended time or proctored exams, and access to note takers (Sullivan-Soydan, 1997). These adjustments create "emotional ramps" instead of concrete ones; an elevator key or a parking pass provides access for someone who uses a wheelchair as well as for someone who risks emotional paralysis due to severe anxiety. Salzer et al. (2008) found that both current and former students with psychiatric disabilities received significant informal support from instructors without going through disability offices.

Academic accommodations for people with disabilities are designed to be negotiated in conjunction with the disability services provider, the student, and the faculty member. While the actual accommodation is not mandated, the student's right to some form of mitigation is and is invoked by the documentation of the disability by a medical expert. In each case, the documentation should provide a clear diagnosis (to be disclosed only to the disability services provider; not to the faculty) and describe the functional impact of the disability on college-related activities like participating in classes, doing homework, taking tests, and managing course loads (Shaw, Madaus, & Dukes 2009; Sullivan-Soydan, 2004).

Training and supervision of providers

The role of the supported education provider is a hybrid one, combining rehabilitation counselor, coach, case manager, and source of hope and inspiration. Providing specialized educational support services to people with psychiatric disabilities may require new knowledge about the policies, procedures, and requirements of post-secondary institutions and legislation and certainly involves the skilled use of mobile communication and other electronic software and equipment. Unger (2008) identifies some specific skills, including assessing strengths and needs, developing service plans, linking to, monitoring, and modifying services and accommodations, providing personal support and encouragement, and evaluating progress. In addition, important characteristics include advocacy skills and the experience of having been a successful student oneself. The role of peer provider is potentially a powerful one in the role of educational support; very often a student needs courage and moral support before or after an exam or some coaching about how to approach a faculty member or respond to questionable feedback. Regular clinical and administrative supervision of the supported education practitioner is essential for recognizing sensitive areas of interpersonal stress to prevent burnout and have access to information and knowledge to stay current.

NEW INITIATIVES

Some new and innovative drivers are changing the landscape of supported education, helping to bolster its implementation and keep it up to date.

Suicide Prevention on Campus

Suicide is a serious and persistent problem on college campuses across the country and has become much more prominent with the campus shootings in recent years. During the 1980s and 1990s, it was difficult to convince campus personnel that they had students with psychiatric disabilities on campus. Even when SEd funding was guaranteed, college presidents were not interested. That has changed. When suicide becomes homicide, the administration pays immediate attention. Long considered the second leading cause of death in young adults, a recent national survey of 1,361,304 college students (ACHA, 2012) identified suicide as the leading cause of death of college-age students. Observed annualize mortality rates per 100,000 students (with 95% confidence intervals) were 6.18 per 100,000 with estimates that approximately 1,350 college students take their own lives each year, roughly 3 young people a day (Eisenberg, 2012; Silverman, 2008). The National Strategy for Suicide Prevention calls more specifically for attention to the problem of college suicide and requests increasing "the proportion of colleges and universities with evidence-based programs designed to address serious young adult distress and prevent suicide" (USDHHS PHS, 2007, p. 66). The impact of this heightened awareness is attention and a new focus on campus mental health supports.

At Boston University, the Student Health Services (SHS) is part of the Healthy Minds Study, a research collaboration project at the University of Michigan that examines mental health issues among college students. Results from the 2006 Healthy Minds Study for Boston University (Eisenberg, 2006) documented that 53% of BU's undergraduate student body reported emotional and mental health difficulties that hurt their academic performance. The most recent annual survey in 2012 (Eisenberg, 2012), using a national sample of 25,000 students at 29 universities, revealed that depression and anxiety remain serious problems for 20 percent of the almost 1,696 BU respondents with 6 percent reporting serious thoughts of committing suicide in the past year. Of significance is the finding that there is a distinct increase in student requests for help. More than half (or 55 percent) of troubled students at BU are asking for and receiving help as opposed to 46 percent in the 2010 study (Eisenberg, 2009). Suicide prevention is not simply a one-time training or a part of orientation, but an essential part of the university's commitment to the well-being of its student body.

Since 2009, Boston University has been committed to college suicide prevention and mental health promotion through the implementation of a Garrett Lee Smith Campus Suicide Prevention Grant funded by the federal Substance Abuse Mental Health Services Administration. Through outreach and awareness activities, peer gatekeeper training, development of a mental health website, and support of student groups, Boston University has emerged as a national leader in campus suicide prevention. Obviously, the problem is not limited to Boston, nor is it going away; clearly suicide prevention is an unanticipated opportunity to improve the campus mental health environment and enrich support services on campuses across the country.

Teaching Challenges and Instructional Methods

Universal design is a natural corollary to the discussion of academic accommodations and the spirit of the disability law and so is briefly discussed here as a new development for use in the classroom. The philosophy of universal design of instruction (UDI; see, e.g., Burgstahler, 2011; McGuire & Scott, 2002) can best be understood in its conceptual origins in the accessibility of physical architecture and the structure of buildings. Ramps and wide doors, for example, accommodate people with mobility impairments, but also provide benefits to someone with a baby stroller or a rolling computer bag. In the classroom, universal design means that all aspects of course delivery and classroom instruction are aimed at students who potentially have broad ranges with respect to ability, disability, age, reading level, learning style, native language, race, ethnicity, and other characteristics.

In practice, UDI means creating a welcoming environment for everyone. The goal is to make content relevant, use multiple examples, implement a flexible curriculum that is organized, and use different styles of learning and assessment (e.g., offer writing assignments, exams, and projects).A detailed syllabus of semester topics, assignments, and due dates can help with executive functioning for all students. Providing multiple ways to demonstrate knowledge and using materials in accessible formats, such as e-textbooks and captioned videos, can improve access for all. For people with psychiatric disabilities who may be uncomfortable or inexperienced with class participation, using a simple rating scale with clearly specified behaviors for expected levels of participation can help to teach expectations as well as evaluate student contributions to class discussions. Universal instruction helps ensure that the course experience is tailored to all, but also, and most importantly, that the learning process is equivalent for any students needing accommodations.

New technology

Distance learning, which is an increasingly available option, is convenient, but offers advantages and disadvantages. Many classes, even those designed as on campus, use a blended approach and require the use of an online course management system, which means the challenges and opportunities offered by distance education also occur in on campus, face-to-face classes. Online classes or class supplements provide 24-hour access to course information, notes, and readings as well as easy access to the professor via email. Students can take the time needed to respond to asynchronous discussions online rather than being on-the-spot in a classroom discussion. Online classes may be isolating, though, and blended classes may have reduced face time with classmates and instructors. Due to limited resources, requiring a computer and online access (and the skills to use them) may limit participation by some people with psychiatric disabilities.

Computing and communications technology has been revolutionized in the last decade with an explosion of electronic devices to access the web, communicate, record, and assist with virtually all aspects of learning. Smart phones, tablet computers, and e-readers are in widespread use, providing instant access to a vast array of written and recorded material. Software applications for these devices abound and proliferate, allowing users to audio and video record easily, translate talk to text (and vice versa), track homework, organize calendars, communicate, and produce written documents and presentations with very little technological expertise. For some, however, the costs of such technology are prohibitive. In addition, while assistive technology continues to develop to provide new access to students, other advances in technology can create different access issues for students with disabilities. For example, although enrollment in online classes has grown exponentially over the past five years (Allen & Seaman, 2010), the access needs of students with learning disabilities have been virtually ignored in the development and implementation of these courses (Madaus, Banerjee, & McKeown, 2011). Ironically, the advances in assistive technology may be the cause of this as web and course designers believe that AT can take care of most access needs (Keeler & Horney, 2007). Furthermore, although Section 508 of the Rehabilitation Act mandates that institutional websites be accessible, research indicates that many are not (Erickson et al., 2009).

SUMMARY

The number of university students with serious mental illnesses continues to rise significantly as do the number of students with mental health problems and the severity of those problems. (Benton, Roberson, Tsen, Newton, & Benton, 2003; Gallagher, 2007). We need to build on what we know works and document the results. We need more evidence to establish the effectiveness of supported education and the factors that facilitate success for people with psychiatric disabilities in postsecondary education. Faculty, administrators, and staff must increase their awareness of the rights and needs of qualified students with psychiatric disabilities and take action in order for these students to feel welcomed and supported on campus and succeed in higher education, and ultimately, careers. Building on the battery of educational and social skills and supports that are required for academic success, we need to measure and document the postsecondary outcomes that result from providing supported education services. Increased knowledge and understanding of the needs, service use, and characteristics of these students is essential for good academic outcomes. Both quantitative and qualitative research is needed to disseminate knowledge to assist faculty and administrators in supporting these students while preserving academic standards and excellence and to eradicate stigma in the hopes that one day it will cease to persist as a major cause of discrimination and exclusion.

BEST PRACTICE GUIDELINES IN SUPPORTED EDUCATION

- Demonstrate a commitment to the supported education philosophy in program description materials and in the process of service delivery.
- Designate a supported education team or specialist.
- Base supported education program eligibility solely on desire to participate and having HS/GED degree, which is necessary for accessing post-secondary education.
- Offer supported education program services that match participant preferences.
- Use a specific supported education educational assessment and work with students to develop a person-centered supported education educational goal and plan.
- Ensure that supported education program activities are congruent with individual treatment plans and include confidence and knowledge building activities.
- Provide individualized enrollment supports and include encouragement.
- Communicate and collaborate with relevant others as needed and as desired by the student.

ABOUT THE AUTHOR

Anne Sullivan-Soydan, ScD is an Assistant Professor in the Department of Occupational Therapy, Sargent College of Health and Rehabilitation Sciences at Boston University. Dr. Sullivan-Soydan has extensive experience in the field of psychiatric rehabilitation and is the author of a number of articles, book chapters, and training manuals on supported education. She is a co-editor of *Supported Education: Models and Methods.* Other areas of interest and expertise include best practices in teaching, clinical supervision, suicide prevention, and eating disorders in people with psychiatric disorders. Anne has worked with the Center for Psychiatric Rehabilitation since 1985 doing supported education research, training, and service initiatives to assist young adults with psychiatric disabilities to return to college. She is also a member of the board of directors of the Massachusetts Psychiatric Rehabilitation Association, and co-chair of the MassPRA Training and Education Committee. A longtime member and past chair of the PRA Education and Training Committee, she directs the PRA preparation course for the CPRP exam several times a year, both online and at the national conference. A fulltime faculty member, her academic courses include abnormal psychology, counseling skills, and human development and disability across the lifespan. She was awarded a Mary Switzer post-doctoral fellowship from NIDRR to study the use of disability services by students with serious psychiatric disabilities on college campuses. Sullivan-Soydan has provided extensive training and technical assistance and is the author and editor of several publications in the areas of psychiatric rehabilitation, education, and mental health both nationally and internationally.

REFERENCES

Allen, I. E., & Seaman, J. (2010). *Learning on demand: Online education in the United States.* Babson Survey Research Group.

American College Health Association. (2010). *National College Health Assessment.* Retrieved on April 12, 2012 from http://www.acha.org

Baron, R. C., & Salzer, M. S. (2002). Accounting for unemployment among people with mental illness. *Behavioral Sciences & the Law, 20*(6), 585-599.

Becker, M., Martin, L., Wajeeh, E., Ward, J., & Shern, D. (2002). Students with mental illnesses in a university setting: Faculty and student attitudes, beliefs, knowledge, and experiences. *Psychiatric Rehabilitation Journal, 25*(4), 359-368.

Benton, S. A., Robertson, J. M., Tseng, W., Newton, F. B., & Benton, S. L. (2003). Changes in counseling center client problems across 13 years. *Professional Psychology: Research and Practice, 34,* 66-72.

Bertram, M., & Howard, L. (2006). Employment status and occupational care planning for people using mental health services. *Psychiatric Bulletin, 30,* 48-51.

Best, L. J., Still, M., & Cameron, G. (2008). Supported education: Enabling course completion for people experiencing mental illness. *Australian Occupational Therapy Journal, 55*(1), 65-68.

Blacklock, B., Benson, B., Johnson, D., & Bloomberg L. (2003). *Needs assessment project: Exploring barriers and opportunities for college students with psychiatric disabilities.* Minneapolis, MN: University of Minnesota, Disability Services.

Brackney, B., & Karabenick, S. (1995). Psychopathology and academic performance. *Journal of Counseling Psychology, 42,* 456-465.

Brockelman, K. F., Chadsey, J. G., & Loeb, J. (2006). Faculty perceptions of university students with psychiatric disabilities. *Psychiatric Rehabilitation Journal, 30*(1), 23-30.

Brockelman, K. F. (2009). The interrelationship of self-determination, mental illness, and grades among university students. *Journal of College Student Development, 50*(3), 271-286.

Burgstahler, S. (2011). Universal design: Implications for computing education. *ACM Transactions on Computing Education, 11*(3), Article 19. doi 10.1145/2037276.2037283.

Byrne, P. (2000). Stigma of mental illness and ways of diminishing it. *Advances in Psychiatric Treatment, 6,* 65-72.

Collins, M. E., & Mowbray, C. (2005). Higher education and psychiatric disabilities: National survey of campus disability services. *American Journal of Orthopsychiatry, 75*(2), 304-315.

Collins, M. E., Bybee, D., & Mowbray, C. T. (1998). Effectiveness of supported education for individuals with psychiatric disabilities: Results from an experimental study. *Community Mental Health Journal, 34,* 595-613.

Collins, M. E., Mowbray C. T., & Bybee, D. (1999). Establishing individualized goals in a supported education intervention: Program influences on goal-setting and attainment. *Research on Social Work Practice, 9,* 483-507.

Collins, M. E., Mowbray, C. T., & Bybee, D. (2000). Characteristics predicting successful outcomes of participants with severe mental illness in supported education. *Psychiatric Services, 51,* 774-780.

Collins, M. E., & Mowbray, C. T. (2008). Students with psychiatric disabilities on campus: Examining predictors of enrollment with disability support services. *Journal of Postsecondary Education and Disability, 21*(2), 91-104.

Cook, J. A., & Solomon, M. L. (1993). The community scholar program: An outcome study of supported education for students with severe mental illness. *Psychosocial Rehabilitation Journal, 17*(1), 83-97.

Corrigan, P. W. (2008). The educational goals of people with psychiatric disabilities. *Psychiatric Rehabilitation Journal, 32,* 67-70.

Corrigan, P. W., & Lundin, R. K. (2001). *Don't call me nuts! Coping with the stigma of mental illness.* Tinley Park, IL: Recovery Press.

Dalke, C. (1993). Making a successful transition from high school to college: A model program. In S. A. Vogel & P. B. Adelman (Eds.), *Success for college students with learning disabilities* (pp. 57-79). New York: Springer-Verlag.

Dobson, K. S., & Kendall, P. C. (Eds.). (1993). *Psychopathology and cognition.* San Diego, CA: Freeman.

DRRK Disability Research. (2010). *Systematic review of supported education literature 1989-2009.* Boston, MA: Boston University Center for Psychiatric Rehabilitation.

Eisenberg, D. (2006). *Healthy Mind Study 2006 school report.* Prepared for Boston University. Ann Arbor, MI: The Center for Student Studies at Survey Sciences Group.

Eisenberg, D. (2009). *Healthy Mind Study 2009 school report.* Prepared for Boston University. Ann Arbor, MI: The Center for Student Studies at Survey Sciences Group.

Eisenberg, D. (2012). *Healthy Mind Study 2012 school report.* Prepared for Boston University. Ann Arbor, MI: The Center for Student Studies at Survey Sciences Group.

Eisenberg, D., Golberstein, E., & Gollust, S.E. (2007). Help-seeking and access to mental health care in a university student population. *Medical Care, 45*(7), 594-601.

Erickson, W., Trerise, S., VanLooy, S., Lee, C., & Bruyere, S. (2009). Web accessibility policies and practices at American community colleges. *Community College Journal of Research Practice, 33*(5), 403-14.

Gallagher R. (2007). *National survey of counseling center directors 2007.* Alexandria, VA: International Association of Counseling Services, Inc. Retrieved on April 24, 2012 from: http://www.iacsinc.org/NsccdSurveyFinal_v2.pdf

Garrett Lee Smith Memorial Act, S. 2634, 108th Cong. (2004).

Hartley, M. T. (2010). Increasing resilience: Strategies for reducing dropout rates for college students with psychiatric disabilities. *American Journal of Psychiatric Rehabilitation, 13*(4), 295-213.

Hefner, J., & Eisenberg, D. (2009). Social support and mental health among college students. *The American Journal of Orthopsychiatry, 79*(4), 491-499.

Heiligenstein, E., Guenther, G., Hsu, K., & Herman, K. (1996). Depression and academic impairment in college students. *Journal of American College Health, 45,* 59-64.

Hembree, R. (1988). Correlates, causes, effects, and treatment of test anxiety. *Review of Educational Research, 58,* 47-77.

Hoffman, F. L., & Mastrianni, X. (1993). The role of supported education in the inpatient treatment of young adults: A two-site comparison. *Psychosocial Rehabilitation Journal, 17*(3), 109-119.

Kadison, R. D., & DiGeronimo, T. F. (2004). *College of the overwhelmed: The campus mental health crisis and what to do about it.* San Francisco, CA: Jossey-Bass.

Keeler, C. G., & Horney, M. (2007). Online course designs: Are special needs being met? *American Journal of Distance Education, 21*(2), 61-75.

Kessler, R. C., Berglund, P., Demler, O., Jin, R., Merikangas, K. R., & Walters, E. E. (2005). Lifetime prevalence and age-of-onset distributions of DSM-IV disorders in the National Comorbidity Survey Replication. *Archives of General Psychiatry, 62*(6), 593-602.

Kessler, R. C., Foster, C. L., Saunders, W. B., & Stang, P. E. (1995). Social consequences of psychiatric disorders, I: Educational attainment. *American Journal of Psychiatry, 152*(7), 1026-1032.

Knis-Matthews, L., Bokara, J., DeMeo, L., Lepore, N., & Mavus, L. (2007). The meaning of higher education for people diagnosed with a mental illness: Four students share their experiences. *Psychiatric Rehabilitation Journal, 31,* 107-114.

Kuh, G. D., Kinzie, J., Buckley, J. A., Bridges, B. K., & Hayek, J. C. (2006). What matters to student success: A review of the literature. Draft commissioned report for the National Symposium on Postsecondary Student Success: Spearheading a Dialogue on Student Success. Washington, DC: National Postsecondary Education Cooperative, 2006. Retrieved April 12, 2012 from http://nces.ed.gov/npec/pdf

Link, B. G., Yang, L. H., Phelan, J. C., & Collins, P. Y. (2004). Measuring mental illness stigma. *Schizophrenia Bulletin, 30*(3), 511-541.

Madaus, J. W., Banerjee, M., McKeown, K. (2011). Online and blended learning: The opportunities and the challenges for students with learning disabilities and attention deficit/hyperactivity disorder. *Learning Disabilities: A Multidisciplinary Journal, 17*(2), 69-76.

Masten, A. S. (2001). Ordinary magic. *American Psychologist, 56,* 227-238.

Manthey, T., Coffman, M., Goscha, R., Bond, G., Mabry, A., Carlson, L., Davis, J., & Rapp, C. (2012). *The University of Kansas Supported Education Fidelity Scale 3.0.* Lawrence, KS: The Office of Mental Health Research and Training, The University of Kansas School of Social Welfare.

McDiarmid, D., Rapp, C., Holter, M., Dykes, D., & Ratzlaff, S. (2006). *The University of Kansas Supported Education Fidelity Scale.* Lawrence, KS: The Office of Mental Health Research and Training, The University of Kansas School of Social Welfare.

McGuire, J., & Scott, S. (2002). Universal Design for Instruction: A promising new paradigm for higher education. *Perspectives, 28*(2), 27-29.

Megivern, D., Pellerito, S., & Mowbray, C. (2003). Barriers to higher education for individuals with psychiatric disabilities. *Psychiatric Rehabilitation Journal, 26*(3), 217-231.

Mowbray C. T., Collins, M. E., & Bybee, D. (1999). Supported education for individuals with psychiatric disabilities: Long-term outcomes from an experimental study. *Social Work Research, 23,* 89-100.

Mowbray, C. T., Mandiberg, J. M., Strauss, S., Stein, C. H., Collins, K. D., Kopels, S., et al. (2006). Campus mental health services: Recommendations for change. *American Journal of Orthopsychiatry, 76,* 226-237.

Mowbray, C. T., Megivern, D., & Holter, M. C. (2003). Supported education programming for adults with psychiatric disabilities: Results from a national survey. *Psychiatric Rehabilitation Journal, 27,* 159-167.

Mowbray, C. T., Korevaar, L., & Bellamy, C.D. (2002). Supported education: An innovation in psychiatric rehabilitation practice. *Canadian Journal of Community Mental Health, 21*(2), 111-129.

Mowbray, C. T., Strauch-Brown, K., Furlong-Norman, K., & Sullivan-Soydan, A. P. (Eds.). (2002). *Supported education: Models and methods.* Linthicum, MD: International Association of Psychosocial Rehabilitation Services.

Mowbray, C. T., & Collins, M.E. (2002). The effectiveness of supported education: Current research findings. In C. T. Mowbray, K.S., Brown, K., Furlong-Norman, & A. P. Sullivan-Soydan (Eds.), *Supported education and psychiatric rehabilitation: Models and methods* (pp. 181-194). Linthicum, MD: International Association of Psychosocial Rehabilitation Services.

Mullen-Gonzalez, M., & Gill, K. J. (in preparation). *Preliminary findings of a multi-site randomized controlled study of supported education.* Unpublished manuscript. Department of Psychiatric Rehabilitation and Counseling Professions, Rutgers University, Scotch Plains, NJ.

Murphy, A. A., Mullen, M. G., & Spagnolo, A. B. (2005). Enhancing individual placement and support: Promoting job tenure by integrating natural supports and supported education. *American Journal of Psychiatric Rehabilitation, 8,* 37-61.

Nolan, J. M., Ford, J. W., Kress, V.E., Anderson, R. I., & Novak, T. C. (2005). A comprehensive model for addressing severe and persistent mental illness on campuses. *Journal of College Counseling, 8,* 172-179.

Oliver, J. M., Reed, K. S., & Smith, B. W. (1998). Patterns of psychological problems in university undergraduates: Factor structure of symptoms of anxiety and depression, physical symptoms, alcohol use, and eating problems. *Social Behavior Personality, 26,* 211-232.

President's New Freedom Commission on Mental Health. (2003). *Achieving the promise: Transforming mental health care in America, final report.* No. Pub. No. SMA-03-3832. Rockville, MD: U.S. Department of Health and Human Services.

Salkever, D. S., Karakus, M. C., Slade, E. P., Harding, C. M., Hough, R. L., Rosenheck, R. A., Swartz, M. S., Barrio, C., & Yamada, A. M. (2007). Measures and predictors of community-based employment and earnings of person with schizophrenia in a multisite study. *Psychiatric Services, 58*(3), 315-324.

Substance Abuse and Mental Health Services Administration (2012) *Supported education evidence-based practices (EBP) Kit.* Publication No. SMA11-4654CD-ROM. Retrieved on March 22, 2103 from http://store.samhsa.gov/product/Supported-Education-Evidence-Based-Practices-EBP-Kit/ SMA11-4654CD-ROM

Salzer, M. S., Wick, L. C., & Rogers, J. A. (2008). Familiarity with and use of accommodations and supports among postsecondary students with mental illnesses. *Psychiatric Services, 59,* 370-375.

Salzer, M. S. (2011). A comparative study of campus experiences of college students with mental illness versus a general college sample. *Journal of American College Health, 60*(1), 1-7.

Shaw, S. F., Madaus, J. W., & Dukes, L. L. (2009). *Preparing students with disabilities for college success: A practical guide to transition planning.* Baltimore, MD: Brookes Publishing Company.

Silverman, M. M. (2008, April). *Turning violence inward: Understanding and preventing campus suicide.* Presented to Violence on Campus: Prediction, Prevention, and Response, Columbia University Law School, New York, NY.

Stein, C. H. (2005). Aspirations, ability and support: Consumers' perceptions of attending college. *Community Mental Health Journal, 41,* 451-468.

Sullivan-Soydan, A. P. (2004). Supported education: A portrait of a psychiatric rehabilitation intervention. *American Journal of Psychiatric Rehabilitation, 7,* 227-248.

Sullivan-Soydan, A. P. (1997). *Frequently asked questions by educators about students with psychiatric disabilities: Tips and resources on the Rehabilitation Act, ADA, academic adjustments, and support.* Boston, MA: Boston University, Center for Psychiatric Rehabilitation.

Surgeon General of the United States. (1999). *The Surgeon General's call to action to prevent suicide.* Washington, DC: United States Department of Health and Human Services, Public Health Service.

Svanum, S., & Zody, Z. (2001). Psychopathology and college grades. *Journal of Counseling Psychology, 48,* 72-76.

Tagayuna, A., Stodden, R. A., Chang, C., et al (2005). A two-year comparison of support provision for persons with disabilities in postsecondary education. *Journal of Vocational Rehabilitation, 22,* 13-21.

Unger, K. V. (1990). Supported postsecondary education for people with mental illness. *American Rehabilitation, 16,* 10-14.

Unger, K. V. (1993). Creating supported education programs utilizing existing community resources. *Psychosocial Rehabilitation Journal, 17*(1), 11-23.

Unger, K. V., & Pardee, R. (2002). Outcome measures across program sites for postsecondary supported education programs. *Psychiatric Rehabilitation Journal, 25*(3), 299-303.

Unger, K. V., Pardee, R., & Shafer, M. S. (2000). Outcomes of postsecondary supported education programs for people with psychiatric disabilities. *Journal of Vocational Rehabilitation, 14*(3), 195-199.

Unger, K. V., Anthony, W. A., Sciarappa, K., & Rogers, E. S. (1991). A supported education program for young adults with long-term mental illness. *Hospital and Community Psychiatry, 42,* 838-842.

U.S. Department of Health and Human Services. (2007). *PHS: National strategy for suicide prevention: Goals and objectives for action.* Rockville, MD: Author.

U.S. Department of Labor. Employment projections: Education pays. Bureau of Labor Statistics, Current Population Survey. Retrieved May 10, 2013 from http://www.bls.gov/emp/ep_chart_001.htm

Warwick, I., Maxwell, C., Statham, J., Aggleton, P., & Simon, A. (2008). Supporting mental health and emotional well-being among younger students in further education. *Journal of Further and Higher Education, 32,* 1-13.

Weiner, E., & Wiener, J. (1996). Concerns and needs of university students with psychiatric disabilities. *Journal of Postsecondary Education & Disability, 12,* 2-9.

Weiner, E., & Wiener, J. (1997). University students with psychiatric illness: Factors involved in the decision to withdraw from their studies. *Psychiatric Rehabilitation Journal, 20,* 88-91.

Yahaya, A., Ramli, J., Hashim, S., & Ibrahim, M. A. (2009) Analysis of students with psychiatric disabilities in higher education. *Journal of Social Sciences, 5*(4), 362-369.

CHAPTER 13

WELLNESS

Dori Hutchinson
Margaret Swarbrick

ABSTRACT

Psychiatric rehabilitation practice is well positioned to support wellness and health. The design and delivery of services can be aligned to help people acquire knowledge, skills, and support so they can live, learn, and work in their communities while developing and maintaining optimal health. This chapter outlines the underpinnings of wellness, whole health, and health promotion models. Promising innovative wellness practices (or approaches), including wellness coaching, health promotion programs, and whole health and integration models are presented. Challenges, concerns, possibilities, and practical suggestions for programs, practices, and the workforce are reviewed.

PREMATURE DEATH RATES FOR PEOPLE LIVING WITH PSYCHIATRIC DISABILITIES HAVE RISEN dramatically in the United States over the last twenty years from an average of 10-15 years to, now, 25 lost years of life (Parks, Svendsen, Singer, Foti, & Mauer, 2006). Sixty percent of premature deaths not related to suicide are due to conditions including ischemic heart disease, pulmonary disease, and metabolic disorders (Joukamaa, Heliovaara, & Knekt, 2001; Lambert, Velakoulis, & Pantelis, 2003; Lawrence, Holman, Jablensky, & Hobbs, 2003). People with psychiatric disabilities are at much higher risk than the general public for developing substance abuse disorders and are at higher risk for HIV infection and AIDS (Razzano, 2005; McKinnon, Wainberg, & Cournos, 2001). Many are dying from preventable health conditions at an accelerated rate compared to individuals without a mental illness diagnosis. Co-occurring medical conditions and early mortality are significantly impacting the recovery trajectory of many people being served by psychiatric rehabilitation practitioners.

Americans who live with psychiatric disabilities experience the largest health disparity in the United States (Center for Mental Health Services, 2010). There are a variety of factors contributing to this health disparity. One disturbing issue is that many people encounter an array of serious adverse health consequences induced or accelerated by atypical antipsychotic medications (Allison, Mackell, & McDonnell, 2003; Meltzer, 2005; Meyer & Nasrallah, 2003; Whitaker, 2010). Additionally, many receive less (or poorer quality) primary and preventive health care than the general population, and they are generally high users of expensive emergency room services (Folsom, McCahill, Bartels, Lindamer, Ganiats, & Jeste, 2002; Goldberg, Seybolt, & Lehman, 2002). Some choose not to seek necessary medical care due to fear of coercive treatment or commitment to a psychiatric facility or lack of adequate insurance (Hahm & Segal, 2005).

These health conditions interfere with people's capacity to work, love, learn, and live well in their communities. Far too often, an individual with psychiatric illness dies an untimely death due to a heart attack or various complications of diabetes. Crushing poverty, lack of access to health education, lack of access to healthy and affordable choices and environments, polypharmacy, and pervasive, entrenched health beliefs all conspire to negatively impact the lives of people with psychiatric conditions.

In September 2007, the Center for Mental Health Services sponsored a National Wellness Summit for People with Mental Illness (CMHS, 2010). The summit gathered together a broad range of stakeholders to develop plans to deal with the considerably shortened life expectancy and reduced quality of life associated with living with a serious mental illness. Three targets areas of work for the field of psychiatric rehabilitation were identified: data and surveillance, education and training, and policy and practice. The wellness pledge developed in the summit is:

> We envision a future in which people with mental illnesses pursue optimal health, happiness, recovery, and a full and satisfying life in the community via access to a range of effective services, supports, and resources.
>
> We pledge to promote wellness for people with mental illnesses by taking action to prevent and reduce early mortality by 10 years over the next 10-year time period.

Putting the pledge into practice requires that practitioners grapple with difficult issues, (Swarbrick 2010), including identifying what service providers and service users need to know to make this pledge a reality; how we get and disseminate that knowledge; how we help everyone involved implement a wellness focus on an individual level, and at the same time, support organizational efforts and initiatives; how we deal with conflicts that may arise between an existing medically oriented service approach and one focused on wellness; how we help people with psychiatric disabilities overcome years of poor health habits that have resulted in disability and health risk factors; and how we help every member of the psychiatric rehabilitation community overcome a history of being encouraged to place more importance on symptom management than on wellness.

There is a growing recognition that the field must now, more than ever, provide person-centered, integrated, and holistic services to address the identified health concerns. There are changes and challenges ahead for psychiatric rehabilitation (PsyR) practice to meet the total health needs of peers who face numerous social inequities (under and unemployment, poverty, prejudice, etc.) in addition to having or being at risk of developing co-occurring mental health and medical conditions. We must re-examine practices and embrace a framework of wellness in our programs. We must assert that people with psychiatric disabilities have a right to optimal health.

PsyR practice is well positioned to support wellness and health. The design and delivery of services can be aligned to help people acquire knowledge, skills, and support so they can live, learn, and work in their communities while developing and maintaining optimal health. This chapter outlines the underpinnings of wellness, whole health, and health promotion models. Promising innovative wellness practices (or approaches) are described, including wellness coaching (Swarbrick, Hutchinson, & Gill, 2008; Swarbrick, Murphy, Zechner, Spagnolo, & Gill, 2011), health promotion programs (Hutchinson, 2011), and whole health and integration models. Challenges, concerns, and possibilities are reviewed, along with practical suggestions for programs, practices, and the workforce.

WELLNESS DEFINED

In response to the fierce urgency for change resulting from the high mortality and co-morbidity rates, paired with a strong belief in mental health recovery, innovative programs and practices have emerged that promote whole health and wellness. Wellness, whole health, and health promotion are important concepts in PsyR practice.

Wellness involves the total individual—body, mind, and spirit—within an ever-changing environment and flow of events (Dunn, 1961, 1977). It is oriented toward maximizing the individual's potential within the environment (Dunn, 1961, 1977). Wellness is a dynamic, ongoing, active process of becoming aware of and making choices towards a satisfying lifestyle. It is often characterized by creating and sustaining a lifestyle that includes a self-defined balance of health habits, such as adequate sleep/rest, nutrition, exercise, partici-pation in meaningful productive activity, adequate social contact, and supportive relationships (Swarbrick, 1997, 2006). An individual defines, creates, and adapts patterns of behavior that may or may not lead to balance and satisfaction.

The 8 Dimensions

The key to achieving wellness is finding a balance by establishing and maintaining healthy habits and routines in these eight dimensions.

Physical: Areas within the physical dimension include nutrition and food choices, physical activity and exercise, smoking cessation, and stress management—recognizing physical symptoms of stress and stress reduction via physical activity and self-care. To address this dimension, a person creates and sustains a self-defined balanced routine (e.g., adequate sleep and rest, walking, moderate levels of activity and productivity to promote health and counteract negative stress responses). This requires knowing how to care for minor illnesses, knowing when professional medical attention is needed, and serving as an informed and active partner in one's own healthcare team for acute and long-term health conditions and preventive care.

Spiritual: This dimension represents a broad concept that encompasses one's personal beliefs and values and recognizes our search for meaning and purpose in human existence and includes the development of a deep appreciation for the depth and expanse of life and natural forces that exist in the universe.

Emotional: In addition to the capacity to manage one's feelings, the emotional dimension includes the realistic assessment of one's limitations and the ability to cope effectively with pain, stress, and adversity. People who are "well" in this dimension show the ability to live and work independently, while realizing the importance of seeking and appreciating the support and assistance of others. They have the ability to take on challenges, take risks, and recognize conflict as being potentially healthy. Emotional wellness also involves self-acceptance and contentment in pursuit of daily activities.

Social: Connection with others is an important part of being human, and achieving social wellness means contributing to the environment and community and recognizing the interdependence between others and nature, along with our ability to communicate with those around us, our personal relationships, important friendships, and connections to the larger community. Social wellness includes family relationships, romantic and intimate relationships, and sexual activity of one's choice.

Occupation and Leisure: Wellness in this dimension requires an opportunity to participate in activities that are meaningful, rewarding, and make the individual feel that s/he has unique gifts, skills, and talents to contribute. Occupational wellness means finding and participating in activities that are in line with personal values, interests, and beliefs. For most, occupational wellness includes choosing, getting, and keeping a competitive job.

Intellectual: In addition to formal education, lifelong learning, and passing one's knowledge on to others, intellectual wellness includes creative abilities and expanding our knowledge and skills while discovering the potential for sharing those gifts with others.

Financial: Wellness in this dimension refers to subjective perceptions and objective indicators of individuals' personal financial status. Objective indicators of financial circum-stances include measures such as income, debt, savings, and aspects of financial literacy including knowledge of financial products and services, planning ahead, and staying on budget. Subjective perceptions include individuals' satisfaction with their current and future financial situation.

Environmental: Where we spend our time influences how we feel, including our living, learning, and working spaces and the larger communities where we participate as citizens. Wellness in the environmental dimension involves recognition that PsyR practice environments can support or deplete a person's wellness. Light, fresh air, cleanliness, fragrances, sound, temperature, posted messages, and colors are important considerations in creating healthy environments.

EMERGING BEST PRACTICES

With recognition of the need to improve physical wellness for people with psychiatric disabilities, traditional approaches for improving health are being adapted, and innovative approaches are being developed and studied. These include health promotion and disease prevention, the establishment of health and wellness centers, coaching and educational strategies, and integrated care.

Health Promotion

Health promotion is a process of enhancing wellness through education, guidance, and support that contributes to positive behavioral change. It involves empowering people to assume responsibility for their own individual, healthy lifestyle patterns. Prevention is designed to promote health and to avoid health problems before they start. Secondary prevention is the early recognition of problems in an effort to halt disease development or progression. By identifying underlying causes and changing contributing behaviors, PsyR practitioners can influence health outcomes. Many untimely deaths and hospitalizations in the U.S. are linked to largely preventable behaviors, such as tobacco use, alcohol abuse, sedentary lifestyle, and overeating.

Recovery and wellness education is a practical solution to assist people in developing improved functional health. Classes on food education, stress hardiness, supported physical activity, sexuality and intimacy, mindfulness techniques, tobacco cessation, and health literacy teach important knowledge and skills that assist people in making informed decisions about their wellness (Hutchinson, 2011). These types of classes are easily integrated into traditional group services and schedules. Some insurance companies and state Medicaid systems will reimburse for health promotion and prevention services if they are provided within the context of medical necessity. Healthcare system reforms will continue to increase opportunities to engage in prevention and wellness services.

Health promotion and prevention campaigns target lifestyle habits with the goal of preventing disease and associated disabilities, such as focusing on establishing healthy habits and using strategies to prevent recurrence of acute episodes. PsyR principles and practices are congruent with health promotion; both acknowledge the need to individualize services to unique health needs and personal goals, and appreciate individuals' capacity for self-determining their own health promotion activities (Hutchinson, Gagne, Bowers, Russinova, Skrinar, & Anthony, 2006). Relevant principles include: (1) Health promotion recognizes the *potential* for health and wellness; (2) *active participation* in health promotion activities is ideal; (3) health education is the cornerstone of health promotion; and (4) health promotion addresses the characteristics of the environments in which people live, learn, and work (Hutchinson et al., 2006).

Health and Wellness Centers

Health and wellness centers are an emerging program model that has been successfully implemented to assist individuals in gaining health knowledge and skills. These centers offer programs designed to provide targeted wellness interventions that include comprehensive wellness and health literacy classes, physical activity interventions, nutritional courses, and healthy meals. Staffing is diverse and represents multiple perspectives, including psychiatric rehabilitation, nursing, social work, medicine, exercise physiology, psychology, and nutrition.

Many staff members have had personal experiences as users of the mental health system and are trained as health coaches, recovery education facilitators, and certified fitness instructors.

The Center for Psychiatric Rehabilitation in Boston developed a pilot health and wellness center known as Hope and Health in 2004. The Hope and Health program was a health promotion program designed to enhance the functional health of persons who lived with and were under medical and psychiatric treatment for both a psychiatric illness and a secondary medical condition. The aim of this program was to increase participants' knowledge, skills, attitudes, and helpful beliefs about their health and health promotion practices. There were two phases to the program: a 16-week educational program and a 16-week partnership with a wellness coach who provided community support to help participants implement their new lifestyle practices into their daily lives.

During the first phase of the program, people with psychiatric disabilities attended classes four days a week from 10 a.m. to 3 p.m. Interventions included physical activity, food education, illness management and recovery education, and health literacy education. The second phase of the program provided wellness coaching by providers who had psychiatric disabilities as well as staff without psychiatric disabilities. Wellness coaching helped participants implement their newly learned skills through weekly meetings, which supported access to community health resources, such as YMCAs and affordable food stores, and provided motivational support for continuing daily physical activity, shopping for, cooking and eating healthy foods, and practicing healthy coping skills.

The program evaluation data demonstrated that the Hope and Health participants experienced significant positive changes in their physical activity levels and in their eating habits. Perceptions of health responsibility, stress management, illness management, personal confidence, and hope were all positively impacted. The program also served to help individuals develop readiness to engage in other community programs and services that promoted healthy role functioning. Individuals went on to participate in programs that promote physical activity (e.g., the local YMCA), educational programs (e.g., community college), part-time employment, community diabetes management programs, and recovery education programs (St. Pierre, 2008). This wellness program was then successfully implemented in four-day treatment centers in Massachusetts in an effort to provide wellness programming through an outpatient hospitalization model of care.

Camp Wellness

The Hope and Health program model has been adapted in Tucson, AZ, in a unique collaboration between the University of Arizona's Recovery through Integration, Support and Empowerment program (RISE), the UA Department of Family and Community Medicine, and the Behavioral Health Community Partnership of Southern Arizona, which is funded by the Arizona Department of Health Services, the state Medicaid program, and the Substance Abuse and Mental Health Services Administration (SAMHSA). These groups have combined expertise and resources to develop a free-standing community health program for individuals in recovery. The health and wellness center, known as Camp Wellness, is a nine-week full-time program that seeks to increase the health knowledge, skills, and health status of adults who are eligible for state Medicaid funds and have a diagnosis of a serious mental illness. Individuals are referred by case managers and attend four days a week from 10 a.m. to 4 p.m. They enrolled as students and participate in daily hour-long classes in food education, cooking skills, supported physical activity, health education, mindfulness, stress management, and tobacco-free lifestyle education. Health mentors, who are people with psychiatric disabilities, also teach the courses and provide peer support in the community once the program ends.

The program actively promotes wellness as a resource for recovery and then assists participants in beginning to not only contemplate change, but to make small changes to improve their health. Students have the opportunity to practice newly learned skills with support from their health mentors. Other staff members, who educate, support, and direct the program, include Certified Psychiatric Rehabilitation Practitioners, a registered nurse and rehabilitation counseling educator, a family physician, and a public health specialist. Camp Wellness is financially self-sustaining with all provided services billed as Medicaid reimbursable encounters. Program evaluation data suggests that students are losing weight, moving more, choosing healthier options, and feeling hopeful about their recovery.

In Shape

Another wellness program that has been successfully implemented both programmatically and financially is the InShape Program at Monadnock Family Services in Concord, NH. The InShape pilot program, initially funded through the Robert Wood Johnson Foundation's local funding Partners Program, involved 300 participants in 35 towns in New Hampshire. This program matched a person with a wellness trainer and a health club membership in the person's community. Participants worked with their trainers in supported exercise and learned about diet modifications to improve their overall physical fitness. Program evaluation of InShape indicated that physical and mental health improved for program participants (Shiner, Whitley, Van Citters, Pratt, & Bartels, 2008). Monadnock Family Services expanded InShape to other communities through replication and adaptation.

In February 2009, two mental health centers, the Providence Center in Rhode Island and the Genesee County Community Mental Health Center in Flint, Michigan, engaged with Monadnock Family Services in a year-long training process to become certified InShape providers. In addition, the state of New Hampshire approved Medicaid reimbursement of InShape services. InShape has demonstrated that people who participate in the program significantly increase their activity levels and lose weight.

Coaching and Educational Strategies

Several approaches have been developed for helping people set and achieve wellness goals. These include both group- and individual-oriented strategies and share a person-centered process built on the value of self-determination.

Peer Support Whole Health

The Peer Support Whole Health (PSWH) training was developed by Appalachian Consulting Group and the Georgia Mental Health Consumer Network as part of a federal grant. Some of the tools used in the training have been adapted from the Health and Recovery Peer Project, based on the Chronic Disease Self-Management Program developed at Stanford University, and the Relaxation Response Program from the Benson-Henry Institute for Mind-Body Medicine at Massachusetts General Hospital.

PSWH is a person-centered planning process that helps participants examine their health life-style; focus on their strengths, interests and natural supports; and create and sustain personally defined healthier lifestyle habits and disciplines. The training is offered for peer specialists to enable them to help someone choose, get, and keep a whole health goal. PSWH is built on the premise that people should not be forced or coerced into changing their unhealthy lifestyle habits; rather they should be supported in examining their interests and strengths and cultivating supports for long lasting positive changes. The program helps people create new habits through meeting on a weekly basis and helps them gain the support needed to facilitate effective changes. The PSWH program focuses on the health lifestyle domains of healthy eating, physical activity, restful sleep, stress management/relaxation response, service to others, and support network.

Peer wellness coach

Faculty in the department of Psychiatric Rehabilitation and Counseling Professions at the University of Medicine and Dentistry of New Jersey, School of Health Related Professions, and peers at Collaborative Support Programs of New Jersey worked together to create a new workforce role, a peer wellness coach (Swarbrick, Murphy, Zechner, Spagnolo, & Gill, 2011). In this peer wellness coach model, peers apply the principles and processes of coaching, effective communication skills, and motivational enhancement strategies to helping an individual achieve the goal of lifestyle improvement for higher levels of wellness. There is a specific focus on the relevant physical wellness as areas that often represent a challenge for people with psychiatric disabilities, including low levels of physical activity and a sedentary lifestyle, nutrition and dietary education, diet and glucose monitoring for diabetes prevention and management, oral hygiene and dental health practices, reduction or elimination of tobacco use and other addictive substances, and HIV/AIDS education.

Peers learn to collaborate and act as coaches, helping to guide people toward successful and long-lasting behavioral change (Swarbrick, Hutchinson, & Gill, 2008). Wellness coaches provide ongoing individualized support and reinforcement. A coach supports other peers in setting and achieving their goals. The coach helps each participant to find his or her own solutions by asking questions that promote insight into his or her situation. A coach holds the individual accountable so that if s/he agrees to a plan to achieve a goal, a coach will help build the motivation needed to complete the plan. A coach uses a variety of methods tailored to the individual to move through the process of setting and reaching goals. The wellness coach guides the peer toward successful and durable behavioral change. Coaching strategies and other communication skills are used to help set and achieve wellness goals.

Although initially developed as a peer-provided service, the wellness coaching approach is being adapted to train non-peer service providers, who then incorporate wellness coaching into their role, and as desired by people using services, include wellness goals and wellness plans into the larger service planning process.

Healthy Changes Initiative

The Massachusetts Department of Mental Health (Mass DMH) has recognized the essential role of wellness in recovery from psychiatric illness, and in light of the significant risk of early death and significant disabling illness among people they serve, Mass DMH established the Healthy Changes Initiative (http://www.mass.gov/eohhs/consumer/behavioral-health/mental-health/healthy-changes.html). The mission of the Healthy Changes Initiative is to improve the quality of life, health, and wellness of individuals at risk for illness and premature death and eliminate the significant health disparity among individuals with serious mental illness. Taking a multi-level approach, Mass DMH has infused wellness into their programs in a variety of ways. Health education is provided in all programs with a focus on providing information and skills to improve health literacy and to support nicotine cessation, weight management, and physical activity. Under this initiative, environmental modifications that support wellness have been made at Mass DMH programs, such as providing access to fitness equipment, bike paths, and walking trails; and offering healthy choices in vending machines. Programs use motivational interventions to promote behavioral and cultural change and have hired peer wellness coaches to teach and inspire peers to develop healthy lifestyles.

Healthcare Reform and Integrated Care

Healthcare reform is underway to ensure that all Americans have access to quality healthcare although how best to accomplish this (and fund it) is an ongoing debate. There is a strong need for the comprehensive integration of physical and mental health care as well as prioritizing holistic health promotion services that can prevent the onset of serious and costly medical co-morbidity (Koyanagi, 2004). The Center for Integrated Health Solutions, a collaborative partnership between SAMHSA and the federal Health Resources Services Administration (HRSA), funded a primary and behavioral health care integration program. This initiative aimed to improve the health status of people with psychiatric disabilities by supporting coordination and integration of primary care services in 55 publically funded community-based behavioral health settings across the U.S. Services included enhanced screenings and referrals as well as wellness and prevention services that focus on tobacco use, nutrition, and physical activity. This initiative served as the benchmark program for integrated behavioral and physical health care that is a main component of healthcare reform.

CHALLENGES, CONCERNS, AND OPPORTUNITIES

People with psychiatric disabilities, peer providers, practitioners, provider agencies, and administrators in policy and finance must collaborate to move from words to deeds to address this health crisis. It is our duty to change programs, policies, and practices to support the whole health choices of people with psychiatric disabilities. While there are challenges and concerns relative to implementing wellness and health promotion, there are significant opportunities to implement change in sustainable ways that are principled, collaborative, and fiscally responsible.

We have an ethical obligation to challenge our programs, policies, and practices to promote whole health and wellness without coercion and without the creation of a tyranny of health. It is not the responsibility of PsyR providers to change the health behaviors and lifestyles of the people who use their services. Rather it is our responsibility to change our programs, policies, and practices to support the possibility, the hope, and the reality of healthy lives for people with psychiatric disabilities and to support people in making the change that they desire in their health behaviors and lifestyles. Smokers and people who are obese already experience prejudice in our society (Stuber, Galea, & Link, 2008; MacLean et. al, 2009). Because prejudice around obesity and nicotine use plays a role in reducing willingness to seek medical care, we do not want to contribute to this reluctance to seek help by disempowering, judging, or labeling people who are not healthy enough.

Wellness offers a framework to help people examine their needs, strengths, and challenges in order to set self-determined goals, grow, and realize their full potential. Wellness centers on health and engenders a positive attitude. A focus on health and personal responsibility can strengthen optimism and a belief in the capacity to exert personal control in managing self-care needs. An individual may feel more empowered to manage life crises, stress, and disappointments and to direct attention to his or her own strengths, needs, and resources (internal, external, and support); and this can lead to increased resilience. People will assume an active role of self-monitoring health and increasing activity in the dimension where they perceive there may be an imbalance. This framework may be a challenge for some settings and practitioners who are concerned with risks and experience a need to do for or protect people with psychiatric disabilities rather than empower them to do for themselves.

Wellness is multi-dimensional and holistic, meaning we need to avoid a narrow focus only on the physical dimension and consider the interdependence among all eight wellness dimensions. Professionals or programs too often focus exclusively on discrete areas such as diet and nutrition or exercise. While these may be important concerns, telling people what to do is not an effective approach and is inconsistent with PsyR principles and practices. Rather, it is important to help people to come to their own understanding, for instance, about whether, why, and how nutrition and exercise are important, including the impact of physical wellness on other aspects of their being, such as the spiritual, emotional, and occupational dimensions. Similarly, having a sense of purpose and meaning (the spiritual dimension) and an income (the financial and occupational dimensions) are likely to help lead a person to the kinds of choices that preserve and increase physical wellness, and consequently, longevity.

The "business" of PsyR creates perceived barriers to wellness promotion. Program budgets are stretched thin, programs have waiting lists, and there are many people to serve and services to deliver. Adding a new modality seems difficult. Funders will need to strategize to reduce non-service burdens and ensure that various wellness and health promotion activities are billable at an appropriate rate. The Center for Medicare and Medicaid Services (CMS) and local CMS intermediaries will need to work together to see that Medicare Health Behavior Assessment and Intervention codes are used as a vehicle to promote the health of people with psychiatric disabilities.

We can and should consider offering smoking cessation as one of the most important things we can do to reduce illness and early death. Providing opportunities that will support choosing a goal to quit smoking must also recognize that this goal is a choice. For example, service practitioners might ensure that nicotine replacement is available, and agencies might make it a standard of care for assessments and for prescribers to address smoking. Nicotine could be considered as "a drug of abuse" when considering dual disorders treatment. Agencies could offer onsite smoking cessation groups and create smoke free spaces. Practitioners should celebrate every success (even those that do not result in permanent abstinence). Agencies can make smoking cessation literature readily available to all people served, and make every direct service workforce member accountable for offering to help with smoking reduction/cessation, and offer incentives as appropriate. For people who choose to reduce or quit smoking, finding help and support should be easy.

Mental health settings and programs that serve food need to pay maximal attention to providing healthy meals and snacks and exposing people to a variety of healthy diet alternatives. Services that support community living need to include helping people learn healthy meal planning, shopping, and food preparation. At the same time, programs should support and maximize access to physical activity and exercise equipment, such as expanding the availability of exercise assets, including workout videos and therabands, and connecting people to local resources for physical activity. PsyR programs and practitioners can help by negotiating reduced fees at YMCAs, yoga studios, and dance studios; ensuring that our facilities are bicycle-friendly, and eliminating security barriers to the use of staircases.

Every effort needs to be made to help people access the physical healthcare they need. Programs and practitioners need to help people develop and use the skills and practical resources, including funds and transportation, needed to access quality health and dental care. Agency and service providers need to help to dispel emotional barriers to seeking care resulting from experiences of prejudice and past trauma. This might include educating people about the importance of health screenings and offering to accompany them to screenings in order to ensure respectful access and reduce fear. An increasing number of PsyR programs are integrating health screening into their facilities by sponsoring health and wellness fairs as a way to give people empowering health information and normalize the idea of health maintenance for both service providers and service users.

It is very important to pay very close attention to the effect of medications on overall health and wellness. PsyR practitioners reject the idea that symptom reduction is a prerequisite for school, work, or independent housing; similarly, we need to reject the emphasis on symptom stabilization through prescribing complex psychopharmacologic cocktails at high doses and only later (if at all) helping people deal with the consequent disabling and deadly side-effects. Shared Decision Making leading to self-determination (Anthony, 2010) that helps people make their own informed choices about medication use is a critical practice intervention. Early intervention programs for people newly experiencing symptoms can help them cope and recover, possibly without moving onto high doses of medication and providing an opportunity to implement regular health screening and health promotion. Additionally, practitioners need to learn how to monitor blood pressures, glucose and lipid levels, body mass index, and other risk factors for metabolic syndrome in people who choose to take medications.

Practitioners need to know about both treatment and rehabilitation advances to help change the paradigm from a heavy reliance on medication as the prime intervention. For example, the evidence for the co-administration of metformin during antipsychotic therapy in an effort to reduce iatrogenic weight gain is strong and growing (Ehret, Goethe, Lanosa, & Coleman, 2010). Research increasingly supports the ideology "less is more." For example, in young adults who are newly diagnosed with a mental health condition, research indicates that less medication has a strong relationship to positive outcomes, both from a clinical and rehabilitation perspective (Bola, 2005). Interventions such as Open Dialogues, used in Northern Europe, emphasize minimal medication, full empowerment of the person and family, and a strong reliance on wellness to develop strong mental health (Seikkula & Olson, 2003). Advocacy for this kind of change in practice and philosophy is important, but it will create significant tension between self-determination advocates and the practitioners, service users, and their supporters who embrace a medical model. This practice and philosophy of wellness with a reduced emphasis on medication also can create competition and conflict with both the psychopharmacology industry and those who believe, at some level, in medication for social and behavioral control.

Gaps in workforce skill are a significant barrier to redesigning PsyR programs into health and wellness enterprises. However, these changes are practical and achievable through a combination of the existing PsyR focus on the whole person and providers' current skills and experience with the stages of change model, motivational interviewing, and building a strong and trusting therapeutic alliance.

Mental health programs, including residential programs, can be a huge resource for wellness. These provide opportunities to socialize, learn, shop, cook, and eat nutritious meals with mindfulness and companionship, and they are places where physical activity can be enjoyed and nurtured in the community. The frequent staff contact allows a focus on all of the dimensions of wellness, moving people towards independence and wellness in vocation, health care, spirituality, social wellbeing, and education. These are the places where people can either find a meta-environment of hope for recovery and wellness or be doomed to ongoing ill health hopelessness. Unfortunately, many mental health programs lack a framework of health promotion or wellness and are places where poor health is supported through restrictive policies and practices or tolerated through neglect.

Psychiatric hospital environments also can provide specific ways to help people initiate and maintain wellness efforts. Even small community units can find space for stationary exercise equipment and arrange daily access to fresh air. Vigorous regulation enforcement can support these interventions as part of the clinical treatment environment. Smokers often receive nicotine replacement therapy during hospital stays, and hospitals can and should offer people continuation therapy (e.g., prescriptions and supplies) along with linkages to cessation resources in the community. Hospitals can provide people with medical and dental exams along with skills teaching to manage their ongoing health conditions.

Every practitioner and program must continually look at the messages being sent (intentional and unintentional), the stumbling blocks erected, and whether service providers show true concern for the wellness of people served. Programs must build a culture of health collaboration. If health promotion is a human issue, it offers an opportunity to build bridges and relationships together around developing optimal health in ourselves and in our rehabilitation environments. As part of this, programs should establish a culture where the role of the broader wellness team—everybody from chiropractors to clergy to wellness coaches to yoga teachers—is honored. Practitioner roles need to shift from solely that of mental health clinician to include educator and coach. In addition, agencies may find they need to support the health and wellness of staff.

Health as a resource for overall recovery can and should be marketed. Programs can help people discover the Personal Medicine® (Deegan, 2004) that promotes their wellness. In accordance with the basic tenets of PsyR, health and wellness can serve as program frameworks, replacing the focus on disease and disability. Programs and practitioners can use the language of health and wellness and establish the development of wellness skills and supports as the goal of program interventions. Program and agency leaders need to support this vision, and reinforce the message of wellness. This can all lead to a Wellness Culture, where interaction between a person's mental, physical, spiritual, sexual, and social health is nurtured and expected—one that inspires hope and expects wellness.

CONSIDERATIONS, FACTORS, AND IMPLICATIONS

Trauma and the fear of re-traumatization play a powerful role in reduced use of medical care by people with psychiatric disabilities. Many people have experienced physical, emotional, and sexual abuse before and during treatment for their mental health conditions. The experience of a serious mental illness, often including forced hospitalizations, physical restraint, and/or police encounters, serves as a source of trauma or re-traumatization for many people. That history may well include use of physical restraint for routine medical and dental procedures (Glassman, Caputo, Dougherty, Lyons, Messieha, Miller, Peltier, & Romer, 2009). People with such experiences are naturally less comfortable placing themselves in settings where they may be fully undressed or physically restrained. The trauma of prejudice, including prejudice around obesity and smoking, can also play into this aspect of care avoidance. The provision of peer support and the use of health peer mentors is a very effective strategy to support people in their quest to use health services while avoiding re-traumatization.

The fragmentation of health care in our society is magnified for many people with psychiatric disabilities. The lack of financial resources and reimbursement strategies for wellness and health promotion and prevention practices are formidable barriers. This is compounded by the prejudice and discrimination that exists within our system of care. Transportation issues aggravate healthcare access, especially for many people outside of our cities. Health and wellness for people with psychiatric disabilities is not universally valued as worthwhile or cost-saving to the system. In spite of federal, state, peer, and professional calls to action for integrated healthcare, research, and policy change, this message has not yet trickled down to the front line of service delivery. There is much we can do to help ensure people have access to quality, timely services and supports. PsyR practitioners have an opportunity to forge new roles by working in integrated settings and assertively advocating for wellness changes in local programs.

Integrating wellness into mental health services makes sense; many of the strategies are straightforward and uncomplicated and are recognized as evidence-based or best practices for the general population. Yet some resist implementing wellness services into our programs and practices. It is time to move from talking about wellness to creating the conditions in our programs and practices that will allow the people we serve to live with health and wellness. Without health, people cannot recover or develop the lives they want to live. It is our responsibility, as providers who value the lives of our consumers, to empower our system, programs, and providers to understand the urgency of wellness, explore creative solutions, and ensure that they happen.

SUMMARY

It is imperative that PsyR educational programs prepare our workforce to better meet the needs of the people we serve. This will involve placing more emphasis on building competencies needed to help people achieve health as a critical foundation for recovery. Information, alone, regarding the health disparities that people with psychiatric disabilities experience will have little effect on reducing those disparities and increasing longevity.

The process of what PsyR practitioners do must be as much the focus as the outcome. Without understanding our processes, we will never improve our effectiveness. Information and recovery-based attitudes are an essential foundation, and workforce development and educational programs need to be skills-oriented with a focus on the skills of health promotion and wellness. The psychiatric rehabilitation field is poised to lead the broader field of mental health in implementing wellness and health promotion models that are adaptive, holistic, and proactive. There are great opportunities for the PsyR professional to design, deliver, and evaluate health and wellness promotion programs and practices that can effectively support people with psychiatric disabilities in living well and recovering meaningful roles in society.

BEST PRACTICE GUIDELINES FOR WHOLE HEALTH AND WELLNESS

• Emphasize wellness skills by shifting traditional groups to wellness classes.

• Promote the fact that health is a personal resource for recovery and that people have a right to optimal health. Advertise, market, and incent positive wellness in programs and environments.

• Resist negativity and work to overcome barriers by offering rides to clinics, stipends for fitness club memberships, health promotion literature for people who speak varied languages, have visual impairments, and/or have limited literacy.

• Teach people to examine their lifestyle habits and behaviors as a form of health empowerment. Use a shared decision making process to support setting self-determined goals and making informed choices about their health and healthcare, including the use of psychiatric medications.

• Encourage people to remember that health and wellness behaviors are an area of life over which they have control.

• Help people seek gainful employment and pursue a career as this can be instrumental in helping them create good health habits and transcend the negative effects of poverty. Teach people the necessary wellness skills for the stamina and resiliency necessary for successful tenure at work and in other valued social roles.

• Gain leadership support to add a focus on health as a critical resource for recovery.

ABOUT THE AUTHORS

Dori S. Hutchinson, Sc.D. has worked at the Center for Psychiatric Rehabilitation at Boston University since 1984. She currently serves as director of the services division, which assists people who live with mental health challenges in assuming their rightful roles as students, employees, residents, and members of their communities.

Margaret (Peggy) Swarbrick, Ph.D., OTR, CPRP, FAOTA is the director of the collaborative support pprograms of the New Jersey Institute for Wellness and Recovery Initiatives and a part-time assistant faculty in the department of psychiatric rehabilitation and counseling professions at the University of Medicine and Dentistry of New Jersey (UMDNJ) School of Health Related Professions (SHRP).

REFERENCES

Anthony, W. A. (2010). Shared decision making, self-determination and psychiatric rehabilitation. *Psychiatric Rehabilitation Journal, 34(2),* 87-89.

Allison, D. B., Mackell, J. A., & McDonnell, D. M. (2003). The impact of weight gain on quality of life among persons with schizophrenia. *Psychiatric Services, 54,* 565-567. doi: 10.1176/appi.ps.54.4.565

Bola, J. R. (2005). Medication-free research in early episode schizophrenia: Evidence of long-term harm? *Schizophrenia Bulletin, 32(2),* 288-296.

Books, A. (2009). *Food education for people with serious psychiatric disabilities: An evidence-based recovery curriculum.* Boston, MA: Boston University Center for Psychiatric Rehabilitation.

Center for Mental Health Services. (2010). *The 10 by 10 Campaign: A national action plan to improve life expectancy by 10 years in 10 years for people with mental illnesses. A report of the 2007 National Wellness Summit.* HHS Publication No. (SMA) 10-4476. Rockville, MD: Center for Mental Health Services, Substance Abuse and Mental Health Services Administration.

Copeland, M. E. (1997). *Wellness recovery action plan.* Peach Press, Brattleboro, VT.

Deegan, P. (2004). *The importance of personal medicine.* Retrieved from http://www.patdeegan.com/blog/posts/importance-personal-medicine

Dunn, H. L. (1961). *High-level wellness.* Arlington, VA: Beatty Press.

Dunn, H. (1977). What high level wellness means. *Health Values, 1*(1), 9-16.

Ehret, M., Goethe, J., Lanosa, M., & Coleman, C. I. (2010). The effect of metformin on anthropometrics and insulin resistance in patients receiving atypical antipsychotic agents: A meta-analysis. *Journal of Clinical Psychiatry, 71*(10), 1286-1292. doi: 10.4088/JCP.09m05274yel

Folsom, D., McCahill, M., Bartels, S., Lindamer, L., Ganiats, T., & Jeste, D. (2002). Medical comorbidity and receipt of medical care by older homeless people with schizophrenia or depression. *Psychiatric Services, 53,* 1456-1460.

Goldberg, R. W., Seybolt, D. C., & Lehman, A. F. (2002). Reliable self-report of health service use by individuals with serious mental illness. *Psychiatric Services, 53,* 879-881.

Glassman P., Caputo, A., Dougherty, N., Lyons, R., Messieha, Z., Miller, C., Peltier, B., & Romer, M. (2009). Special Care Dentistry Association consensus statement on sedation, anesthesia, and alternative techniques for people with special needs. *Special Care in Dentistry, 29*(1), 2-8.

Hahm, H., & Segal, S. P. (2005). Failure to seek needed health care among the mentally ill. *American Journal of Ortho Psychiatry, 75*(1), 54-62.

Hutchinson, D. S., Gagne, C., Bowers, A., Russinova, Z., Skrinar, G. S., & Anthony, W. A. (2006). Framework for health promotion services and for people with psychiatric disabilities. *Psychiatric Rehabilitation Journal, 29,* 241-250.

Hutchinson, D. S. (2011). The recovery education center: An integrated health promotion and wellness program. *Psychiatric Rehabilitation Journal, 34(4),* 321-324.

Joukamaa, M., Heliovaara, M., Knekt, P., Aromaa, A., Raitasalo, R., and Lehtinen, V. (2001). Mental disorders and cause-specific mortality. *The British Journal of Psychiatry, 179,* 498-502.

Koyanagi, C. (2004). Get it together: How to integrate physical and mental healthcare for people with serious mental disorders. Washington, DC: Bazelon Center for Mental Health Law.

Lambert, T.J., Velakoulis, D., & Pantelis, C. (2003). Medical comorbidity in schizophrenia. *Medical Journal of Australia, 178*(9 Suppl), S67-S70.

Lawrence, D. M., Holman, C. D. J., Jablensky, A. V., & Hobbs, M. S. T. (2003). Death rate from ischaemic heart disease in Western Australian psychiatric patients 1980-1998. *British Journal of Psychiatry, 182,* 31-36.

MacLean, L., Edwards, N., Garrard, M., Sims-Jones, N., Clinton, K., & Ashley, L. (2009). Obesity, stigma, and public health planning. *Health Promotion International, 24*(1), 88-93.

McKinnon, K., Wainberg, M. L., & Cournos, F. (2001). HIV/AIDS preparedness in mental health care agencies with high and low substance use disorders caseloads. *Journal of Substance Abuse, 13,* 127-135.

Meltzer, H. (2005). The metabolic consequences of long-term treatment with olanzapine, quetiapine, and risperidone: Are there differences? *The International Journal of Neuropsychopharmacology, 8,* 153-156.

Meyer, J. M., & Nasrallah, H. A. (2003). *Medical illness and schizophrenia.* Washington, DC: American Psychiatric Publishing, Inc.

Parks, J., Svendsen, D., Singer, P., Foti, M. E., & Mauer, B. (2006, October). *Morbidity and mortality in people with serious mental illness* [technical report]. Retrieved July 8, 2010 from http://www.nasmhpd.org/general_files/publications/med_directors_pubs/Technical%20Report%20on%20Morbidity%20and%20Mortaility%20-%20Final%2011-06.pdf

Razzano, L. A., & Hamilton, M. M. (2005). Health-related barriers to employment among people with HIV/AIDS. *Journal of Vocational Rehabilitation, 22*(3), 179-188.

Seikkula, J., & Olson, M. E. (2003). The open dialogue approach to acute psychosis: Its poetics and micropolitics. *Family Process, 42*(3), 403-18.

Shiner B., Whitley, R., Van Citters, A. D., Pratt, S. I., & Bartels, S. (2008). Learning what matters for patients: Qualitative evaluation of a health promotion program for those with serious mental illness. *Health Promotion International, 23*(3), 275-82.

St. Pierre, C. (Ed.). (2008). Wellness and recovery: The vision and the pledge. *Recovery and Rehabilitation Newsletter, 4*(3), 1-6. Retrieved from http://cpr.bu.edu/wp-content/uploads/downloads/2011/11/Wellness-and-Recovery-Pledge.pdf

Stuber, J., Galea, S., & Link, B. G. (2008). Smoking and the emergence of a stigmatized social status. *Social Science & Medicine, 67*(3), 420-30.

Swarbrick, M., Murphy, A., Zechner, M., Spagnolo, A., & Gill, K. (2011). Wellness coaching: A new role for peers. *Psychiatric Rehabilitation Journal, 34*, 328-331.

Swarbrick, M. (2010). Lived experience: Recovery and wellness concepts for systems transformation. In M. Scheinholtz (Ed.), *Occupational therapy for advanced practice: Considerations for mental health practice*. Bethesda, MD: American Occupational Therapy Association.

Swarbrick, M. (2006). A wellness approach. *Psychiatric Rehabilitation Journal, 29*, 311-314.

Swarbrick, M. (1997, March). A wellness model for clients. *Mental Health Special Interest Section Quarterly, 20*, 1-4.

Swarbrick, M., Hutchinson, D., & Gill, K. (2008). The quest for optimal health: Can education and training cure what ails us? *International Journal of Mental Health, 37*(2), 69-88.

U.S. Department of Health and Human Services. (1999). *Mental health: A report of the Surgeon General.* Rockville, MD: U.S. Department of Health and Human Services, Substance Abuse and Mental Health Services Administration, Center for Mental Health Services.

Vandiver, V. (2008). *Integrating health promotion and mental health: An introduction to policies, principles, and practices.* New York: Oxford University Press.

Whitaker, R. (2010). *Anatomy of an epidemic: Magic bullets, psychiatric drugs, and the astonishing rise of mental illness in America.* New York: Crown Publishing.

COMMUNITY INTEGRATION

Mark S. Salzer
Richard C. Baron
Seble-Mariam Abate Menkir
Lori Breen

A B S T R A C T

Community integration practice promotes opportunities for individuals with psychiatric disabilities to live full lives in the community like everyone else. Such practice is viewed as a cornerstone of psychiatric rehabilitation and is a right based on the Americans with Disabilities Act and grounded in the social model of disability. Specific practices that support community integration are consistent with the core competencies and evidence-based practices of psychiatric rehabilitation. This chapter includes an historical overview of community integration and its foundations in U.S. law and policy. Community integration practices and principles are described to provide a framework to better understand how community integration relates to promoting recovery. A program description illustrates how community integration practice increases opportunities for veterans with psychiatric disabilities to live full, meaningful lives. Finally, policy, program, and individual challenges associated with community integration practice are also offered.

COMMUNITY INTEGRATION IS A STRONGLY HELD VALUE AND GOAL IN MENTAL HEALTH POLICY AND practice that has become a unifying concept in the public mental health system for people with psychiatric disabilities (Bond, Salyers, Rollins, Rapp, & Zipple, 2004; Carling, 1995; Flynn & Aubry, 1999). Based on the far reaching rights movements, legislation, and judicial decisions, community integration emerged as "the opportunity to live in the community and be valued for one's uniqueness and abilities, like everyone else" (Salzer, 2006, p. 1). Focusing on opportunity to participate emphasizes self-determination and choice about what one does in the community, and inhibits the development of practices that might force either partici-pation that is not desired by the person, participation that occurs in segregated settings, or participation in which interactions with a broad-range of community members is unlikely. The promotion of community integration, understood as the enhancement of opportunity, is viewed as being at the core of psychiatric rehabilitation (Salzer, 2006).

The ultimate goal of community integration is to help individuals express themselves in communities of their choice. In practice, it involves first the articulation of an individual's desires, hopes, and dreams. Goals may range from learning to use public transportation or acquiring a personal vehicle to going on a recreational outing with friends and earning a degree and becoming employed. Ideally, drawing on natural supports in the community creates a process where the individual will no longer have to rely on professional services.

Every endeavor considered and/or undertaken includes the concept of risk, a term that may have positive consequences as well as potentially challenging ones. The benefits of overcoming fears include breaking down previous barriers, having a sense of accomplishment in trying and/or succeeding, and possibly achieving more than what was anticipated. The related negative effects of risk include fears that may turn into reality, a discussion of possibility that raises fears of failure, and fear of relapse that could cause an individual to temporarily or permanently lose all the meaningful participation that was gained. Each step taken towards increasing community participation brings with it gains and losses. It is also recognized that it is a struggle to maintain wellness when aspects of one's life are in flux.

The Practice of Community Integration: Seble's Story

One of our co-authors understands the importance of community integration from her personal experience.

> I live with bipolar disorder and have also struggled with use of illicit substances. Fundamentally, I discovered that success in my recovery is built on the ability to connect with individuals and build trusting relationships. Hope-instilling conversations promote opportu-nities for individuals to express their passions and to build on innate abilities. The power of strengths-based approaches, such as Motivational Interviewing, has worked against substantial odds. Individuals who appear unresponsive come alive when simply encouraged to share their own stories.
>
> Entrenched in a locked ward for three months during my last hospitalization, I was mired in psychosis, paranoia, and delusional thinking. Hopelessness, regret, depression, and destitution plagued me. A stranger took a few moments to listen empathically during a conversation and created an opportunity for me to examine my own statements. During the course of the conversation, I came to realize that who I had hoped to be and what I had become were disjointed and disconnected; this was the turning point in my recovery and community integration journey.

I decided to get help for myself, and luckily, it arrived in the form of a newly assigned paid supporter. With her help, I began to weave the tattered threads of my life into a cohesive whole. The hope she held for me, and the hope she instilled in me, helped me re-envision myself as a human being again. At the same time, it was, quite frankly, horrible to realize the value of time lost to illness, opportunities squandered, and potential unrealized—this was the ultimate grief.

Through the early stages of recovery, I was constantly and consistently encouraged to focus on what was in my power to achieve. Each step was painful, and in overcoming my fears and taking risks along the way, I was able to build a reserve of resilience that carries me to this day. The key in taking risks is to construct potential responses to unforeseen circumstances. Risk-taking also helps to continuously build skill sets and coping mechanisms to strengthen the individual's flexibility in addressing issues that may arise. Risk is mitigated by increasing information and knowledge and through building relationships based on trust.

COMMUNITY INTEGRATION: AN HISTORICAL PERSPECTIVE

Building on the personal perspective of Seble's Story, the experience of community integration is best understood through its grounding in the rights of the individual to opportunity and growth in the community. Historically, community integration has its foundation in the disability rights "Normalization Movement" for people with mental retardation and developmental disabilities. This movement originated in Denmark in the 1950s followed by the social model of disability that arose in the 1960s (Wolfensberger, 1970, 1972). As a result of these social and progressive movements, human services initiatives emerged to support and enable people with disabilities "to function in ways considered to be within the acceptable norms of his/her society" (Wolfensberger, 1970, p. 67). Similarly, Nirje (1980) defined normalization in terms of "making available to all mentally retarded people patterns of life and conditions of everyday living which are as similar as possible to the circumstances and ways of life of society" (p. 33). In both of these definitions, community integration is understood as the extent to which people have the opportunity to participate fully in the community to the same extent as other citizens. Community integration includes the extent to which individuals are physically present in ordinary settings, activities, and contexts (physical integration) and are able to participate in social interactions and relationships (social integration; Wolfensberger, 1972). Community integration also includes a person's unique experience of community and belonging (psychological integration; (Aubry & Myner, 1996; Wong & Solomon, 2002).

The social or contextual model of disability does not deny impairments, but recognizes that "disablement," or limited activity and community participation, results from a society that fails to ensure opportunities for full and meaningful roles for all citizens (Oliver, 1990). Disability is viewed as resulting from a person-environment interaction that does not maximize opportunities for full community participation.

A disability rights movement that emerged out of this new understanding of disability successfully advocated for the Americans with Disabilities Act (ADA, 1990), which was signed into law in 1990. Title II of the Act "[r]equires governments to give people with disabilities an equal opportunity to benefit from all programs, services, and activities (e.g., education, employment, voting, transportation, recreation, etc.)," thereby establishing the promotion of community integration in the law.

Another important landmark event for disability rights was the 1999 ruling of the U.S. Supreme Court in what is now known as the Olmstead Decision (*Olmstead vs. L.C.,* 1999).

With the Olmstead Decision, the court ruled in favor of Elaine Wilson and Lois Curtis, who claimed that they were unjustly being confined in an institution rather than being allowed to live in a community-based setting. The court concluded that unnecessary institutionalization is a form of discrimination prohibited by the ADA. In response to this decision by the court, the U.S. Department of Justice created the 2001 "Integration Regulation," which required that "services, programs, and activities must be delivered in a way that enables individuals with disabilities to interact with non-disabled people to the fullest extent possible." As a result of this legislative act and the judicial ruling, community integration was validated and established as an inherent right for all people with disabilities, which expanded their right to live, study, work, and recreate alongside and in the same manner as people without disabilities (Racino, 1995). The ADA and Olmstead decision drove the formation of the President's New Freedom Commission on Mental Health, and this perspective on community integration is fully present in their resulting report (DHHS, 2003).

Indicators of Limited Opportunities for Community Integration

There would be cause for celebration if community integration were viewed solely from the standpoint of whether more people were living in institutions than in community settings. Data indicate that the number of individuals who reside in state/county-funded psychiatric institutions has declined from a high of 558,922 in 1955 to 52,632 in 2004 (Atay, Crider, Foley, Male, & Blacklow, 2006). Significant advances have also been made in identifying and implementing rehabilitation approaches in community settings that have proven effective for adults with psychiatric disabilities (Salzer, Blank, Rothbard, & Hadley, 2001). Multimillion dollar research investments have been made by the federal Center for Mental Health Services and the National Institute of Mental Health focusing on, for example, Assertive Community Treatment, Illness Management and Recovery, and cognitive remediation as well as supported employment, supported independent living, and peer support. Equally as important, advocacy efforts by people who have personally experienced the mental health system have dramatically influenced policies and practices, leading to a greater focus on the development of programs emphasizing recovery, full participation, and independent living.

Nevertheless, while persons who experience psychiatric disabilities are now more likely to be physically in the community rather than in institutions, they are too often not of the community like everyone else. Most indicators reveal continuing levels of isolation, impoverishment, and despair, and opportunities for fuller and more satisfying lives in the community remain beyond the reach of many. The following indicators emphasize these disparities:

Employment: In the area of employment, people with psychiatric disabilities would, could, and should work (Baron & Salzer, 2002). Yet only 25% are working or looking for work, a number that is consistently and substantially lower than for any other disability group (Trupin, Sebesta, Yelin, & LaPlante, 1997). Supported employment models show positive results in many areas, but also relatively short job tenure and small increases in annual income, resulting in little possible movement out of poverty (Baron & Salzer, 2002; Draine, Salzer, Culhane, & Hadley, 2002).

Finances: In terms of economic independence, nearly 70% are almost entirely dependent on Social Security programs for financial and medical support, representing the largest disability category receiving SSI/SSDI and the disability group that is most likely to remain dependent on SSA benefits for a lifetime (GAO, 1996). Current work-focused, evidence-based practices do not yet enable people to leave the public disability income rolls and move toward financial independence (Cook et al., 2008).

Education: In education, more than 33,000 students with mental illnesses are enrolled in colleges and universities (Souma, Rickerson, & Burgsthler, 2002), a number that appears to be increasing over time (Sharpe, Bruininks, Blacklock, Benson, & Johnson, 2004). However, 86% of students with mental illnesses withdraw from college prior to completing their degrees (Kessler, Foster, Saunders, & Stang, 1995), a figure that is much higher than the approximately 37% withdrawal rate for the general student population (Beginning Postsecondary Students Longitudinal Study, 2001).

Housing: For housing, research has found that persons with psychiatric disabilities are heavily concentrated in some of the most impoverished and resource poor inner-city neighborhoods where opportunities for community participation are limited (Metraux, Caplan, Klugman, & Hadley, 2007).

Social networks: Valued social roles and family and friendship networks are limited both in size and scope (McDonald-Miszczak, 2000) for people with psychiatric disabilities, and relationships are viewed as less supportive and less satisfying than those in other groups (Pattison et al., 1975). Mothers with a psychiatric disability are almost three times more likely to lose custody of their children compared to other mothers, even after controlling for poverty (Park, Solomon, & Mandell, 2006).

Leisure and recreation: There is less opportunity for leisure and recreation for people with psychiatric disabilities, which results in more limited physical activity and consequently impacts overall health and wellness. These limitations are believed to be partially responsible for the increased health morbidity and mortality of these individuals (Parks, Svendsen, Singer, Foti, & Mauer, 2006).

Prejudice and discrimination: Despite significant public education initiatives, individuals with serious mental illnesses continue to be viewed in negative ways by the general public (DHHS, 1999, 2003), and many believe they may be unpredictable and/or violent (Hinshaw, 2007; Phelan, 2000). This leads to discrimination in employment, housing, and social relationships (Carling, 1995; Corrigan, 1999).

Empowerment: Despite the many opportunities for empowerment (Salzer, 1997), self-determination continues to be viewed more as a privilege rather than as a right (Chamberlin, 1999), and people report feeling invisible (Carling, 1995) and unwelcome in human service settings. Although there was evidence of a slowdown in the rate of deinstitutionalization after Olmstead (*Olmstead vs. L.C.,* 1999), current data indicate that for the first time in 50 years, there has been an increase in the number of institutionalized individuals with psychiatric disabilities.

COMMUNITY INTEGRATION FRAMEWORK AND OVERVIEW

At the heart of promoting community integration is a consistent commitment to expanding opportunities in all life domains, leaving to individuals the responsibility to prioritize the types of participation that are most meaningful to them and determine the degree to which they wish to participate. We identify twelve domains of community life and a vision of what full opportunity for community participation like everyone else could look like in each.

1. *Housing opportunities* in which people live where they choose to live and can afford to live, choosing neighborhoods, residential settings, roommates and/or relatives, and access to local housing resources in ways that suit them

2. *Employment opportunities* in which people for competitive wages in mainstream community settings

3. *Educational opportunities* in which people pursue their own educational goals, seeking personal growth and/or career training in both specialized mental health settings and mainstream educational programs

4. *Social and intimate relationships* where people can establish a balance of friendships with others who may or may not have psychiatric disabilities and can draw on those friendships for support and reciprocate as they can; people also have the opportunity to pursue, enjoy, and benefit from romantic and intimate relationships.

5. *Family relationships* that people can draw on for the nurturing aspects of their given or chosen families and contribute to family life by playing normal supportive roles as parents, siblings, and children in the lives of those they love

6. *Peer relationships* in which people have the opportunity both to benefit from the experiences and assistance of others with psychiatric disabilities—both from peer counselors and peer run programs—and to serve as peer staff and peer volunteers themselves

7. *Religion and spirituality* that provides individuals the opportunity to participate in the religious and spiritual activities they find most supportive, drawing upon and giving to the life of congregations

8. *Leisure and recreation opportunities* in which people can participate in a wide range of hobbies, sports, travel, and artistic endeavors in their communities, and both enjoy and contribute to these activities

9. *Civic life opportunities* wherein people have the opportunity to participate in a wide range of civic activities, such as serving as volunteers, advocates, and voters, that shape and strengthen their communities

10. *Health and wellness options* to ensure that people both receive the quality of health care needed to sustain healthy lives and take responsibility for maintaining their own, and their loved ones', physical and emotional health

11. *Financial resources* wherein people can manage their own finances with whatever help and assistance they choose, making individual choices about earnings, expenditures, and savings

12. *Self-determination* to ensure that people make decisions about the key issues that affect their lives

The framework for promoting opportunities in each of these domains is grounded in the social model of disability. As mentioned earlier, this ecological model emphasizes the importance of the interplay between environmental or external factors (referred to as barriers) and individual characteristics (strengths and impairments) in understanding the disablement and lack of opportunity to participate. Interventions to counteract disability require a sophisticated understanding of how the external barriers and individual impairments, independently and interactively, limit opportunity. Increased opportunities can result from actions that target the external barriers or individual impairments with an expectation that maximum opportunities are achieved when both are targeted. Common barriers include stigma and discrimination, poverty, transportation, laws, and policies. Common individual impairments include internalized stigma and demoralization, losing sight of goals, skills that may have atrophied or never been achieved, and lack of support for dealing with illness-related symptoms that interfere with achieving life goals. These barriers and needs will be discussed in more detail later in the chapter.

Opportunity can be viewed as a gradient, or a continuum, with levels that can differ for each life domain. That is, an individual may have more opportunity in the areas of housing and employment, but less in leisure and recreation or spirituality/religion. However, opportunity across domains may not necessarily be independent. For example, certain external barriers and individual impairments may similarly affect opportunity in multiple domains. The ultimate goal of community integration practice is the promotion of opportunity to a point that enables participation across domains, but with the understanding that the degree of subsequent participation is not the definitive metric for assessing success. Individual choice and self-determination about the types and degree of participation is paramount in a community integration framework. Mandating participation would be counter to community integration principles.

Neither researchers, practitioners, policymakers, family members nor anyone else is able to reliably predict which individuals will and will not be able to take advantage of opportunities to become more engaged in life in the community. Because neither symptoms nor compliance nor past failures have served as substantial barometers of future success, the community integration approach argues for ensuring that all individuals with psychiatric disabilities be provided the opportunity to pursue their goals—to work or to own a home or to volunteer or any of a myriad of personally meaningful goals. Moreover, when they have the opportunity to do so, individuals in recovery have consistently proven themselves far more capable of managing their own lives and achieving their own goals than others have imagined. Maximizing opportunity has been proposed as essential for creating environments that fully promote full participation in meaningful social roles and well-being and recovery (Salzer, 2006) and initiatives to promote community integration can occur, and should occur, at the policy, program, and practice levels.

Community Integration Principles and Practice

We can conceptualize community integration practice as the application of the following 10 principles organized into three areas: recognizing rights, roles and responsibilities; promoting opportunities for participation like everyone else; and utilizing effective, evidence-based strategies:

Recognizing rights, roles, and responsibilities

- Principle 1. Community integration is a right. People with psychiatric disabilities have a right, like everyone else, to participate in those aspects of community life that they find most meaningful. Exclusion, either as a result of public policy or societal values, must be challenged at every turn on legal, economic, and moral/ethical grounds.

- Principle 2. Community integration offers opportunities for participation in varied roles. People with psychiatric disabilities seek opportunities to play varied roles in their communities across all domains of community life—as neighbors and workers, as friends and family, as volunteers and civic activists, as congregants and students, and more.

- Principle 3. Community integration promotes a sense of responsibility. Like everyone else in the community, people with psychiatric disabilities can be expected to carry a range of responsibilities, not only to monitor their own health and welfare but also to be responsive to the needs and concerns of their communities.

Promoting opportunities for participation

- Principle 4. Community integration facilitates opportunities for participation in the community over participation in the institution/agency. Competitive employment is preferred over sheltered workshops; going to a movie theater rather than watching movies at the agency; going to a community gym rather than using agency equipment; playing bingo at the local church or community center over bingo in the program; and taking public transportation over agency van transportation.

- Principle 5. Community integration facilitates opportunities for self-directed rather than staff-directed activities. People have the same opportunities to choose what they do to the same extent as everyone else.

- Principle 6. Community integration facilitates opportunities for participation with a full-range of community members rather than only with others from a program or within the disability community.

Using effective evidence-based practices

- Principle 7. Community integration promotes self-determination. People choose which domains of community life to pursue, at what pace, and with whatever level of support services they believe is best.

- Principle 8. Community integration utilizes natural supports and mainstream resources. Rather than relying only upon paid mental health professionals, community participation strategies use natural supports (e.g., family, friends, and neighbors, etc.) as well as mainstream community services and opportunities available to anyone else.

- Principle 9. Community integration seeks to identify barriers to opportunity and develop strategies for overcoming those barriers. People with psychiatric disabilities and the programs that serve them seek to identify attitudinal, professional, and policy barriers that limit or discourage community participation and then seek to eliminate those barriers.

- Principle 10. Community integration seeks to identify the supports that individuals with psychiatric disabilities need to successfully participate in community life. Practitioners and programs provide the full-range of supports and services people may need to actively and successfully participate in community life.

Socio-Environmental Barriers and Individual Needs

It is particularly critical in community integration practice to identify and address socio-environmental barriers and individual needs. While the values and rights of our society promote the full participation and inclusion of persons with psychiatric disabilities in all areas of community life, poverty and discrimination, among other barriers, hamper our current ability to achieve these goals. These factors, compounded by the lack of an adequate range of effective supports, keep individuals with psychiatric disabilities socially isolated and dependent on the mental health system for meeting their social, psychological, and subsistence needs (Beels, 1981).

Socio-Environmental Barriers: There are many barriers to community integration in one or several of the aforementioned life domains. To address these environmental and/or institutional barriers in the years ahead, the field will need to draw on established strategies and develop innovative approaches. A few of the most prominent barriers to opportunity are described below, many of which impact several life domains, and these will often be best addressed by a combination of public policy advocacy and a determined partnership between individuals, family members, policymakers, and providers.

Discrimination: The negative stereotypes attached to mental illnesses remain profound and often lead to discrimination, which serves as a barrier to decent housing, good jobs, new friends, family life, and religious participation, among other life domains. Providers and people in recovery can work together on three types of initiatives: first, strengthening and enforcing anti-discrimination statues and regulations; second, framing widespread public education campaigns that promote community understanding; and third, structuring opportunities at local levels for individual community members to meet and get to know individuals with mental illnesses across a wide range of life dimensions (e.g., at work, as neighbors, through church, etc.—that is, within the context of everyday community life.)

Disempowerment: Mental health systems, in both institutional and community settings, have often been criticized for an unintentional but systemic tendency to disempower the people who use their services. Staff members often make decisions for the people they serve and restrict their choices, undermining their self-confidence to select the goals, treatments, and supports that make the most sense to them. The consumer empowerment and self-help movements offer an antidote to the disengagement of people in recovery in their own lives, emphasizing both the need for each person to be the primary decision-maker in setting individual goals and treatment/rehabilitation/recovery plans, as well as emphasizing the effectiveness of self-help groups, peer specialists, consumer-operated programs, and policy advocacy.

Poverty: Participation in community life is often hampered by lack of economic security. Renting or buying a decent home, participating in a sports league, going back to school, or even having transportation to a good job—all often strain limited personal budgets. These are problems many other citizens share, with and without disabilities, and require a focus on two kinds of strategies: (1) increasing the level of cash assistance (and in particular increasing disability payments); and (2) expanding the emphasis on employment outcomes in mental health and vocational rehabilitation programs so that people in recovery have the earned income they need to re-engage in their communities.

Transportation: Similarly, many people experiencing psychiatric disabilities note that getting to the job, going to a family gathering, attending church, making doctors' appointments, or showing up in class on time often depends on reliable, safe, and available transportation. The strategies that address transportation problems are often difficult in urban settings but are particularly troublesome in suburban and rural communities where public transportation is spotty or non-existent. Several strategies have emerged in recent years in which service users and providers press public agencies for altered or expanded public transportation routes, collaborate with other service systems (e.g., for people who are elderly or have physical disabilities) for specialized van services, sponsor car pools, or subsidize car ownership.

Individual Needs and Supports: There are, as well, many opportunities to frame supports as people re-connect to their communities, and ensuring access to the supports they need must also draw on established program models or practices and develop new initiatives. This is an area that is well understood by psychiatric rehabilitation professionals and in which psychiatric rehabilitation practices traditionally shine. Individual supports can be provided in both programmatic packages, including many of the evidence-based models (e.g., supported employment, supported education, social skills training) or through the skilled work of individual practitioners. The provision of supports to promote community integration is well-known and understood by psychiatric rehabilitation practitioners. A few of the key support practices are described below and are based on the core psychiatric rehabilitation competencies described elsewhere (Salzer, 2006).

Peer and Other Natural Supports: Peer support has been identified as a best practice in mental health services (Salzer & MHASP Best Practices Team, 2002) and combined with natural supports, such as friends, family members, and other unpaid community members, is an essential adjunct to non-peer, paid support staff services. The supports these individuals offer limit the temptation of viewing community integration as a medical issue and heighten exposure to receiving help and opportunities for reciprocity that is most typical for most citizens. Finally, these supports further reduce dependency on the mental health system and increase independence.

Setting Goals and Establishing Priorities: Some individuals may need assistance in establishing community integration goals. Agencies can be helpful by making a cornerstone of their work communicating to service providers and service users alike that everyone is encouraged to rethink their participation in various domains of community life. Individual supporters can play a critical role in helping people who have grown used to living their lives within the behavioral health system to re-engage in the community and determine which domains of community life are of most importance to them. This can involve not only an assessment of their current levels of community participation but also the barriers they see before them as they take advantage of new opportunities.

Assessing Community Opportunities and Resources: People without disabilities make great use of community opportunities and resources, and psychiatric rehabilitation practitioners can do more to support an individual's access to community resources. This requires a two-pronged approach. On the one hand, a greater knowledge about and connection to community resources (jobs programs, religious congregations, civic associations, local clubs, etc.) can help individuals identify their own participation goals; on the other hand, supporters and individuals in recovery will also need to work together in helping community organizations become more open and accessible to participation by people with mental illnesses, strengthening the likelihood that participation will be successful.

Skills Training: Participation in community life—particularly for those who have been disengaged from work, discouraged from socializing, and disconnected from family life—may require individuals to build new skills or expand on their current array of skills. This includes, but is not limited to, social skills, cognitive skills, basic life skills (e.g., budgeting and bill paying, cooking, laundry), and specific skills needed in specific types of participation. Each individual will have an opportunity to decide whether those skills can be best learned in the protective environment of the agency/program or within mainstream programs available to and accessed by anyone in the community.

Personal Assistance: Participation in community life can be a substantial challenge, and many individuals may look for assistance at a very immediate level. Agencies can help by freeing staff—as in supported employment and supported education programs—to provide mobile, individualized supports on-site if necessary or accompany a person to church or a bowling league or a civic meeting. Other personal resources, such as a family member, a friend, or a peer specialist, can play a similar role. Often untapped are the resources of community organizations themselves, which are sometimes able to offer personal assistance (mentoring) on their own to ensure that a new member feels welcome and is helped to begin to function independently.

COMMUNITY INTEGRATION IN PRACTICE

With the Veterans Health Administration's adoption of a recovery philosophy and principles, VA Medical Centers across the country are implementing Psychosocial Rehabilitation and Recovery Centers (PRRCs), many of which replace day programs that previously served veterans with serious mental illnesses (Veterans Health Administration, 2008, pp. 5, 27-29). The goal of these psychiatric rehabilitation-based programs is to inspire and assist veterans in creating or re-creating self-determined roles in the community (T. Smith, personal communication, January 15, 2008).

The Veterans Empowerment Center at the Philadelphia VA Medical Center

The veterans it serves have named Philadelphia's PRRC *The Veterans Empowerment Center* (VEC). The VEC has adopted the community integration framework and principles described above and has placed a strong emphasis on providing supports in veterans' communities to maximize opportunities for veterans to connect to natural supports, mainstream resources and activities, and self-determined roles.

The VEC's structure, which continues to change, is based on the experiences, feedback, and self-reflection of veterans, VA staff, students, consultants, and volunteers (VEC's leadership team) with the goals of facilitating community integration, self-direction, increased hope, empowerment, and better quality of life. The VEC uses psychiatric rehabilitation evidence-based practices, including peer support, as well as unique approaches developed with veterans, including the utilization of a Community Integration and Recovery Plan, mobile support and community partnering. The VEC leadership team has met regularly since VEC's inception, and each week collaborates to continue to develop and monitor program activities to ensure that all new and existing activities meet the VEC's mission and reflect recovery and community integration principles. The VEC also holds bi-annual retreats and has created a strategic plan and subsequent workgroup activities. From these meetings, retreats, and VHA directives, the VEC team has created or identified the following core activities. All activities are designed and delivered reflecting the core values of the VEC: to be community-oriented, strengths-based, and veteran-centered. All activities are designed to encourage empowerment, self-advocacy and to acknowledge veterans' progress.

Goal Exploration and Identification: VEC staff partners meet with veterans to help them explore their hopes and dreams and identify their goals and action plans.

Individual Supports: VEC staff partners assist veterans to take action steps to meet their goals. Activities may include assisting veterans in addressing barriers, providing individualized supports, and increasing the availability and use of natural supports and resources. Individual supports are likely to occur in veterans' communities.

Groups: Evidence-based psychiatric rehabilitation groups, such as Social Skills Training (SST), Illness Management and Recovery (IMR) and Family PsychoEducation (FPE), in addition to Wellness and Recovery Action Planning (WRAP), Health & Wellness and other psychoeducational groups, are offered on-site and in the community.

Peers: Peer counselors or Certified Peer Specialists offer individual and group supports and act as role models. Veterans also act as role models and offer support to each other.

Community Partnering: VEC actively partners with community organizations to provide opportunities for veterans to connect to these community resources as well as to provide venues to meet with veterans in their own communities.

Veteran Empowerment: Veterans are encouraged to participate in the planning, operation, and evaluation of the VEC program and activities. Veteran self-determination and shared decision-making are core values of the VEC.

Long Term Supports: VEC is exploring this area with the intent of developing alumni activities such as a speaker's bureau. VEC supports are available to Veteran's at any point in their Recovery. Veterans may return to the VEC upon their needing additional support.

Community Integration and Recovery Plan (CIRP)

The Community Integration and Recovery Plan was designed to encourage a specific discussion between veterans and VEC staff about all areas in which they are interested, such as employment, education, dating, developing friendships, leisure and recreation, and the environmental barriers and individual impairments that may be limiting their opportunities in these areas. This is followed by the creation of a co-developed plan requiring collaboration between the veteran and staff supporter to address each barrier and provide needed supports. The plan includes specific steps and timelines to achieve the goal.

Consistent with best practices in person-centered planning, the first step in CIRP planning is to meet with the veterans to explore and identify their goals in each community integration domain. While many veterans quickly identify a goal or goals, others have a more difficult time doing so. Some veterans say that they have become used to others making decisions for them or that they are afraid to "get better" and lose their financial benefits. Veterans and their staff partners may use one or more approaches or tools to explore their interests, skills, and strengths. Veterans who are concerned about losing their disability benefits may still identify a goal that is meaningful to them, and staff help them review the costs and benefits associated with achieving that goal. Another strategy is to ask veterans to rate their level of satisfaction in life domains such as employment, social relationships, and leisure/recreation in order to identify areas they would like to focus on. Two additional strategies include using a *Goal Exploration Worksheet* that prompts veterans to answer open-ended questions about their interests, strengths, current and desired activities, and current supports; and providing opportunities for veterans to create vision boards to help them explore what they would like to add to their lives. Once veterans identify goal(s), the veteran and his/her staff partner use the CIRP (Community Integration and Recovery Plan) to continue goal-setting and related activities.

The CIRP is completed by or with the veteran at the veteran's pace. Action steps may be identified and completed to achieve a specific goal or simultaneously work across numerous goals. The CIRP is reviewed at least once every three months, but can be reviewed and edited at any time—daily, weekly, bi-weekly, or whenever the veteran and staff together decide that it will be beneficial.

For this example, one Veteran, John, expressed a desire to work and identified his strengths and skills as intelligence, motivation, and marketability (among others) related to achieving his goal. He identified environmental barriers, including those related to a lack of support from important people in his life. He chose to address this issue first. John and his VEC staff partner (James) discussed options and resources, and John decided to see if his parents would participate in family psychoeducation.

John's second target area was addressing his discomfort using public transportation, including a perceived lack of knowledge about public transportation and skills in using it. John and James brainstormed about what might help him increase his comfort and the frequency of his use of public transportation. In addition to identifying ways to obtain information, John, with help from James, decided that they would travel together on public transportation to a place that John always wanted to go. Later, one of John's friends was included as a supporter for John to use public transportation. While his primary goal was employment, John expressed a desire to make changes in other areas of his life as well. The steps taken to increase his use of public transportation not only increased John's comfort and ability to commute, but made it possible for him to travel to other desired locations and engage in other types of community activities.

Mobile Support and Community Partnering

The VEC team identified the need and desire of veterans to be supported in their own communities in the early stages of program development. The interactions between the veterans and their staff partners occur in typical community settings and do not require dedicated office space. Conversations can occur at a coffee shop, library, church, shopping mall, or other places where people typically gather. Mobile support, delineated in action steps on the CIRP, can take the form of accompanying a veteran to a credit counseling agency to help him establish credit so that he can rent an apartment. Support may occur by helping a Veteran join a gym, sign up for a community college course, or open a checking account or other activities to help a veteran reach his or her self-determined goal.

As much as possible, skills, peer support, and psychoeducational groups are also held in the community rather than the VA medical center. These groups do require more confidential space, and VEC staff have developed partnerships with libraries, churches, recreation centers, and other organizations to secure private individual and group meeting space. Providing supports in the community emphasizes the mission of enhancing connections and partici- pation in the community and is achieving results. For instance, a veteran attending a VEC peer support group located at a local library is now volunteering at that library on a weekly basis. A partnership developed at another library resulted in library staff offering free basic computer skill training for veterans. A trip to a veterans' museum, organized by a VEC veteran, provided an opportunity for veterans to learn to use public transportation with veterans and VEC Staff providing support. Other partnerships help connect veterans to existing community resources, such as those that help people with disabilities find work, go to school, or learn new skills.

CHALLENGES TO IMPLEMENTING
COMMUNITY INTEGRATION PRACTICES

While the concept of community integration is central to psychiatric rehabilitation, programs and practices will need to continue to evolve in response to growing evidence that recovery and community participation is possible for everyone with a psychiatric disability. Moreover, strategies for effectively addressing the external barriers that are increasingly being found to be major factors that limit community participation also need to be fully incorporated into psychiatric rehabilitation practice.

Practitioners will also need to develop new ways of working with people on a day-to-day basis that emphasize a greater focus on engagement and work in the community rather than agency-based supports and activities. Psychiatric rehabilitation providers may need to examine the degree to which group housing programs, agency-operated businesses, drop-in centers, social clubs, and group outings tend to reaffirm the distance between people with psychiatric disabilities and the community, thereby limiting rather than expanding opportunities to live like everyone else. Some settings will find it a challenge to identify new ways for providers to encourage the people who use their services to consider the options of moving beyond the warm embrace of agency programming and into the life of the community. This will be the further evolution of mobile psychiatric rehabilitation programs, consistent with the various evidence-based support models our discipline has developed (e.g., supported housing, employment, education, socialization). Site-based psychiatric rehabilitation programs will need to reflect on how they can most successfully facilitate opportunities for participation in the community while not abandoning the people who choose not to pursue these opportunities at the current time.

Practitioners will need to learn even more about the types of community resources available and reassess the role they can play in assisting individuals in taking full advantage of opportunities in the community. Even with a clear mission, a program's or practitioner's tendency, traditions, and comfort zone may result in a drift back towards traditional service provision in secured settings. Providing mobile support can be challenging even for attuned staff. It often requires not only significant changes in thinking about the work we do, but how we go about doing it. Consistently implementing community integration practices requires that we create or identify our own supports and action steps. It is easy to concentrate on the program, the group, or the problem rather than on our intended focus, the people we are partnering with and their hopes and dreams in their own communities. We need to regularly remind ourselves of our mission and seek feedback from persons in recovery and colleagues to keep us on track.

Promoting community integration also means consciously calibrating our views of professional responsibilities with the dignity of risk that comes with making choices from among a full-range of opportunities (Perske, 1972). Living in the community like everyone else means exposure to risk like everyone else. Promoting opportunities for meaningful lives in the community and choice means exposure to risk like everyone else. Choice means the ability to choose nothing, even if we believe that it is not in a person's best interest. At least one state has explicitly adopted a dignity of risk posture for how services are delivered to adults with serious mental illness. Arizona Administrative Code, Title 9, Chapter 21 allows for some element of risk in services in order for individuals with serious mental illnesses to have opportunities for "normal experiences." However, this does not mean we should abdicate our professional responsibilities. Instead, efforts to assess and manage risk need to be taken, including identifying potential risks, assessing the probability and severity of harm, and developing and implementing proactive solutions to minimize risks and reactive solutions should an incident occur (Burns-Lynch, Salzer, & Baron, 2010).

SUMMARY AND FUTURE DIRECTIONS

The field of psychiatric rehabilitation was born during a time when deinstitutionalization, a major community integration initiative providing opportunities for people to live in the community, was picking up steam. The field is again at the forefront in theory, research, and practice as efforts to create systems that promote recovery are the driving service delivery paradigm. An emphasis on promoting community integration—increased opportunities for people to live in the community like everyone else—is central to psychiatric rehabilitation and is a critical approach to facilitating recovery.

Psychiatric rehabilitation has firmly established itself as the leading discipline in developing, researching, and implementing support services that increase opportunities. To remain consistent with our ways of thinking and our identified practice competencies, psychiatric rehabilitation must increase our recognition of the impact of socio-environmental barriers on community participation, develop and research effective strategies for overcoming these barriers, both systemically and at the individual level, and make sure that our policies, programs, and practices fully attend to barriers. Without these steps, community integration, participation, and ultimately opportunities for recovery, will not be fully realized.

BEST PRACTICE GUIDELINES FOR COMMUNITY INTEGRATION

- Challenge exclusion, prejudice, and discrimination, recognizing that community integration is a right.
- Create opportunities for participation in varied roles and across all domains of community life.
- Promote a sense of responsibility, not only for people with psychiatric disabilities to monitor their own health and welfare, but also to help them be responsive to the needs and concerns of their communities.
- Facilitate opportunities for participation in the community rather than focusing on participation in institution- or agency-based activities.
- Provide opportunities for self-directed rather than staff-directed activities.
- Help people connect with a full-range of community members, rather than only with others from a mental health services program or within the disability community.
- Base services on an individual's choice of which domains of community life to pursue, at what pace, and with whatever level of support services they believe is best.
- Support the use of natural supports and mainstream resources rather than relying only upon paid mental health professionals.
- Identify barriers to opportunity and develop strategies for overcoming those barriers.
- Provide the full-range of supports and services people may need to actively and successfully participate in community life.

ABOUT THE AUTHORS

Mark Salzer, Ph.D. is a professor and chair of the Department of Rehabilitation Sciences at Temple University. He is also the principal investigator and director of the Temple University Collaborative on Community Inclusion of Individuals with Psychiatric Disabilities (www.tucollaborative.org), a research and training center funded by the National Institute on Disability and Rehabilitation Research. Dr. Salzer has been the principal investigator on numerous federally funded research grants (NIH, SAMHSA, NIDRR) and has published more than 75 articles and book chapters on the delivery of effective community mental health and rehabilitation services to individuals with psychiatric disabilities. His work specifically focuses on identifying and eliminating barriers to full community inclusion (e.g., work, school, intimate relationships, spirituality, friendships, or parenting), promoting the development and utilization of effective supports and mainstream community resources, and enhancing the development and effectiveness of peer support programs.

Richard C. Baron is the director of knowledge translation for the Temple University Collaborative on Community Inclusion of Individuals with Psychiatric Disabilities and has been a leading researcher, trainer, and policy analyst on the issues surrounding competitive employment for people with mental health conditions for over 40 years, including two NIDRR Switzer Fellowship publications on employment issues.

Seble-Mariam A. Menkir is a recovery initiatives specialist with the Department of Behavioral Health and Intellectual disAbility Services in the city of Philadelphia where she participates in various policy and training initiatives in the system's recovery transformation. She is also an individual with lived experience regarding recovery from mental health challenges.

Lori Breen received her master's in social work in 2000. In 2007, she acquired her certification in non-profit executive leadership, expanding her expertise into program design and governance. In 2002, Lori led a county-sponsored pilot aimed at transforming traditional mental health services into recovery-oriented services and supports. Since then, she has been partnering with people diagnosed with mental illness in developing programs and initiatives designed to reconnect individuals to themselves, their communities, and meaning and purpose in life.

REFERENCES

Americans with Disabilities Act. (1990). 12101-12213.

Atay, J. E., Crider, R., Foley, D., Male, A. A., & Blacklow, B. (2006). *Admissions and resident patients, state and county mental hospitals, United States, 2004.* Rockville, MD: Center for Mental Health Services.

Aubry, T., & Myner, J. (1996). Community integration and quality of life: A comparison of persons with psychiatric disabilities in housing programs and community residents who are neighbours. *Canadian Journal of Community Mental Health, 15*(1), 5-20.

Baron, R. C., & Salzer, M. S. (2002). Accounting for unemployment among people with mental illness. *Behavioral Sciences & the Law, 20*(6), 585-599.

Beels, C. C. (1981). Social networks and the treatment of schizophrenia. *International Journal of Family Therapy, 3*(4), 310-315.

Beginning postsecondary students longitudinal study. (2001). Retrieved from http://nces.ed.gov/surveys/bps/somefindings.asp

Bond, G. R., Salyers, M.P., Rollins, A. L., Rapp, C. A., Zipple, A. M. (2004). How evidence-based practices contribute to community integration. *Community Mental Health Journal, 40*(6), 569-588.

Burns-Lynch, B., Salzer, M., & Baron, R. (2010). *Managing risk in community integration: Promoting the dignity of risk and supporting personal choice.* Philadelphia, PA: Temple University Collaborative on Community Inclusion of Individuals with Psychiatric Disabilities.

Carling, P. J. (1995). *Return to community: Building support systems for people with psychiatric disabilities.* New York: The Guilford Press.

Chamberlin, J., Powers, L. (1999). History and definition of self-determination and consumer control proceedings from the National Leadership Summit on Self-Determination and Consumer-Direction and Control. Bethseda, MD.

Cook, J. A., Blyler, C. R., Leff, H. S., McFarlane, W. R., Goldberg, R. W., Gold, P. B.,... Razzano, L. A. (2008). The employment intervention demonstration program: Major findings and policy implications. *Psychiatric Rehabilitation Journal, 31*(4), 291-295. doi: 10.2975/31.4.2008.291.295

Corrigan, P. W., & Penn, D. L. (1999). Lessons from social psychology on discrediting psychiatric stigma. *American Psychologist, 54,* 765-776.

DHHS. (1999). *Mental health: A report of the Surgeon General.* Rockville, MD: U.S. Department of Health and Human Services, Substance Abuse and Mental Health Services Administration, Center for Mental Health Services, National Institutes of Health, National Institute of Mental Health.

DHHS. (2003). *Achieving the Promise: Transforming mental health care in America: Executive summary.* Rockville, MD: DHHS Pub. No. SMA-03-3832.

Draine, J., Salzer, M. S., Culhane, D., & Hadley, T. (2002). Role of social disadvantage in crime, joblessness, and homelessness among persons with serious mental illness. *Psychiatric Services, 53,* 565-573.

Flynn, R. J., & Aubry, T. D. (1999). Integration of persons with developmental or psychiatric disabilities: Conceptualization and measurement. In R. J. Flynn & R. LeMay (Eds.), *A quarter century of normalization and social role valorization: Evolution and impact* (pp. 271-303). Ottawa, ON: University of Ottawa Press.

GAO. (1996). *SSA disability: Program redesign necessary to encourage return to work. Report to the chairman.* Washington, DC (GAO #/HEHS 9662): Special Committee on Aging of the U.S. Senate, U.S. General Accounting Office.

Hinshaw, S. (2007). *The mark of shame: Stigma of mental illness and an agenda for change.* Oxford University Press.

Kessler, R. C., Foster, C. L., Saunders, W. B., & Stang, P. E. (1995). Social consequences of psychiatric disorders, I: Educational attainment. *American Journal of Psychiatry, 152,* 1026-1032.

McDonald-Miszczak, L., Maki, S. A., Gould, O. N. (2000). Self-reported medication adherence and health status in late adulthood: The role of beliefs. *Experimental Aging Research, 26,* 189-207.

Metraux, S., Caplan, J. M., Klugman, D., & Hadley, T. R. (2007). Assessing residential segregation among Medicaid recipients with psychiatric disability in Philadelphia. Journal of Community Psychology, 35(2), 239-255. doi: 10.1002/jcop.20145

Nirje, B. (1980). The normalization principle. In K. E. Nitsch & R. J. Flynn (Eds.), *Normalization, social integration, and community services* (pp. 31-50). Baltimore, MD: University Park Press.

Oliver, M. (1990). *The politics of disablement.* London, UK: Basingstroke Macmillians.

Olmstead vs. L.C., 527 U.S. 581 (1999).

Park, J. M., Solomon, P., & Mandell, D. S. (2006). Involvement in the child welfare system among mothers with serious mental illness. *Psychiatric Services, 57*(4), 493-497.

Parks, J., Svendsen, D., Singer, P., Foti, M. E., & Mauer, B. (2006). *Morbidity and mortality in people with serious mental illness.* Alexandria, VA: National Association of State Mental Health Program Directors, Medical Directors Council.

Pattison, E., Defrancisco, D., Wood, P., Frazier, H., Crowder, J. (1975). A psychosocial kinship model for family therapy. *American Journal of Psychiatry, 132,* 1246-1251.

Perske, R. (1972). The dignity of risk. In W. Wolfensberger (Ed.), *Normalization: The principle of normalization in human services* (pp. 194-200). Toronto, ON: National Institute on Mental Retardation.

Phelan, J. C., Link, B. G., Stueve, A., & Pescosolido, B. A. (2000). Public conceptions of mental illness in 1950 and 1996: What is mental illness and is it to be feared? *Journal of Health and Social Behavior, 41*(June), 188-207.

Racino, J. A. (1995). Community living for adults with developmental disabilities: A housing and support approach. *Journal of the Association of Persons with Severe Handicaps, 20,* 300-310.

Salzer, M. (2006). Introduction. In M. Salzer (Ed.), *Psychiatric rehabilitation skills in practice: A CPRP preparation and skills workbook.* Columbia, MD: United States Psychiatric Rehabilitation Association.

Salzer, M. S. (1997). Consumer empowerment in mental health organizations: Concepts, benefits, and impediments. *Administration and Policy in Mental Health, vol 24,* 425-434.

Salzer, M. S., Blank, M., Rothbard, A., & Hadley, T. (2001). Adult mental health services in the 21st century. In R. W. Manderscheid & M. J. Henderson (Eds.), *Mental health, United States, 2000* (pp. 99-112). Washington, DC: United States Government Printing Office.

Salzer, M. S., & Mental Health Association of Southeastern Pennsylvania Best Practices Team. (2002). Consumer-delivered services as a best practice in mental health care and the development of practice guidelines. *Psychiatric Rehabilitation Skills, 26*(3), 355-382.

Sharpe M. N., Bruininks B. D., Blacklock B. A., Benson, B., & Johnson, D. M. (2004). *The emergence of psychiatric disabilities in postsecondary education* (Vol. 3). Minneapolis, MN: University of Minnesota, National Center on Secondary Education and Transition.

Souma, A., Rickerson, N., & Burgsthler, S. (2002). *Academic accommodations for students with psychiatric disabilities.* Seattle, WA: Washington University.

Trupin, L., Sebesta, D., Yelin, E., & LaPlante, M. P. (1997). *Trends in labor force participation among persons with disabilities 1983-1994.* San Francisco, CA: University of California, Disability Statistics Rehabilitation Research and Training Center, Institute for Health and Aging.

Veterans Health Administration. (2008). *VHA handbook 1160.01: Uniform mental health services in VA medical centers and clinics.* Washington, DC: Department of Veterans Affairs, Veterans Health Administration.

Wolfensberger, W. (1970). The principle of normalization and its implications to psychiatric services. *American Journal of Psychiatry, 127,* 291-297.

Wolfensberger, W. (1972). *The principle of normalization in human services.* Toronto, ON: National Institute on Mental Retardation.

Wong, Y. L. I., & Solomon, P. (2002). Community integration of persons with psychiatric disabilities in supportive independent housing: A conceptual mode and methodological considerations. *Mental Health Services Research, 4*(1), 13-28.

ADVOCACY

Kathy Muscari

A B S T R A C T

This chapter emphasizes the importance of the practice of advocacy in obtaining resources, services, and supports to which people have a right. Advocacy as a best practice is also highlighted because there are important systems changing reasons for helping professionals to become skilled advocacy leaders. Advocacy strategies that help define a course of action are included. Exemplary advocacy programs are discussed as well as targets and tactics, challenges and concerns, implementation, and other considerations. PsyR practitioners want people to be able to pursue their potential. Skilled advocacy, gained through educational programs, such as West Virginia's *Leadership Academy* or Maryland's *The Anti-Stigma Project,* sets the stage for system transformation and creates the difference leading to improved services, lives, and communities.

SYSTEM TRANSFORMATION IS ABOUT DISRUPTING THE STATUS QUO AND FUNDAMENTALLY CHANGING delivery of services and supports so people have easy, on-going access to up-to-date information and personalized quality care. Advocacy, whether individually or collectively applied, is a practical skill for bringing about social inclusion and needed change in policies, programs, and practices. PsyR practitioners have unfortunately encountered systems and situations where opportunities for those they serve are blocked or non-existent. Acting as change agents, people who use and provide services are increasingly working to implement agency, legislative, legal, community, and self-advocacy strategies.

IMPORTANCE OF SYSTEM TRANSFORMATION AND ADVOCACY FOR RECOVERY

I want to help make things better. Yes, I've learned a lot from my rehab counselor, such as empowerment and recovery. Sometimes, we both speak out for people on the streets ... like testifying at the state house on homelessness. [Housing is] a great need. I know; I've been without a home myself ... and, advocacy is a way to start making a difference—to give back. It changed my life. Someone believed in me. (Consumer Advocate, Interview 2010)

Recovery is defined as the "process of change through which individuals improve their health and wellness, live a self-directed life, and strive to reach their full potential" (SAMHSA, 2012). Health, home, purpose, and community are identified as major dimensions of recovery—all easily fitting into the values and work of PsyR. In America's continuous effort to transform its mental health delivery system toward this recovery focus, psychiatric rehabilitation practitioners are important providers of community-based service. In partnership with people who are managing challenges presented by mental illnesses, including those with co-occurring mental illness and substance abuse issues, these practitioners promote the message that a more satisfying and successful life is possible.

This powerful vision of recovery (as an outcome) and the need for transformation in the nation's mental health system were formally recommended by the President's New Freedom Commission Report, *Achieving the Promise: Transforming Mental Health Care in America* (2003). Since that time, progress toward a better understanding of and support for recovery has occurred. Services and supports have been reshaped to be more consumer and family driven. Psychiatric rehabilitation (PsyR) principles are more aligned with key recovery components. Recovery experiences and personal narratives are increasingly valued. Peers as providers, such as peer support specialists and wellness and recovery coaches, are more commonplace. Statewide self-help advocacy networks are growing. All this has taken place, and continues to occur, through the relentless work of people in recovery, families, providers, policymakers, and others in both public and private sectors.

With recovery named as the "single most important goal" for the mental health service delivery system (Federal Action Agenda, 2005), greater emphasis has been placed on improving all aspects of a person's life. By accepting that mental health recovery is possible, acknowledging its role in overall health, and having a desire to reduce rates of co-morbidity and mortality, attention to wellness of mind/body/spirit has increased. Exciting initiatives, such as integrated primary and behavioral health care and whole health peer support, have been touted by strong advocates. Attending to the whole person fits precisely into the work of PsyR practitioners, who have long supported an array of services that promote holistic well-being. Through their interactions with local resources, experienced PsyR practitioners have a keen understanding of both opportunities and challenges faced daily by the people they represent. When needed change is recognized, PsyR practitioners are often in an informed position to advocate. As PsyR practitioners wear their change agent hats, they demonstrate advocacy skills and become role models for people in recovery. Joining forces to conduct collective advocacy is a powerful tactic for initiating change.

At the federal government level, a former Center for Mental Health Services Director remarked that "transformation is ultimately about new values, new attitudes, and new beliefs; it is about how these changes are expressed in the behavior of people and institutions" (Power, 2004). This important process of transformation begins when PsyR practitioners challenge the status quo—both with and on behalf of the people they serve—through individual connections and organized advocacy (Salzer, 2006). The Substance Abuse and Mental Health Services Administration has taken more of a leadership role in efforts to advance understanding of recovery, "drawing on research, practice, and personal experience of recovering individuals, within the context of health reform" (SAMHSA, 2012), Psychiatric Rehabilitation practitioners can apply for federal grants, join expert panels, and act as advocates to enforce SAMHSA's effort to "ensure that vital recovery supports and services are available and accessible to all who need and want them."

Sometimes transformative change comes about through what the business world calls a disruptive innovation where a simpler, cheaper product or service ultimately upends an established marketplace (Christensen, 1997). Some examples of disruptive innovation in the behavioral health care field include employing peers and community health workers as providers and leveraging information technology in service provision. The *Pillars of Peer Support* Summits (2009-2012) have promoted peer support services as a valuable transformational tool to support recovery for people utilizing state systems of care. Emerging from disruptive innovation, these summits advocated for peer support implementation, reimbursement, involvement in promotion of whole health and well-being, and establishing quality standards. PsyR practitioners are pivotal leaders in supporting this paradigm shift. In many states, Certified Psychiatric Rehabilitation Practitioners (CPRPs) supervise peers as providers.

Advocacy is a key component for PsyR practitioners to understand and use in their role of supporting recovery, promoting social inclusion, and creating system transformation. To assist in eliminating stigma and discrimination, improving services and supports, and establishing venues for people in recovery to convey their messages of hope, skilled advocates are absolutely necessary. This is reinforced by the century-old national Mental Health Association (2010), dedicated to helping people live mentally healthier lives through advocacy, education, and services, believing that "mental health and substance abuse systems transformation will occur only when all stakeholders view recovery as the primary goal."

Psychiatric rehabilitation practitioners use "systematic efforts to help adults with psychiatric disabilities to move forward in their recovery process" (Corrigan et al., 2008, p. 74). They support people in attaining their individualized rehabilitation goals so that meaningful, positive life change is possible. In creating community connections, they provide service functions such as assessment, planning, linking, monitoring, and advocacy. As individual lives improve, whole communities improve.

PsyR practitioners believe people with disabilities can and do contribute to society. Over time, PsyR practitioners have learned much from change agents and advocates with disabilities. These individuals are powerful, transformative advocates, including Clifford Beers, who wrote *A Mind That Found Itself* (1908), exposing psychiatric hospital atrocities from his viewpoint as a patient; Judi Chamberlin, who wrote *On Our Own* (1978) about the growth of community self-help supports and alternative services to treatment; Justin Dart, who helped to pass the *Americans With Disabilities Act of 1990;* and Pat Deegan, whose ideas on shared decision-making (2010) are evident in her *Common Ground* web-based application currently used to involve people in their psychiatric care. Through their role as advocates, PsyR practitioners, in concert with people in recovery, continue to lay the groundwork for transformation and deep-seated systems change to occur.

ADVOCACY AS A BEST PRACTICE

> *Thank you for the opportunity to be part of the Leadership Academy. This is the first time I've attended anything like this in my life. I've learned a lot about advocacy and running meetings and creating action plans. My confidence is better; I now have skills I can put to use. I want to get started on building a respite center in my town. Thanks for believing in me!* (Speech from Oklahoma Key Leadership Academy graduate, May 2010)

Best practices are associated with demonstrating positive outcomes, and skilled advocacy is a well-established practice (Clay, 2005; Ezell, 2001; Rubin & Rubin, 2007; Salzer, 2006; Corrigan et al., 2008). Advocacy has been studied and applied in many fields with proven results—both society-focused and government-focused. To improve conditions, lawyers, teachers, manufacturers, social workers, nurses, and ballpark moms all use advocacy. "Today, empowered consumers of mental health services acknowledge the importance of using individual and collective self-advocacy for systems change" (Muscari, 2007, p. 52).

Self-advocacy involves action on one's own behalf, and collective advocacy is enacted when several people with common interests work together on a specific issue. According to Ezell (2001), advocacy "consists of those purposive efforts to change specific existing or proposed policies or practices on behalf of or with a specific client or group of clients" (p. xx).

PsyR practitioners and those they serve have opportunities every day for taking on advocacy issues. Advocacy is about a cause; it is an effort to shape perception or create change. Ezell (2001) points out that there are five important reasons for helping professionals to be advocates: to "create a society that is just, in which all persons have equal opportunities to pursue their potential; ensure that programs and services are accessible, effective, appropriate, flexible, comprehensive, adequate, and efficient; protect existing individual rights and entitlements and to establish new rights and entitlements as needed; eliminate the negative and unethical impact that social institutions, programs, and individuals may have on people; and assure that the least intrusive intervention is utilized to meet the client's needs and achieve the service goal" (p. 6).

Advocacy Strategies

In addition to these reasons to advocate, there are specific advocacy strategies that PsyR practitioners and other advocates consider when deciding upon a best course of action for a cause. These strategies include: self-advocacy, agency advocacy, legislative advocacy, legal advocacy, and community advocacy.

Self-advocacy

Self-advocacy is described by Sally Clay (2005) as people in recovery learning to "identify their own needs and to speak for themselves" (p. 265). Author and researcher Mary Ellen Copeland (2010) considers self-advocacy to be one of five key concepts essential to recovery. Copeland has met people in recovery "who have learned to be their own best advocate [and] many of them are now strong advocates for others with similar issues" (p. 17). An individual practicing self-advocacy gathers confidence and information to purposefully ask for what they need.

Agency advocacy

Agency advocacy is about making change in programs and agencies so that the agency truly benefits people being served. Agency advocates need to know the "differences between rules, regulations, policies, and practices and the agency processes by which each is created" (Ezell, 2001, p. 73).Also, if there is wrongdoing such as inhuman treatment or misused funds, there are bona fide whistleblower laws that protect the rights of people to blow the whistle (see also legal advocacy).

Legislative advocacy

Legislative advocacy is applied when a budget is being addressed by the legislature or a change is proposed involving the law, ordinances, municipal code, or a school board policy. Using legislative advocacy, well-known advocate Dorthea Dix appealed at state and federal levels in the 1800s to help create hospital care for people with psychiatric disabilities, who were then living in chains, poorhouses, and jails.

Legal advocacy

Legal advocacy involves filing suits regarding neglect or rights violations. The Olmstead Act (1999), which promoted community integration and is now upheld in every state, is a result of a legal case in Georgia. There are also laws that protect civil rights. For example, in the United States, the *Rehabilitation Act of 1973* and the *Americans with Disabilities Act of 1990* help with anti-discrimination protection and reasonable accommodations.

Community advocacy

Community advocacy is important when it appears that people who are oppressed are uncared for. Community advocacy often comes in the form of education. Nellie Bly, an undercover journalist who gained admission in the 1880s to a psychiatric institution, and Clifford Beers, a patient/advocate who in 1909 founded the advocacy organization that is now Mental Health America, used their personal experiences to educate the public on what was happening in psychiatric institutions.

Advocacy Tactics

Within each of the advocacy strategies described above, there are tactics that can be used. Tactics refer to the actual change-creating activities applied, such as educating legislators, testifying at hearings, influencing an agency administrator, holding a press conference, and so forth. Media tactics include advertising, editorials, interviews, letters to the editor, public service announcements, webinars, and radio and television talk shows. Responsible use of social media's networking methods can quickly provide relevant information to large numbers of people. A target is the specific thing that needs to be changed, like a state statute, agency policy, or community attitude. Some advocates see targets as specific people who can affect the change. Targeted advocacy, such as anti-stigma education or self-determination support, can be accomplished through an array of proven tactics, including public forums and trainings. Brown (2012) states, "research has shown that, of the three types of anti-stigma interventions—protest, education, and contact—contact and education strategies are the most successful" (p. 1).

When advocacy strategies and tactics are proven through both practice and evidence to be highly effective, they are considered best practices. While PsyR practitioners gain advocacy knowledge from resources, such as texts, journals, films, and lectures, it is through participation in real-life advocacy campaigns—interacting with seasoned advocates who apply practical tactics—that practitioners hone PsyR skills and acquire best practice experience.

Advocacy Guidelines

Advocacy is a focused and purposive effort to create change on behalf of or with specific populations. Because of its change nature, it must always be issue-centered. With this in mind, there are actions generally considered effective because they often lead to successful advocacy results. When using advocacy to help transform conditions, improve services, the following guidelines represent what is currently considered best practice (Avner, 2002; Bobo et al., 2010; Ezell, 2001; Salzer, 2006; TCA Tool-Kit, n.d.; WVMHCA, 2007).

Issues that affect a person's ability to live, learn, work, or participate in environments of his/ her choice are prime targets for advocacy in the field of psychiatric rehabilitation. PsyR practitioners encounter many situations and circumstances where change is needed. Opportunities to rally against social injustice, improve a company policy, or request a reasonable worksite accommodation are fairly common. Without action, change is unlikely. To be effective change agents, PsyR practitioners must carefully identify the target(s) needing change and determine the strategies and related tactics best suited for a successful result.

Conducting a full advocacy initiative is called a campaign. Advocacy campaigns consist of all the planning and actions taken toward achieving the overall goal. The process for conducting effective advocacy does not have to be complicated. Determining a basic plan with manageable steps paves the way. The guidelines listed next describe this advocacy process in more detail and offer some helpful tips.

Identify the issue and hoped-for outcome (goal): People organize because they have an interest in gaining something of importance to them. Their issues of concern may be about such things as obtaining equal rights, helping the poor, getting better healthcare, or protecting the environment. Listening is critical for learning about people's wants and needs. By listening, advocates build trust and respectful relationships. Relationships are essential in creating a foundation for action. PsyR practitioners hear and represent their target population by understanding both the situation (issue) and the hoped for solution (goal).

State your case and the values involved, and then propose a solution: PsyR practitioners are on the alert for worthwhile, impactful issues where advocacy action would result in improving lives and empowering others. Once an issue is identified, details should be carefully gathered and a clear description prepared. When stating the case, include what specific change is hoped for and what help is needed. Mention unifying values, like respect for others or the importance of choice. Proposing a solution is a proactive step. By doing this, advocates strengthen their position, gain followers, and influence decision-makers.

Build a base of supporters, educate them, and invite them to join the effort: To inform and engage others, articulate the vision and goals. Raising awareness helps to mobilize supporters. Supporters can be attracted through activities such as online networking, town meetings, fact sheets, personal stories, and so forth. Look for individuals, groups, and organizations with similar missions. Once a connection is made, encourage people to get involved. Collective advocacy has the advantage of strength in numbers, providing many helping hands. It allows for productive delegation of tasks and taps into a variety of resources, including development of natural leaders.

Create an action plan with strategies, targets, tactics, resources, and timelines: An advocacy plan begins with identifying the issue (target) and the goal desired (hoped for outcome); the type of advocacy (strategy) needed; and action steps (tactics) to be implemented. In simple terms, advocacy groups support good news, oppose bad news, investigate contradictory information, and help develop a solution for unmet needs (WVMHCA, 2007). For example, a local group identifies the need for accessible parking near the town's public library. Having improved parking will increase use of the site by people with disabilities. In planning action, the group decides the change needed requires community advocacy. The mayor, county commission, and library board will be targeted because of their decision-making abilities regarding the issue. Tactics to be used include a letter-writing campaign, media coverage, and an educational town meeting involving key stakeholders. A writer, mailing list, media contacts, and a meeting site for concerned parties are the most obvious resources required to complete the steps involved. A timeline naming people responsible for securing these resources and implementing the activities will be developed. This timeline listing action responsibilities reminds people of what they have agreed to do. Having an action plan in place increases the likelihood an advocacy campaign will occur in an organized and productive fashion. In this case, a solution (more convenient, usable parking) to an unmet need (lack of accessible parking near the library) is the goal.

Take the least conflictual action(s) needed to accomplish the objective: When embarking on an advocacy campaign, prioritizing action steps is wise. Where several options are possible, determine which is the most positive and beneficial. Consider what will bring success with the least difficulty and cost. Weigh out possible consequences, including harm to others. Is there a way to build bridges rather than create conflict? When making choices, check to see if the group's values are being accurately reflected.

Document everything: Gather information so that a position or action rests on facts. Actions based on incorrect information can cause embarrassment and damage reputations. Document everything the advocacy group and other people do. Records help to validate successes, protect against misinformation, and promote the cause. Records provide an historical document of what takes place and can help in planning future events.

Be culturally aware and respectful: Culture affects the way people think and how they behave. Culture is defined as shared values, traditions, norms, customs, arts, history, folklore, and institutions of a group of people. Diversity includes such differences as race, ethnicity, language, gender, nationality, mental ability, and age. Worldview is the way people have learned to think about things as a result of their life experiences (Mead, 2008). Being willing to listen and learn about culture demonstrates respect. Effective advocates demonstrate sensitivity to and understanding of cultural differences. To become more informed about culture, read about different cultural groups, keep up with current political and economic issues, pay attention to the media, read cultural magazines and newspapers, attend cultural events, take classes or workshops, and seek out new experiences (WVMHCA, 2007). Becoming culturally aware helps to build bridges and avoid miscommunication and unintended offenses. A diverse coalition of supporters is a big advantage for an advocate.

Counter negative stereotypes about and discrimination towards the target population: Opponents of the advocacy campaign may use scare tactics and broad generalizations about the target population to undermine the need for change. When serving an at-risk population, such as people with psychiatric disabilities, advocates encounter a variety of misinformation, stigma, and discrimination. Stereotypes are hurtful labels that have been used to create social isolation. Pro-active education is one of the best ways to counter negativity and raise awareness. Provide correct information to the media. Offer positive, prompt responses, based on fact, when these situations arise. Keep the needs of the population being served in the forefront. Role-model dignity and respect.

Monitor changes and follow-up: Once an advocacy campaign toward addressing an issue has begun, follow through. Monitor progress by attending meetings and reviewing the advocacy action plan. Be prepared to adapt to changes as interventions take place. Keep current, so action taken is appropriate and information exchanged is accurate. Success can be viewed as progress toward an ideal. Monitoring keeps everyone abreast of where the situation stands. It helps in creating quick responses. Having successful efforts over time strengthens an advocate's competency and reputation. This is helpful when building a network for future opportunities to create needed change.

CHALLENGES TO IMPLEMENTING ADVOCACY PROGRAMS

Although advocacy is considered an important skill of PsyR practitioners, implementation is sometimes overshadowed by other day-to-day roles and responsibilities. To complicate matters, PsyR programs and resources are rarely funded or implemented primarily for strengthening advocacy efforts. Although advocacy is mentioned at professional workshops and transformation seminars as a necessary vehicle for change, it often lacks the attention in practice that it deserves.

The perception of the importance of advocacy is related to a practitioner's professional preparation in advocacy and participation in advocacy activities at the local, state, and national levels (Tappe et al., 2007). While well-intentioned about making a difference, practitioners do not always choose to apply the skills of advocacy. Some may not fully realize that advocacy is a valid role of a PsyR practitioner. Others may feel inadequately prepared or lack experience in this area. Basic information, through formal and informal learning experiences, is needed to improve knowledge, skills, and positive perceptions for participating in advocacy initiatives. Formal learning experiences include higher education courses, service learning, internships, independent study, and research projects (Tappe & Galer-Unti, 2001, 2006). Informal advocacy learning experience includes such things as mentoring and participating in advocacy activities of relevant organizations.

Along with feelings of inadequate preparation or lack of experience, additional challenges for the PsyR practitioner involve the investment of energy, time, and financial resources required for effective advocacy. With the needs of an organization and the people it serves as the priority, and with existing work demands requiring multi-tasking, it can be difficult to set aside time to conduct a general staff training about advocacy. With funding dollars so competitive, targeted, and stretched, it can be difficult to find resources to fund proven programs like an anti-stigma campaign or leadership training. With so many needs to address, services to provide, and agency requirements to fulfill, time and energy are precious commodities--especially when an agency is short-staffed and existing staff are overloaded.

Few funding streams will pay solely for advocacy work. Avner (2002) notes that while 501(c)(3) nonprofits can lobby, there are legal limits to lobbying expenditures, and they cannot work to influence the outcome of an election (electioneering). As a result, to be successful as an advocate, resourcefulness is required as well as ingenuity. Often, resources are borrowed, such as offices, phones, other staff, transportation, and so forth. Coming up with acceptable tactics that will make a real difference requires time and creativity. While the art of persuasion is helpful, engaging others to assist can be difficult. Advocacy is hard work and becomes a particular challenge when workloads are full, resources are limited, and other demands are pressing. And, in some instances, providers fear alienating employers and funders.

Sometimes PsyR advocates neglect to limit their efforts and take on too much. Becoming too stretched may result in a compromise to one's well-being. Not taking care of one's self likely affects the quality of one's advocacy activities and can lessen one's continued interest in being an advocate. Much like figuring out reasonable goals with the people they serve, PsyR advocates benefit from determining how much advocacy work they can adequately take on. Maintaining a balance can result in better advocacy outcomes. Action steps, such as requesting a day off, spending time with family and/or friends, talking to a supervisor, exercising, applying stress reduction, and implementing time management techniques may help. Self-care is one way to role-model empowerment to others. Teamwork, delegation, and limiting new activities can help with busy schedules.

There are also perceived challenges to working alongside people-in-recovery whether they are advocates in the self-help recovery movement or socially conscious colleagues in a PsyR center that hires people in recovery. Effective advocacy requires peers and non-peer allies to work in partnership. Challenges raised in this arena can create barriers to advocacy efforts and system transformation due to perpetuation of stigma and discrimination, which blocks progress.

Hiring peers as providers is an example of a disruptive innovation that has upended traditional hiring practices and job responsibilities at behavioral health agencies. "Peer employees are individuals who self-identify as peers and are hired either in designated peer positions or in traditional mental health positions" (Corrigan et al., 2008, p. 376). The benefits of hiring people in recovery are undeniable. Personal narratives peers share serve to inspire hope and promote recovery. Awareness of local resources and the ability to hold mutually responsive dialogue regarding similar issues offers a source of comfort and motivation for service recipients. People with disabilities, including those in recovery from psychiatric disabilities, are often described as loyal, working harder and longer to prove their capabilities. Because of this and other findings, promoting employment of people in recovery is a commendable target for advocacy efforts.

Even with evidence that peer counselors, support specialists, navigators, and recovery coaches are making a positive difference, there remains some concern about boundary issues, dual relationships, and the need for special accommodation, such as increased break time and job sharing. There is also some prejudice against peer workers by non-peer providers (Corrigan et al., 2008), particularly in accepting them as equals in the field. In addition, some people in recovery may not accept their peers as having helpful expertise worthy of staff positions. They may consider the peer helper as having been co-opted into the system, possibly losing the perspective of a consumer. People in recovery manage this perception by receiving support from others, participating in self-help groups, following their treatment plans, accessing supervisors for support, and attending trainings (Silver, 2004). Positive aspects of hiring people with personal experience using mental health services include their knowledge about various human service systems, use of beneficial coping strategies, ability to engage other consumers, and being positive role models that inspire hope (Corrigan et al., 2008).

These work-related challenges may call for internal advocacy or agency advocacy. Internal advocates can access information and often personally know and can influence those in charge. They likely understand what strategies would work best in their agency to address issues. PsyR practitioners, particularly those familiar with case management skills, are often internal advocates. If an advocacy problem becomes protection of legal rights, then a reasonable course of action for a PsyR practitioner, who does not have legal expertise, might be to refer the consumer to a legal advocate or national advocacy group.

As Ezell (2001) suggests, "with skill and determination, advocates are sure to produce change" (p. 196). Despite the limitations of needing more practitioners, the lack of adequate advocacy training and the need for raising awareness about the importance of taking action, system transformation is occurring. Regardless of the need for more time, energy, and funds, and the reduction of discrimination and stigma regarding peers as providers, it is amazing what PsyR practitioners are accomplishing through advocacy on behalf of and with the people they serve. In communities across the U.S., PsyR practitioners are being resourceful and creative. At the same time, balance is needed, so burnout is reduced and effective advocacy can continue.

CONCERNS RELATED TO IMPLEMENTING ADVOCACY PROGRAMS

As stated earlier, people advocate because they believe in something, and PsyR practitioners are no exception. They passionately want to make a difference in peoples' lives and improve communities. Recovery is about hope for the future, self-determination, healthy relationships, and meaningful roles in society. Along with self-management and problem-solving strategies, self-advocacy is key to recovery (Copeland, 2004, 2010). Self-advocacy in the system of mental health care often involves co-creating service plans with mental health professionals. There is concern by people in recovery that self-advocacy attempts are not always taken seriously and that treatment planning becomes a rote experience. When expressing a desire for change, people are sometimes labeled as non-compliant and even treated against their will. Mead's *Intentional Peer Support* (www.mentalhealthpeers.com) and Copeland's *Wellness Recovery Action Plan®* (www.mentalhealthrecovery.com) are two recovery-focused programs that emphasize developing mutually supportive relationships and informed self-advocacy. One concern expressed by consumers of services is that implementation of programs like these sometimes becomes co-opted toward system preferences, compromising fidelity to peer support principles. There is also a need for mutual partnerships between traditional mental health service systems and peer-run services in community care. The delivery of mental health care is being challenged and "professionals and policymakers acknowledge that mental health services have failed to help people get the level of care that research has shown to be effective" (Clay, 2005, p. 18). Demand for services and supports is increasing while funds are limited and traditional programs are strained. Studies show peer-run services are filling gaps, providing a social network, and helping to reduce hospitalization. Due to this, mental health administrators must be encouraged to become more open to using recovery-based models and include people with mental illnesses as partners. Within peer groups, there are advocacy programs that assist with "resolving problems encountered with entitlement programs, medical institutions, community agencies, residence, and even their own families" (Clay, 2005, p. 14). A concern of many people in recovery is that peer programs are not always fully recognized by traditional health care services as viable partners in care.

Advocacy is a tool that can be used to help overcome these concerns. Strong advocates inform the public about emerging best practices. They highlight success stories as well as unmet needs. They ask powerful questions, and they work alongside others with similar goals and interests. "These developments have created an unprecedented opportunity for grassroots advocates concerned with psychiatric disability issues to make their voices heard in the shaping of policies and services" (Stringfellow & Muscari, 2003, p. 142). As one example, advocates have helped to raise attention about the need for creating community reconnection opportunities and services for military service members back from deployment, their families, veterans, and others who may be dealing with trauma-related stress. There are opportunities here for PsyR practitioners, including work as volunteers with the American Red Cross. In addition, the U.S. Department of Veteran Affairs has recognized the self-help value of having veterans-in-recovery trained and hired as peer support specialists to assist courageous warriors in need. This fits with the soldier's creed (warrior ethos) of never leaving a fallen comrade.

Advocates listen to and learn from the people they serve. They seek out programs that work, including those that offer skill-building opportunities for self-determination, leadership, collective advocacy, and reduction of stigma and discrimination. West Virginia's *Leadership Academy* and Maryland's *The Anti-Stigma Campaign* are two such programs whose participants have taken hundreds of real-life actions resulting in transformational change.

SUCCESSFUL IMPLEMENTATION: ADDRESSING CHALLENGES AND CONCERNS

Advocacy is about creating a just society with equal opportunities, ensuring there are excellent and accessible programs and services, protecting and establishing rights, eliminating negative and unethical impacts of social entities, and using the least intrusive interventions to meet needs and goals (Ezell, 2001). People in recovery and their families are vital contributing stakeholders in this process.

Advocacy is one way to create momentum for system change and training is needed to help produce transformational leaders. For change at societal and legislative levels, systems advocacy uses tactics such as giving testimony before the legislature, participating in meetings and on boards and committees, and writing letters, sending emails, or making telephone calls to policy makers and representatives. The current system has not fully realized the long-term and beneficial results that are made possible by skilled advocate leaders who identify as people in recovery. Telling personal stories of recovery, including needed supports and services, can be strong tactics. Pratt et al. (2007) summarize the significance of people in recovery in advocacy and system transformation:

Persons who have severe mental illnesses play other important roles in mental health systems as well. They act as policy makers, advocates, researchers, and board members. Their input into how PsyR services are provided is essential to the development of a truly consumer-driven mental health system. Such input helps to ensure consumer satisfaction and contributes to the protection of the rights and dignity of people with disabilities. It is essential for psychiatric rehabilitation providers who are not diagnosed with a mental illness to learn to work in conjunction with the various types of peer providers, activists, and policy makers and to recognize all of the valuable roles that they can play in transforming mental health systems. (p. 366)

Today, there are several consumer-driven advocacy programs that have a strong evidence base and are considered exemplary. When a PsyR agency gets involved with these programs, transformational change becomes a greater possibility. Two such programs, West Virginia's *Leadership Academy* and Maryland's *The Anti-Stigma Project,* are advocacy-based curricula that are educational in nature. Each has been implemented at diverse sites across the U.S., including psychiatric rehabilitation centers where PsyR practitioners and people in recovery have trained together. Experts have commended both programs, which offer participant materials and facilitator information. They have been published in the literature and continue to be targets of research. *Leadership Academy* and *The Anti-Stigma Project* work well with providers and people in recovery by being fully engaged in planning, implementation, and evaluation. Replicated by various populations in the U.S. and in other countries, these programs exemplify the fact that hope and commitment are common in people dedicated to being change agents (Onken et al., 2002).

West Virginia Leadership Academy

I didn't realize there were others who experience what I do until we got together at this training. I've learned a lot about action plans ... our group will be doing our project when we get back home! It wasn't just practice for nothing. It's time to speak out and change things. (West Virginia Leadership Academy graduate, 2011)

The West Virginia *Leadership Academy* is a two and one-half day educational program that offers training in leadership and collective advocacy skills. This educational program has a track record of successful outcomes in creating local system and community change. The concept for *Leadership Academy* came from an Idaho demonstration project in the 1990s. During a 27-month period, this demonstration project had four hundred advocacy outcomes falling into nine basic categories: recognition, community education, policy/legislative changes, leadership appointments, fundraising, improving services, consumer rights, building networks, and strengthening advocacy groups (Hess et al., 2001; Stringfellow, 2000). *Leadership Academy* was further developed through block grant funds awarded to the West Virginia Mental Health Consumers Association, which helped to strengthen their consumer network statewide. WVMHCA's national technical assistance center project (CONTAC) later provided *Leadership Academy* technical assistance for dozens of states with funding through the federal Center for Mental Health Services.

Emphasizing skill development and empowerment through a tell-show-do structure, *Leadership Academy* fits well with PsyR principles and self-help values. Over the two and one-half days of discussion, role-play, audio-visuals, guest speakers, and presentations, *Leadership Academy* participants increase their leadership and advocacy skills. According to the *Leadership Academy Participant Manual* (WVMHCA, 2007), they accomplish this by having the opportunity, for example, to learn about consumer involvement and the forms it can take as well as the etiquette guidelines that help to improve group success and are an important foundation for coalition building. To select a target for advocacy efforts, *Leadership Academy* participants learn about sources of information used to identify community issues, how to identify issues suitable for action-planning by consumer organizations, and the criteria for selecting relevant issues to report to a group. Developing goals and action steps helps with organizing community action groups, and once a coalition is formed, advocates need skills in preparing a meeting agenda, opening the meeting, managing discussions and votes, recording minutes, and managing group records.

One of the chapters in the *Leadership Academy Participant Manual* suggests seven important steps for reporting issues in a way that the group's interest is captured and action is considered (p. 35): (1) state the issue and the source; (2) describe the situation; (3) tell what you would like the group to achieve in this situation; (4) explain what makes the issue relevant to the group; (5) state your opinion of the values involved; (6) suggest one or more steps for the group to consider; and (7) assure a decision (vote) is made on your report. Participants learn how to do these steps through role-play and feedback.

A key component of the Leadership Academy is its emphasis on identifying issues, determining goals, and responding through action steps. It facilitates learning these skills by conducting role-plays representing large and small advocacy group meetings. Leadership Academy participants consider important questions as they work together to plan advocacy campaigns. What can be done? What is appropriate? What are the goals of any particular strategy? Are these goals compatible with the values of the organization? Do we have the resources to act? What are the potential costs and benefits of particular actions? How will we implement our plan?

Most *Leadership Academy* graduates come away from the interactive workshop acknowledging the following statements as a general rule:

- When the issue is good news, reinforce it. (Example: Support a budget increase.)

- When the issue is contradictory information, investigate it. (Example: Clarify a rumor.)

- When the issue is an unmet need, develop a solution. (Example: Expand services.)

- When the issue is bad news, oppose it. (Example: Complain about discrimination.)

Taking action is how things get done. Without action, things stay the same. The *Leadership Academy* suggests possible action steps that PsyR practitioners and people in recovery might use in their advocacy campaigns, with varying degrees of difficulty, and which may be received more or less positively (WVMHCA, p. 109). In determining whether to use one of these actions, advocacy groups must weigh the work involved, the resources required, and the possible costs and benefits involved. Individual and/or group effectiveness and credibility are at stake.

The Leadership Academy has been publicly recognized as making an important contribution to strengthening consumer-led advocacy efforts. Recognizing the need for consumer and civic involvement within the mental health system and local communities, Sabin and Daniels (2002) stated:

> The *Leadership Academy* experience suggests that consumer voice can be strengthened
> through training and practice but that the process requires ongoing support. The U.S. health

care "strategy" places too much faith in market forces ("exit") as the guiding hand for its health care system. All health care systems, whether single payer or market-based managed care, require effective consumer voice and civic advocacy to help address the challenge of caring for individual patients and the needs of a wider population in ways that are clinically informed, ethically justifiable, and politically acceptable. (p. 411-412).

Maryland's The Anti-Stigma Project

You finally decide to get help, and then you're punished for it—pigeonholed into a diagnosis, shamed, labeled, and discriminated against for life. The stigma can be worse than the illness.
(Anti-Stigma Project participant, 1998)

Stigma and discrimination against people with mental illnesses and other disabilities are unfortunately common across society. Our mental health and addiction recovery communities, while improving, are not immune. Policy makers, consumers, administrators, and families are all affected by actions showing stigma and discrimination. Despite our best efforts, the system of mental health care continues to be somewhat fragmented and dysfunctional, including recognizing its own stigmatizing attitudes and behaviors. This is evidenced, in part, by ways in which we do or don't interact with each other—at times demonstrating a lack of dignity and respect. "The stigma within the mental health system damages therapeutic, professional, and personal relationships and creates barriers to providing and receiving competent and effective mental health treatment" (On Our Own of Maryland, Inc., n.d.).

The Anti-Stigma Project is a component of On Our Own of Maryland Inc. a statewide mental health consumer advocacy organization. Started in 1993 in collaboration with the Maryland Mental Hygiene Administration, the project has traveled across the U.S. and to several countries abroad. "The mission of *The Anti-Stigma Project* is to fight stigma by raising consciousness, facilitating ongoing dialogues, searching for creative solutions, and educating all participants within or connected to the mental health community, including consumers, family members, providers, educators, and administrators" (Brown and Wallace, 2007, p. 7). The Anti-Stigma Project's overall goals are to provide a safe and equal playing field and a confidential forum for interactive and collaborative discussion; facilitate the process of reducing stigmatizing attitudes and behaviors in order to create a more responsive, respectful system; strengthen collaborative relationships; enhance consumer involvement, empowerment, and recovery; and enhance access to service, quality of care, and outcomes of care.

Using education to counter discrimination and stigma associated with mental illnesses, The Anti-Stigma Project, according to the *Resource Center to Promote Acceptance, Dignity and Social Inclusion* (2008), offers workshops where participants look at how stigma affects their personal and professional lives. Participants are exposed to several facilitation methods, including assessments, role-play, and group discussions that fit various learning styles. They work with participants in reviewing videotaped interviews with people affected by stigma. According to On Our Own of Maryland, Inc., the workshops are team-facilitated by trainers who have experience in mental health, addictions and recovery, and education and communications.

Through this educational series, attitudes shift from "I don't do that" to "Yes, I do" to "I can change." According to evaluations collected, participants agreed the workshops could be seen as agents for concrete behavioral change and indicated they would pass along the information learned. One of the organization's videos, *Stigma … in Our Work, in Our Lives,* has been well received. Some general principles, offered through The Anti-Stigma Project's *Stigma: Language Matters* brochure (1998), provide concrete suggestions for avoiding stigmatizing language: (1) don't focus on a disability, (2) don't portray successful people with disabilities as superhumans, (3) don't sensationalize a disability, (4) don't use generic labels, (5) don't use psychiatric diagnoses as metaphors for other situations, (6) do put people first, not their disabilities, and (7) do emphasize abilities. The Anti-Stigma Project's 2013 DVD entitled *Distorted Perceptions: How Stigma Impacts Recovery* is a training tool including 25 thought-provoking interviews with a widely diverse group of people. It examines the impact of stigmatizing beliefs, attitudes, and behaviors on all stakeholders in the healthcare system. It also addresses ways stigma complicates collaboration between mental health and addictions entities, often creating barriers to receiving and providing competent services.

Although the designers of the *Anti-Stigma Project* did not intentionally build on effectiveness research, their intervention design is both contact- and education-based, which are the most effective strategies for changing negative public attitudes (Brown, 2012). The project's success has resulted in expansion "to include law enforcement, government, education, and somatic healthcare," and On Our Own has taken the work to eight other states and abroad (p. 2). The researchers for the project conclude that the training has a positive effect. Specifically, "the immediate benefits for consumers attending the *ASP* workshop included greater belief in their ability to overcome psychiatric-related problems, increased awareness of stigma within the mental health system and lower levels of prejudice toward their fellow consumers. Providers participating in the workshop exhibited increased awareness of stigma within the mental health system, lowered levels of prejudice toward people with psychiatric illnesses, and improved attitudes regarding the personal capabilities of people with mental illness. In summary, the *ASP* workshop raises awareness, improves attitudes, decreases stigma, and fosters a sense of personal recovery" (p. 2).

In their article on lessons learned from *The Anti-Stigma Project,* educators Arthur and Brown (2002) emphasize the importance of questioning assumptions, listening carefully, asking questions, getting to know people as people, and knowing at a heartfelt level that change is possible.

SUMMARY

Sometimes leaders have to shake things up. Other times they just have to grab hold of the adversity that surrounds them. Whether change comes from outside challenges or inside challenges, leaders make things happen. (Kouzes & Posner, 2007, p. 164)

PsyR practitioners have a professional obligation to develop their advocacy skills and become strong leaders for positive change. Anthony and Huckshorn (2008) suggest that "in the field of mental health, interpersonal skills and problem solving skills … that make someone a good clinician are fundamental to effective leadership" (p. 13). PsyR advocates applying their leadership skills "try to create the system, program, and/or unit where they can do good work and in which consumers can prosper" (Anthony & Huckshorn, 2008, p. 13). As explained throughout this chapter, the best practice of advocacy is an essential part of systems transformation. In a position statement supporting systems transformation, Mental Health America (2010) encourages mental health advocates to educate decision makers that recovery is possible and is the expected outcome of proper treatment and supports; to correct misinformation reported in the media with positive, factual, and prompt responses expressed with the dignity we demand for people with a mental illness; to promote policies that are consistent with the recovery philosophy; and to identify opportunities for people in recovery to have meaningful involvement in advocacy efforts in addition to the planning, delivery and evaluation of mental health services.

Similarly, Backs and Federici (USPRA, 2006) believe "systems change is an important responsibility for psychiatric rehabilitation practitioners" (p. 337). They list such key practitioner skills as intervening to stop discrimination and advocating for better access to public resources, policy changes, systems integration among resources, responsive services, civil protections, and changes to support optimal living. Social change advocate Shery Mead (2008) promotes advocating in the context of building community relationships. She suggests direct, honest, respectful communication with interest and curiosity about different ways of thinking.

In order to improve services, lives, and communities, transformational change is a must. Fortunately, PsyR practitioners are motivated change agents. Through their practice of effective advocacy, PsyR practitioners are making a positive difference. They are working to provide equal opportunities and ensure that the least intrusive interventions are used to meet needs. PsyR practitioners realize there are services to which people have a right. They apply advocacy skills to change policies, programs, and practices.

In supporting individual and collective empowerment, in helping to eliminate stigma and discrimination, in moving people toward their goals, in creating social inclusion, in disrupting static systems, skilled advocacy is an excellent and necessary tool. Educational programming (such as the *Leadership Academy* and *The Anti-Stigma Project*) is just one tactic in the strategy of community advocacy that PsyR practitioners, people-in-recovery, and others can apply. As PsyR practitioners continue to seek out proven tactics, it is suggested that "the explosion of technology and freedom of the Internet provide a multitude of possibilities for revitalized advocacy efforts" (Galer-Unti, 2010). It takes everyone working together, energized by common concerns, to provide the transformational leadership necessary to create beneficial results. Advocacy is a key practice the field of psychiatric rehabilitation, providing opportunity for practitioners and other change agents to achieve many successes for individuals and the public. The proven practice of advocacy exemplifies the voice(s) and power of individual and collective self-determination.

BEST PRACTICE GUIDELINES FOR EFFECTIVE ADVOCACY CAMPAIGNS

- Identify the issue and hoped-for outcome (goal).
- State your case, identify the values involved, and propose a solution.
- Build a base of supporters, educate them, and invite them to join the effort.
- Create an action plan with strategies, targets, tactics, resources, and timelines.
- Take the least conflictual action(s) needed to accomplish the objective.
- Document everything.
- Be culturally aware and respectful.
- Counter negative stereotypes and discrimination.
- Monitor changes and follow-up.

REFERENCES

Americans with Disabilities Act of 1990. Pub. L. No. 101-336, 2, 104 Stat. 328. (1991).

Anthony, W. A., & Huckshorn, K. A. (2008). *Principled leadership in mental health systems and programs.* Boston, MA: Center for Psychiatric Rehabilitation.

Arthur, T., & Brown, J. (2002). The anti-stigma project: Lessons learned, part I. *On Our Own of Maryland, Inc. Consumer Network News, 2,* 9-10.

Avner, M. (2002). *The lobbying and advocacy handbook for nonprofit organizations: Shaping public policy at the state and local level.* St. Paul, MN: Wilder Publishing Center.

Backs, A., & Federici, M. (2006). Systems competencies. In Salzer, M.S. (Ed), *Psychiatric rehabilitation skills in practice: A CPRP preparation and skills workbook* (pp. 337-386). Linthicum, MD: USPRA.

Beers, C. W. (1908). *A mind that found itself: An autobiography.* New York: Longmans, Green & Company.

Bobo, K., Kendall, J., & Max, S. (2010). *Organizing for social change: Midwest academy manual for activists.* (4th ed.). Santa Ana, CA: Forum Press.

Brown, J. (2012). Illuminating the possibilities: The Anti-Stigma Project seen as a clearly effective tool. *On Our Own of Maryland Consumer Network News, 18*(4), 1-2.

Brown, J. K., & Wallace, A. T. (2007, May). *The Anti-Stigma Project in Maryland: A collaboration between On Our Own of Maryland and the Maryland Mental Hygiene Administration.*[slide presentation] NASMHPD Fifth Annual Summit of State Psychiatric Hospital Superintendents. Bethesda, MD.

Chamberlin, J. (1978). *On our own: Patient controlled alternatives to the mental health system.* New York: McGraw-Hill.

Christensen, C. M. (1997). *The innovator's dilemma: When new technologies cause great firms to fail.* Boston, MA: Harvard Business School Press.

Clay, S. (Ed.). (2005). *On our own, together: Peer programs for people with mental illness.* Nashville, TN: Vanderbilt University Press.

Copeland, M. E. (2010). *WRAP plus.* Dummerston, VT: Peach Press.

Copeland, M. E., & Mead, S. (2004). *Wellness recovery action plan & peer support: Personal, group and program development.* West Dummerston, VT: Peach Press.

Corrigan, P. W., Mueser, K. T., Bond, G. R., Drake, R. E., Solomon, P. (2008). *Principles and practice of psychiatric rehabilitation: An empirical approach.* New York: The Guilford Press.

Daniels, A., Grant, E., Filson, B., Powell, I., Fricks, L., Goodale, L. (Ed). (2010, January). *Pillars of Peer Support: Transforming mental health systems of care through peer support services.* Retrieved from www.pillarsofpeersupport.org

Daniels, A. S., Fricks, L., Tunner, T. P. (Eds.). *Pillars of Peer Support II: Expanding the role of peer support services in mental health systems of care and recovery.* Retrieved from www.pillarsofpeersupport.org

Daniels, A. S., Tunner, T. P., Ashenden, P., Bergeson, S., Fricks, L., Powell, I. (2012, January). *Pillars of Peer Support III: Whole health peer support services.* Retrieved from www.pillarsofpeersupport.org

Deegan, P. E. (2010). A description of a web application to support shared decision making. *Psychiatric Rehabilitation Journal, 34*(1), 23-28.

Ezell, M. (2001). *Advocacy in the human services.* Belmont, CA: Wadsworth/Thompson Learning.

Galer-Unti, R. (2010). Advocacy 2.0: Advocating in the digital age. *Health Promotion Practice, 11,* 784-787.

Hess, R. E., Clapper, K. H., & Gibison, F. P. (2001). Empowerment effects of teaching leadership skills to adults with a serious mental illness and their families. *Psychiatric Rehabilitation Journal, 24,* 257-265.

Kouzes, J. M., & Posner, B. Z. (2007). *The leadership challenge* (4th ed.). San Francisco, CA: John Wiley & Sons, Inc.

Mead, S. (2008). *Intentional peer support: An alternative approach.* Self-published manuscript. Retrieved from http://www.mentalhealthpeers.com

Mental Health America. (2010). *Position statement 11: In support of recovery-systems transformation.* Retrieved February 5, 2012 from http://www.nmha.org/positions/recovery-systems

Muscari, K. D. (2007). Examining Kouzes and Posner's five leadership practices in statewide mental health consumer advocacy networks: A multi-site descriptive survey study. *Dissertation Abstracts International* (UMI No. AAT3278156).

Olmstead v. L.C., (98-536) 527 U.S. 581. (1999).

On Our Own of Maryland, Inc. (n.d.). *The Anti-Stigma Project.* Retrieved February 5, 2012 from http://www.onourownmd.org/asp.html

On Our Own of Maryland, Inc. (Winter, 2013). Distorted perceptions: How stigma impacts recovery. *Consumer Network News, 19*(4), 7.

Onken, S., Dumont, J., Ridgway, P., Dorman, D., & Ralph, R. (2002, October). *Mental health recovery: What helps and what hinders? A national research project for the development of recovery facilitating system performance indicators.* Alexandria, VA: National Technical Assistance Center for State Mental Health Planning (NTAC), National Association of State Mental Health Program Directors (NASMHPD).

Power, A. K. (2004, December). *Remarks by A. Kathryn Power.* National Consensus Conference on Mental Health Recovery and Systems Transformation. Washington, DC.

Pratt, C. W., Gill, K. J., Barrett, N. M., & Roberts, M. M. (2007). *Psychiatric rehabilitation.* San Diego: Academic Press.

President's New Freedom Commission on Mental Health. (2003). *Achieving the promise: Transforming mental health care in America, final report.* No. Pub. No. SMA-03-3832. Rockville, MD: U.S. Department of Health and Human Services.

Rehabilitation Act of 1973. Pub. L. No. 93-112, H.R. 8070. (1973).

Resource Center to Promote Acceptance, Dignity and Social Inclusion. (2008). *The Anti-Stigma Project, Baltimore, Maryland.* Retrieved February 5, 2012 from http://promoteacceptance.samhsa.gov/campaigns/Program_Details.aspx?ID=33

Rubin, J. J., & Rubin, I. S. (2007). *Community organizing and development* (4th ed.). Needham Heights, MA: Allyn & Bacon.

Sabin, J. E., & Daniels, N. (2002). Strengthening the consumer voice in managed care: IV. The leadership academy program. *Psychiatric Services, 53*(4), 405-411.

Salzer, M. S. (Ed.). (2006). *Psychiatric rehabilitation skills in practice: A CPRP preparation and skills workbook.* Linthicum, MD: USPRA.

Silver, T. (2004). Staff in mental health agencies: Coping with the dual challenges as providers with psychiatric disabilities. *Psychiatric Rehabilitation Journal, 28,* 165-171.

Stringfellow, J. W. (2000). The relationship of participation in a collective advocacy training program to the attitudes toward authority of consumers of mental health services. *Dissertation Abstracts International, 61*(03), 1700. (UMI No. 996594).

Stringfellow, J. W., & Muscari, K. D. (2003). A program of support for consumer participation in systems change: The West Virginia Leadership Academy. *Journal of Disability Policy Studies, 14*(3) 142-147.

Substance Abuse and Mental Health Services Administration, U.S. Department of Health and Human Services. (2005). *Transforming mental health care in America. Federal action agenda: First steps.* DHHS Pub. No. SMA-05-4060. Rockville, MD: U.S.D.H.H.S.

Substance Abuse and Mental Health Services Administration. U.S. Department of Health and Human Servcies. (2012). *SAMHSA's working definition of recovery.* [Brochure]. PEP12-RECDEF.

Tappe, M., & Galer-Unti, R. (2001). Health educators role in promoting health literacy and advocacy for the 21st century. *Journal of School Health, 71,* 477-482.

Tappe, M., Galer-Unti, R., & Radius, S. (2007). Health education faculty's advocacy-related perceptions and participation. *American Journal of Health Studies, 22*(3), 186-195.

Texas Commission on the Arts. (n.d.). *Tools for results tool-kit: Advocacy, the basics.* Retrieved February 5, 2012 from http://www.arts.state.tx.us/toolkit/advocacy/basics.asp

The Anti-Stigma Project. (1998). *Stigma: Language matters.* [Brochure]. Baltimore, MD: On Our Own of Maryland, Inc. & Maryland Mental Hygiene Administration.

West Virginia Mental Health Consumers Association. (2007). *West Virginia Leadership Academy: Consumer involvement in leadership, civic participation, and organization skills (participant manual).* Charleston, WV: Phoenix Publications, WVMHCA.

CHAPTER 16

TRANSFORMING PROGRAM CULTURE

Lori Ashcraft

If you want to truly understand something, try to change it.
– Kurt Lewin

ABSTRACT

Changing organizational culture is an important aspect of creating services that promote recovery. While it can be a daunting task, it is not impossible, and rising to the challenge can unleash energy and enthusiasm to fuel the transformation process. We hope for and work towards positive change for the people we serve. Demonstrating a willingness to change ourselves and the culture of our programs and systems is the most effective way to model the change process to those we serve. This chapter describes how to recognize the need for program culture change and offers recommendations for how to change the way we do our work to be more person-centered and recovery-oriented. The author describes her own experience in transforming program culture and includes points based on the experiences of people using her agency's services. Practical approaches that demonstrate how this transformation can take place are described and implications for practice are delineated. Examples include how to transform a physical environment to convey and support recovery and how to develop language and communication skills that enhance recovery conversations.

CHANGING ORGANIZATIONAL CULTURE IN BEHAVIORAL HEALTH CARE PROGRAMS HAS NEVER BEEN AS important as it is now for two significant reasons. First, we now believe that recovery is possible, and the way to promote recovery is to change our approach to planning and providing services from the way we have operated in the past. Second, healthcare reform will call upon us to contribute our best work in the area of recovery since this is the most valuable contribution we have to make to ensure integrated systems of service delivery. We know that culture is pervasive and elusive. Culture lives, not on paper or in computers or in bricks and mortar, but in the hearts and minds of those who populate the organization—staff, supervisors, customers, administrators, boards of directors, and family members. The values and beliefs held in the hearts and minds of these individuals are the bedrock of the culture of an organization. The visible signs of culture can usually be detected in the place (the program setting), the people in the program and how they interact, and the practices used in program operation. These are each described a little later on in the chapter.

Cultural transformation is more than rewriting the rules and sending out a memo instructing people to change their approach to their work; it requires preparing people for a new experience. We all naturally resist change in order to protect ourselves from one of the scariest things with which we human beings have to deal—the unknown.

The academic version of organizational culture is that it is a collection of basic assumptions "invented, discovered, or developed by a particular group … as it learns to cope with its problems" (Schein, 1990, p. 111). Those assumptions are then shared with new group members and help to define the right way to think and to act. Rather than summarizing the vast professional literature on organizational culture, this chapter will focus on what we need to consider when transforming a traditional behavioral healthcare organization into an organization focused on wellness and recovery.

RECOGNIZING THE CULTURE OF AN ORGANIZATION

I first met Edmond about ten years ago when our company Recovery Innovations hired him as a peer support specialist. It didn't take long for us to become friends as well as colleagues. One of our common bonds was related to medications. In spite of numerous attempts to get by without them, neither of us was able to do this successfully. So we partnered with each other and supported each other in taking our medications as they were prescribed. We also promised to tell each other if we were having problems associated with the medications to help both of us get an objective look at what was happening.

One afternoon, I looked out my office window and saw Edmond sitting on a bench in the courtyard talking to someone only he could see. Given our agreement to point out signs that could be related to medication issues, I went out and sat down on the bench with him. After opening with a little chit chat, I asked him how he was feeling.

"Not good," he said. "I've run out of meds, and I'm not going back to the clinic."

"Why is that?" I asked.

"I hate going there," he said. "I feel awful just walking in the door because they all know everything about me. I know they have their team meetings, and they talk about all of us, so all of them know about me—even those I don't know anything about. The longer I wait in the waiting room, the worse I feel. The receptionist acts like she's afraid of me. She probably knows all about me too. Then they have that guard there—you know we can't even go behind that yellow line anymore without him standing up and acting mad. The last time I was in there, my friend Madeline was waiting too. She had to use the bathroom and it was occupied, so she tried to use the staff bathroom. The guard jumped up and chased her off like she was about to commit a major crime. I know I need to get my prescriptions refilled, but I just don't want to go back there. The minute I walk in the door, I begin to feel like a 'mental patient' and I've worked too hard to get over that feeling. It cripples me."

Edmond's situation illustrates the importance of having a program culture that is open and friendly. If this particular clinic had been irresistibly inviting, respectfully supporting Edmond in his attempts to stay well, they would have witnessed a whole different side of him. Instead, they unwittingly brought out his tendency to resist and resent situations that made him "feel like a mental patient."

What is organizational culture? If we're going to transform it, where can we find it? What does it look like? One sign of culture can be found in the policy and procedure manuals, but changing those manuals is not going to create transformation all by itself. Organizational culture is pervasive and elusive. It's in the organizational air, like pollen on a spring day. It's like dust that settles quietly over everything, leaving a cloudy film that we can write our names in with a moist fingertip. Edmond knew that the values, beliefs, and actions of the people working at the clinic form the bedrock of the culture of that organization. This is why he described his feelings about the clinic by talking about the staff. The visible signs of culture can usually be detected, as Edmond observed, in the staff and how they interact, in the facilities where they are located, and in the practices used to operate the program.

Cultural transformation involves a lot more than simply rewriting the rules and sending out a memo instructing people to change their approach to their work. It starts with preparing the hearts and minds of people for a new experience. If you think this is going to be easy, think again. Plowing through layers of rhetoric, history, and antiquated information to reach hearts and minds is challenging. It's impossible to do by bullying or bossing people around. Instead, it takes time, imagination, creativity, and a commitment to inviting everyone to the table. It also takes a commitment to role model a transformed way of being.

When we talk about cultural transformation, we're not just asking for change; we are asking for a revolution. Change is different from transformation in many ways. Primarily, change is based on what we already know and emanates from the past. When we change, we rearrange what we already know from past experiences. Transformation, on the other hand, is based on the unknown and emanates from the future. It often requires us letting go of what we have learned from past experiences and stepping into a whole new paradigm. Human beings usually resist change, and they are likely to resist transformation even more.

THE PROCESS OF TRANSFORMING CULTURE

The challenge we face is that of moving through the resistance with as little effort as possible and engaging those hearts and minds in the transformation process. Two words come to mind for me when we talk about transformation, and they aren't the usual administrative-type words that populate books on managing organizations; they are inspiring and irresistible. Presenting the opportunity for transformation in ways that are inspiring and describing outcomes that are irresistible are the keys to engaging the hearts and minds. Remember, this is where the culture is held, so it's an important place to begin the process. Once the hearts and minds are on board, we continue to present transformation in ways that are inspiring and irresistible and that function like muses to create the courage, excitement, and energy that will transport an organization through a change in culture. The most effective approach to carrying this out is to do it with sincerity and authenticity. It is much more than a cheerleading process. It's a balancing act between respecting existing beliefs and values while, at the same time, nudging people out of their comfort zone in the direction of their potential for greater things. As a leader in the transformation process, you may grow weary of this balancing act early on and find yourself resorting to bossing, blaming, and shaming. Try to resist this urge. It will only set you back and, ultimately, it will take longer to reach the point of transformation due to greater resistance.

Reflecting on my own experience, I realize that I have a lot of patience with people who are beginning their own personal recovery journey. In contrast, when working with organizations that are beginning their journey of culture transformation, I tend to be very impatient. Their resistance aggravates me. Their reluctance to try new approaches frustrates me. My impulse is to start wagging my finger at them. This, of course, is not the most effective approach. I have to remember to get out of my own way and recall the fundamental truth about the transformation process: Organizations transform the same way people recover and require the same basic conditions of hope, choice, empowerment, and a plan for change. Once I remember the similarities, I am able to approach cultural transformation for organizations using the same tools that effectively support the recovery process for individuals. Let's take a look at how this works.

Critical Components

People who have successfully initiated their recovery journey often tell us that it began when they had hope that they could lead a much more meaningful and fulfilling life. If they weren't able to believe this, to hold the hope, often there was someone else who held the hope for them. Organizational hope works the same way. When people in the organization catch a glimpse of a vision that their work can be more meaningful and that their outcomes can change dramatically for the better, their resistance changes substantially.

Once people begin their journey of recovery, it is important that they begin to exercise their ability to make choices. By making choices, a person's ability to become self-determining is strengthened, and he or she is able to take the next steps on a recovery journey. Choice is very important for organizations as well. If people in the organization are given a choice and voice in how the journey will unfold, they are much more likely to get on board, own the outcomes, and enjoy the trip. Also, it is helpful for organizations to have an opportunity to consider the options, make choices, and find their own unique path toward transformation.

Once people have hope and have been encouraged to make choices, we can support their recovery through empowerment by engaging them in empowering conversations. Empowering conversations usually include pointing out strengths, past successes, and opportunities for further recovery. Organizations, too, benefit from empowering conversations. What are their strengths, and how can they use their strengths to launch a transformation process? What successes have they had in the past? How have they used their resources to make a difference for the people they serve? What partnerships have they built that can support their transformation? Once organizations begin to appreciate their strengths, they can use them to move toward their goals.

People who begin their recovery journey do best if they have a plan—a roadmap that will help them stay on track with the goals they want to reach and the dreams they want to make come true. This is not necessarily a treatment plan; it's a personal plan—the plan the person puts together to guide his or her steps toward recovery. It's a dynamic document that gets revised as the person continues to learn and grow. Organizations also benefit from a roadmap leading them toward transformation. As with an individual, the plan needs to be owned—born from an organic process that is informed by the hearts and minds of those in the organization. It, too, is a dynamic document that can change as the process unfolds and more is learned about the landscape.

Getting Everyone on Board

Who are the people of the organization who will need to unite in order to bring about a transformed culture? We'll start at what a traditional organization considers the bottom of the classic organizational pyramidal structure—just below the front-line workers. Here's where we find the service users—the people for whom the whole organization is supposed to exist. Note that a recovery philosophy suggests turning the pyramid upside down with the service users on top where the decisions are made but, for now, we'll follow the more traditional organizational chart to minimize confusion. What can you do?

People using services

People using services support organizational transformation in many ways. Start by checking your attitude. If you see yourself as a powerless victim who has no influence over what happens with the organization, get over that right away. Owning your own personal power is one of the first steps toward personal recovery, and it is essential if you are going to make a contribution to the transformation process. Another attitudinal check point is to let go of any resentments and enragements you may hold toward the organization. You will be most effective if you become a partner than if you become a complainer or a nagging finger-pointer. Think about how the organization could change in ways that would really support your recovery and start talking to people about your ideas. Talk to other service users, your treatment team, and the organization's administration. Let them know that you see things that can change for the better and that you want to be part of the solution.

Try not to get angry or frustrated and for heaven's sake, don't take it personally if you don't see change happening right away. Give the organization a chance. Remember, it needs hope and choice and empowerment the same way you do. Be reasonable and persistent. Don't give up. Service users still outnumber service providers, and if you all get your act together, transformation will be inevitable.

Front-line workers

Front-line workers are next when moving up from the bottom of the classic organizational pyramid. As a front line worker, you may feel like one of the least important parts of the system, but this is not true. You are the eyes and ears, the arms and legs, and perhaps most important, you are the voice that communicates what you are experiencing first hand. If you go about your job just putting in time, you cannot convey the important information you are able to gather from the people being served and the communities they live in. In order to move transformation forward, keep your ears and eyes wide open. Listen to what service users are saying. Listen to their families. Share what you hear with your colleagues and supervisors. Think about the implications of what you are hearing. Use your critical thinking abilities to consider what it means. Report this up the ladder so that the people who make policy decisions will have pertinent and up-to-date information to guide planning and cultural transformation.

Some service providers feel threatened by the inclusion of peer employees, making it hard to see the benefits they have to offer and creating resistance to integrating them into the workforce. Take an honest look inside and see if this is happening within you. If not, congratulate yourself. If so, realize that peers are not coming to take your job but to contribute new things, to enhance what you do, and to free you up to use more of the skills you have been trained to do.

Supervisors

Supervisors populate the middle of the pyramid and are the wild card in this cultural transformation process. Your position—between the line staff below you and the managers above you—means that you can make or break just about any efforts to change. The implementation of transformation—the day to day work of actually making it happen—falls heaviest on you. You are in a position to inform and influence those above you on the pyramid and those below you. You hold the key to change; how you use that key will determine the degree and the speed of your organization's transformation. To move transformation forward, your ability to role model the changes can impact the culture in a positive way. Being open to input from service users and the staff who report to you also holds hope for the people who are above you and below you in the organizational structure. Once a transformational path has been agreed upon, move it into action and keep it going. Don't accept mediocrity as a standard. Set the bar high enough that it challenges you and your team to stretch beyond your comfort zone. Use your influence and energy to keep the momentum up.

Leaders

Leaders at the top of the pyramid include the bosses and directors. If you, as a leader, stay in a positive frame of mind and reflect enthusiasm and excitement, your organization will be more able to manage change and work toward a transformed culture. Keep summarizing the progress that has been made and stay focused on the goal. Most importantly, listen. Keep holding the hope, giving choices, and empowering your staff to transform the culture. And yes, keep inspiring people and creating irresistible opportunities for them to contribute to the transformation.

WHAT A TRANSFORMED CULTURE LOOKS LIKE

There are at least three areas that require assessment and attention in the process of transforming organizational culture: the space, the people, and the practices.

Transformed Space

Let's face it; most of what we do is intangible. People who work in psychiatric rehabilitation usually have to painstakingly explain our purpose and process to others in order for them to really understand what we're doing. A facility, on the other hand, is tangible. It provides a visual representation of what we're all about. It's touchable. We can smell it (sometimes literally). Our facilities say a lot about us. The building tells us about some of the underlying beliefs of a culture. Our buildings give us an opportunity to reflect a recovery culture and to send a message to our staff, the program participants, and the community. We can do this without saying a word simply by having facilities that reflect respect for our mission and purpose.

The usual message that our facilities convey is one of control, risk management, and lack of respect for the people who use our services. These things fly right in the face of a recovery culture. If we want people to recover, we have to stop seeing our role as one of controlling and managing people. We need, instead, to inspire them to live up to their potential. The way we design our facilities says a lot about how we see our role and mission and how we see the participants.

Most behavioral health facilities (especially inpatient facilities) seem designed for the convenience of the staff. The physical layout and the schedule often take power away from participants sometimes to make things more convenient and comfortable for staff. Rules may dictate what participants will eat, what they are allowed to wear, and whether they can smoke (as well as when and where). The message to participants seems like, "This is not your place. It's our place." This message does not set the stage for recovery. It does just the opposite. It endorses and reinforces a culture that actually makes it harder to recover.

A facility that reflects recovery values and principles and sets the stage for a recovery culture communicates a different message. It sounds more like this: "I'm serious about your recovery; I have high expectations for our staff and for those who participate in our services. Our role is to empower people to take their lives back." A recovery-oriented facility is not a destination but is more like a "service" station—a place to renew and reenergize and inspire people to move forward on their recovery journey and maximize their potential. How do we get a facility to give this message and reinforce a recovery culture?

We may be so accustomed to the personality of our facilities and the silent messages they convey that we no longer notice or question the power that they have to shape our culture. There are some specific areas to notice next time you have the courage to look your facility with a critical eye. These include the building itself, the neighborhood, the internal layout, and the décor inside.

The building conveys a recovery message

How can a building reinforce a recovery message? Think of your program as being a center that's part of a community instead of as an isolated office or a clinic or residential program. This will give you the flexibility to be more agile as you grow into the knowledge of what it takes to establish a recovery culture that hosts a recovery-oriented program. It allows you to add new components and to eliminate those that have outlived their usefulness. Above all, it avoids the identity of being solely related to illness. What about the door? What does the signage look like? Is there an inviting and optimistic "Welcome" sign? Is the entrance welcoming and friendly? Can you add some potted plants or a few flowers? It always helps to have some comfortable places to sit outside in both good and inclement weather. People often like to sit near the entry, so they can greet people they know who are coming in. Can you turn some parking spaces into a little park and picnic area?

The neighborhood

What surrounds the facility? Many programs settle for being in an unsavory part of town because the rents are low or maybe because they've worn themselves out trying to fight the "Not in My Back Yard" (NIMBY) phenomenon. Staff may have internalized the low expectations and the discrimination associated with those who participate in the programs. They no longer notice that the building is surrounded by concrete parking lots in an undesirable part of town with dead or non-existent landscaping, cluttered and dirty sidewalks, dirty windows, and a shabby paint job.

A recovery culture is easier to sustain if the location is in an upbeat part of town where regular people come and go, is easily accessible, and has places to eat nearby. Find a balance between peacefulness (not a lot of roaring traffic) and an active and alive community. A free-standing facility is usually better than being in a large multipurpose complex. This affords more of an opportunity to be distinct and unique and have a recovery identity.

What's the community climate? Do the neighbors and adjacent businesses resent and fear the presence of your program? The more you can invite the community in to your program and minimize the us and them mentality, the more you will reduce the discrimination and fear that often divides and separates us. One of our primary intentions is to build bridges to the community, so recovering people will have a place to belong. The more we can model how to do this, and create linkages to natural supports, the easier it will be for people to flow though our programs and not get stuck in dependency.

The importance and message of space

The internal layout and the décor are loaded with subtle (and not-so-subtle) messages that impact the culture. These messages reinforce, for both staff and participants, an attitude that either reflects recovery values or extinguishes them. Try to set aside everything you know about what a facility should look like, so you can be open to considering special aspects that support a recovery culture.

What about the lobby? First impressions create a lasting influence, so a lobby needs to reflect the message you want people to know about the facility. A big open room with rows of old, dirty, and hard chairs does not send a recovery message. Smaller spaces with congregate sitting arrangements can be more natural and relaxed as well as more comfortable and welcoming.

What about the walls? Recovery environments don't adhere to the low stimulation concepts that often guide the interior decorating plans of behavioral health facilities. Recovery happens best in settings that are attractive and comfortable. This means colorful walls, interesting pictures, and inspiring affirmations that strategically reinforce recovery messages. Recovery is about focusing on potential and positive outcomes, so get rid of the "no" signs (as in no smoking, no loitering, no eating or drinking, no entrance beyond this point). Brightness and joy on the walls that lightens the spirit and affirms hope for both staff and participants has a subtle yet strong influence on the culture.

If your facility includes nursing stations or staff-only offices, find a way to eliminate them. They tend to be places where staff goes to get away from participants under the guise of doing paperwork and documentation. A recovery culture is open with staff and participants interacting continually. Paperwork should not be something staff members do in the absence of the participant, but with the participant. A "culture without walls" goes a long way toward reinforcing the level of relationship that supports recovery. If there is a need for private conversations, they can occur in interview rooms set aside for that purpose.

If you are really going to promote wellness, you need to serve healthy food and teach the people who use our services how to prepare it either at their own place of residence or in the facility right along with you. A place to prepare food, with enough cooking space for teaching, can also provide a foundation for serving snacks or even catering outside events. A snack bar with tables and chairs offers a place where people can sit and talk or use a computer and could even be open to your neighbors who may want to drop in for a cup of coffee. This will help with community integration. Instead of waiting for the community to invite us out, take the initiative and invite them in.

Does your space help people stay connected? Connectedness is a key principle of recovery. Having a way for people to stay connected to their natural supports is very important. One suggestion is to include a communication center where people can go online, use the phone, charge their own equipment, or make copies of their resumes.

If the people who attend your program need a place to clean up, then include a washer and dryer in your building plans and also a shower. This can provide another training opportunity to help people get involved with maintaining a healthy life style. Also, keep the place clean—not Pine-Sol® clean, but tidy and well organized.

If your facility has overnight capacity, the question of privacy versus risk management needs to be considered. To promote recovery, guests need to have their privacy respected. This means, for example, sharing a bathroom with as few people as possible. This also might mean giving up some notions about line of sight to keep people under constant surveillance. Although this change may raise questions about risk, in a recovery culture, risk is shared and not the sole domain of staff. People who are trying to recover need to maintain as much control as possible over their circumstances. Certain features in the environment, like the anti-ligature devices designed to prevent hanging that now dominate most overnight facilities, give a message to people that they cannot be trusted, they are not safe, and they will make poor decisions. Provide as many options for freedom and choice as you can. For example, ask, could people in our program take their own medication if they had a place to keep it secure? Could they keep track of their own appointments with doctors and other staff?

Transforming People

In addition to giving our facilities a presence and a voice that will reinforce and echo the recovery culture, we need to understand the daily happenings that can promote a recovery culture. If you've been feeling like you are boldly going toward something, but aren't sure what, this will help you pin down the essentials.

Creating a recovery culture takes a lot more than adding recovery to the sign you have on the door. This sign-changing exercise has taken place frequently across the country and has become a major disappointment to funding sources and service participants alike. Having the word "Recovery" on the front door has unfortunately become meaningless. We need to go much deeper, but what will we be looking for?

Who greets people when they arrive at your program? The people in the lobby set the tone for everything that happens in the program. They play a very important role in the way your culture is experienced. Is someone there to greet people with a smile, or is there a preoccupied receptionist talking through a little hole in a glass window? Is there a relaxed feeling of openness and positivity, or is there a serious looking security guard with a sign in sheet who never smiles and won't let people pass a certain point without an escort?

Since culture originates in the hearts and minds of the direct service staff, let's take a close look at who they are and at what they are doing. Do you employ people with lived experience? If you do, are they valued and acknowledged? Are they fully integrated with all the rights and responsibilities of a "regular" staff person? Are they in leadership positions? If they have a peer-specific role, is that role well defined?

Direct service staff members need to be welcoming and friendly. Look around at the people working in your organization—what do they do to connect with people? Do they understand and practice the importance of developing real relationships with people? Are they hopeful and excited about each person's plans and goals? Do they have high expectations for themselves and for the people they are serving? Are they inspiring and encouraging? Do they treat each other and the people they are serving with dignity and respect?

All of the people working in your organization need to have knowledge of recovery values. Those values need to be obvious through the actions of staff. Do they use recovery language? Do they give choices and avoid force, coercion, and strong-arm persuasion tactics? Are they willing to partner with the person in risky choices?

Some of the most important questions to ask when determining the extent to which recovery is present in the culture have to do with power. Where is it? Who has it? How is it used? Since the person using services has to take the lead in his/her own recovery process, that person is the one who needs the power. The organization's job is to make sure power is transferred to the person. There are many signs to look for when it comes to a power shift, such as whether people using services routinely are informed about their rights and responsibilities in the recovery partnership. Has staff been trained in transferring power to the person? Are they skilled and knowledgeable in ways of empowering people to take the lead in their recovery process? Are they reluctant to give over the power to the person for fear of creating risk? Do staff recognize that it is their responsibility to empower people, so they can be instrumental in their own transformation, rather than to fix people? Has staff been trained to recognize their own strengths and potential? Are their strengths and potential reinforced constantly by colleagues, supervisors, and the organizational culture?

Since recovery is mobilized through the process of conversation, the discussions we have with people need to promote and reinforce recovery. Listen for whether regular conversations provide evidence of a recovery culture. Is there talk about recovery instead of just stability and safety? Are conversations between staff and participants (and between supervisors and staff) sequenced to build self-confidence and motivation? Are the conversations among staff and those between staff and program participants carried out with recovery language rather than jargon/clinical/illness-based words? Is the conversation more about listening than directing? Is the conversation inspiring instead of controlling and managing the person? Is there a lot of talk about choices and options rather than compliance? Is there an absence of threat and coercion? Is there a strong interest and curiosity in each person's priorities? Are the staff at all levels curious about and fascinated by the perspectives of the people using services?

Transformed Practices

Program practices include the overall focus of the program, general practices, and policies and procedures as well as how you document your services and track your progress towards desirable outcomes.

The focus of organizational culture

What is the focus of your organizational culture? This is a "big picture" question, so stand back, squint, and see what comes into focus. Is the attention of the culture focused on what's strong or what's wrong with each person? Obviously, a recovery culture would have a focus on what's strong in both staff and people being served. Are challenges viewed through the lens of potential instead of past disappointments? Do staff see "puzzles" instead of "problems" (Bishop, 2010)? When corrective action is needed, is the focus on supporting each person and helping them grow rather than just eliminating a problem? Is there a focus on abilities and accomplishments—a "whole person" approach instead of a singular focus on challenges or pathology?

Staff competencies

Have staff been trained in recovery practices? Training staff in recovery practices needs to be a high priority for a recovery organization with ample opportunities for staff to develop new recovery skills and to engage in life-long learning. Are staff members able to use negative or challenging circumstances as learning opportunities for both themselves and for the person instead of experiencing them as failures? Do staff have the knowledge, skill, and confidence to help a person recover and confidence in the person to recover? Lack of confidence, especially, is a major cause of burnout that can usually be addressed and fixed through training that is interesting and provocative.

Tracking recovery outcomes

Do the outcomes that you measure to track your overall progress include items that are important to the people using your services? For example, does your organization strive to support people in having safe and stable housing, finishing school, starting vocational training, getting a job, and forming meaningful relationships? Are these personal outcomes routinely measured and valued more than system-focused outcomes like medication compliance, symptom reduction, reduced hospitalizations, and fewer incident reports?

Relevant policies

Many programs are still operating according to policies that were developed before we knew recovery was possible. Rather than support the use of recovery approaches, old policies tend to get in the way of recovery processes and services being carried out. Take a fresh look at your policies. Do they promote recovery, or do they hold it back? You may be tempted to put off rewriting polices since it's a tedious job, but you must eliminate policies that create barriers to the transformation process. A recovery culture involves program participants and staff in reviewing and rewriting policies and procedures.

Systematic documentation

Paperwork may seem innocuous—simply what we have to do to satisfy reimbursement criteria—but clinical documentation is a powerful process that has a strong influence on the culture. It forces staff to look at people and their problems in ways that persuade them to either focus on strengths and potential or on pathology and problems. Aligning the documentation process with recovery values will support the development of a recovery culture in a powerful way. Review your documentation procedures and clinical records. Is there evidence of an expectation that the person will recover and not just become stable? Has the person been given information about the organization and its goals so s/he can understand what is supposed to happen there and what s/he can expect? Do the forms use recovery language, and are they written in person-first language? Is there a requirement to periodically review the person's plan and measure accomplishments and progress toward goals? Do people using services routinely get copies of assessment results and service plans?

One critical theme in the overall paperwork process is that the person using services must be the primary driver of service planning. Who seems to own the treatment plan: the person, the staff, the organization, or the funding agency? Does the treatment plan aim for self-determination? As the person desires, the process also needs to build in inclusion of others outside the system. Has attention been given to involving family and friends as supporters?

Developing a crisis response

Nothing interferes more with a recovery culture than the use of seclusion and restraint, which gives everyone the message that it is impossible to maintain order in any other way. It is an insult to both service users and service providers. Although many overnight facilities have stopped using this approach altogether, licensing regulations sometimes require a room to be dedicated to this purpose. The very presence of a restraint room impacts the culture. It takes some creative imagination to come up with ways to disguise this room to keep its influence as low as possible. If your program doesn't use physical seclusion and restraint, take a look at any other ways that you might be restraining and secluding people. Do you use coercion or persuasion to force people to do what you think is best? Do you avoid and isolate people when they don't behave in ways that you would prefer? If you are doing this, you might as well get the leather restraints out because you are interfering with the recovery process nearly as much as you would be if you were physically restraining and secluding them. This approach does not support a recovery culture.

Example of Successful Implementation

In the spring of 2000, Gene Johnson, founder and CEO of Recovery Innovations, attended a workshop at a national conference where attendees talked about their experience of being put in restraints (G. Johnson, personal communication). Accounts of their experiences were troubling and heart-rending. At the end of the workshop Gene made a declaration: "We've got to stop using restraints in our crisis programs." At the time the company operated two large crisis programs in Maricopa County, AZ, that served around 1,300 people each month. We had already begun to work hard on changing the culture in our company to reflect recovery principles and practices. If we could change this one practice, it would send a message about our commitment to stop doing business as usual. It would also boost our efforts to transform our culture.

Before the culture shift took place, staff working in the crisis programs tended to operate in a crisis mode of management, reacting instead of responding thoughtfully to each situation. They were often overlooking the person's inherent strengths and resources by focusing primarily on the problems. This left them trying to solve problems instead of promoting a response of recovery. The futility of this task left them worn out and feeling hopeless and helpless.

By their very nature, crisis services are usually delivered in a brief period of time, usually less than 23 hours. Such a tight timeline can cause staff to focus on "moving people on" or "clearing the room" in order to be able to serve the next arrivals without exceeding the census. The focus on "moving on" can compromise the quality of service since it doesn't make it a priority to give people a renewed sense of hope and self-determination that could add meaning and purpose to their lives. It doesn't necessarily help them manage their life circumstances, so they could avoid this experience in the future. Furthermore, it doesn't allow for the type of relationship where staff can gain a sense of meaning and purpose from their work, and it doesn't increase staff skill in promoting recovery.

Gene's announcement to the staff of eliminating the use of seclusion and restraint did not meet with a positive response. This was a huge culture shift, especially since the use of seclusion and restraint has always been seen as a necessary part of the crisis programs. Some staff threatened to leave. Some considered calling the federal Occupational Safety and Health Administration because they believed the company was putting them at risk. Others just felt that the company didn't care about them anymore.

This was hard for Gene to hear, but he stayed the course. Because his genuine beliefs and concerns were evident, staff had the courage to try this new approach even though many still didn't believe it would work. His interactions with the staff were enthusiastic and optimistic about what could be accomplished.

One of the first things instituted was a search for any information that would support the move toward "zero restraint" (see Huckshorn, 2005; NASMHPD, 1999). The search gathered facts on the danger of using restraints and the number of deaths attributed to the use of them, personal stories from people who had been restrained that described the destructive and toxic effect it had on them, and the review of other programs that had tried to eliminate this practice. Next, policies were rewritten to reflect the change in culture. This was quickly followed by redesigning the in-service training to include the goal of eliminating seclusion and restraint and shifting staff actions toward practices that would promote recovery.

While all these changes cleared the way for the culture to move closer toward the elimination of seclusion and restraints, the one change that had the most impact was the addition of peers to the crisis teams. The peer workers continually reminded the non-peer staff that being in restraints was the worst thing that ever happened to them and that it had set their recovery back significantly. Also, when staff could see the reality of recovery for former users of crisis services, they had further evidence that people seen in crisis do recover.

Once these changes were in place, the company began to measure the outcomes. Were the new practices working? Were the number of restraints and seclusions decreasing? Staff began to experience some success as the numbers started to decrease, and this gave them the hope that they could keep lowering the incidences. Soon they took on the goal themselves. It was no longer just the goal of the company, but a personal goal of the staff. They came up with more and more ways to get better at avoiding the use of restraints. They enlisted the help of the people being served to help them reach their goals. If they did resort to restraining someone, there was a sense of failure and sadness among the staff. The culture was changing. Eventually, restraint was eliminated altogether, and with only one or two exceptions, has not been used since. Now, whenever there is something to do that is really hard, the company remembers that they have already done the impossible. "Zero Restraint" has become their metaphor for transformation.

SUMMARY

Changing organizational culture is often necessary to create services that promote recovery. We hope for and work towards positive change for the people we serve. Demonstrating a willingness to face the existing limitations of our programs and a willingness to change ourselves makes it possible to make the needed changes happen and models the change process to those we serve. By examining every aspect of the organization—the space, the people, the practices—and comparing what exists to what could (and should) be, you can see both your goal and your path to change. Everyone within the organization from the top to the bottom (however those are defined) has a role to play in changing your program culture. In the words of Barack Obama during a February 2008 speech, "Change will not come if we wait for some other person or some other time. We are the ones we've been waiting for. We are the change we seek."

BEST PRACTICE GUIDELINES FOR TRANSFORMING PROGRAM CULTURE

1. Recognize and acknowledge the fears and challenges that people will experience when you ask them to do things differently. Change is not something human beings do gracefully.

2. Send a strong message of hope and possibility through every aspect of your program. Talking about recovery is not enough. Leaders who set a tone of optimism and enthusiasm related to the benefits of change will have the best results.

3. Provide clear expectations that will help staff choose to commit to the new way. Goals that are set in collaboration with all involved will allow for progress to be measured and celebrated.

4. Include everyone involved in the program in some way, so they can be part of identifying, designing, and implementing needed changes. This way everyone can feel ownership and recognize their responsibility for making the program fully and consistently recovery-oriented.

5. Provide ongoing training. This is essential, so the organizational culture needs to embrace the necessity of continuous learning and improvement.

ABOUT THE AUTHOR

Lori Ashcraft, Ph.D. is the executive director for the Recovery Innovations/Recovery Opportunity Center. After a full career in California that included serving as the deputy director for community programs of the State Department of Mental Health, she re-located to Arizona where she accepted the position as director for adult services for the Regional Behavioral Health Authority and served as a professor for the University of Arizona teaching psycho-social rehabilitation and managing one of eight SAMHSA funded employment demonstration programs. It was during this time that Lori became involved in the recovery movement. Through training with Mary Ellen Copeland and help from colleagues at Boston University, her commitment to recovery principles became a passion. When META Services (now Recovery Innovations), opened the Recovery Education Center in the fall of 2000, Lori accepted the position as executive director of the center.

Some of the ideas in this chapter were also mentioned in *Behavioral Healthcare* magazine. The author, Lori Ashcraft, serves as a columnist for *Behavioral Healthcare* magazine and her contributions and aspirations are in close alignment with the mission of the publication.

REFERENCES

Huckshorn, K. (2005). *Six core strategies© to reduce the use of seclusion and restraint planning tool.* Alexandria, VA: National Technical Assistance Center, National Association of State Mental Health Program Directors.

NASMHPD (National Association of State Mental Health Program Directors). (1999). *Reducing the use of seclusion and restraint, part 1.* Retrieved from http://www.nasmhpd.org/publicationsmeddire.cfm

Schein, E. H. (1990). Organizational culture. *American Psychologist, 45*(2), 109-119.

CHAPTER 17

LEADERSHIP DEVELOPMENT

LEADERSHIP IN PSYCHIATRIC REHABILITATION ORGANIZATIONS

Anthony M. Zipple
Daniel Billingsley
Ron Otto
Greg Salustro
Catherine L. Batscha

ABSTRACT

This chapter addresses leadership as an essential component of psychiatric rehabilitation services. An historical perspective includes the importance of a leadership vision to build psychiatric rehabilitation programs and to attract staff and resources to make that vision a reality. Leadership is defined, and essential leadership traits are emphasized. Strategies to develop organizational leaders are clearly delineated. Leadership among people using services and peer advocates is also emphasized as a crucial piece of leadership development, and strategies are suggested for developing peer leadership.

LEADERSHIP HAS ALWAYS BEEN AN ESSENTIAL COMPONENT OF PSYCHIATRIC REHABILITATION SERVICES. The PRA founders and the founders of Fountain House, Thresholds, Hill House, Fellowship House, and other seminal psychiatric rehabilitation organizations needed to be great leaders. They were building novel programs when established mental health systems doubted that such programs were possible. They succeeded in defining a vision and attracting staff and resources to make that vision live.

Leadership in psychiatric rehabilitation is just as important today. Program leaders still need to innovate as they serve people coming from jails and prisons, help people with complex medical conditions, and support the development of peer-driven services. They need to attract staff members who are passionate and committed about changing the world— one life at a time—despite being paid less than workers in many other industries. Finally, the world continues to change rapidly with fiscal challenges, managed care, and evolving cultural values, making development and management of psychiatric rehabilitation services a continuing challenge. We need leaders to do more than get things started; we also need leaders to build, grow, evolve, and sustain what they initiate. Leaders will define the strategic challenges and find the way through them. Clearly, leadership in psychiatric rehabilitation will continue to be essential.

WHAT IS LEADERSHIP?

Every book on leadership begins with its own definition. Despite differences, most share essential common elements of inspiration, direction, and staff mobilization. Three definitions of leadership illustrate these essentials and are particularly relevant to psychiatric rehabilitation. In *The Leadership Challenge,* perhaps the most widely read book on leadership currently in print, Kouzes and Posner (2008) define leadership as inspiring others to want to strive for shared aspirations. Leaders are not people who command and control. They touch the hearts of their followers and find a way to inspire followers to work on shared goals.

Several other definitions stress the inspirational role of leadership and its relation to followers. For example, Gary Wills (1994) defines a leader as "one who mobilizes others toward a goal shared by leaders and followers" (p. 17). A definition particularly relevant to psychiatric rehabilitation comes from Anthony and Huckshorn (2008), who define leadership as "creating a shared vision and mobilizing others toward specific organizational goals consistent with the vision" (p. 11). What is particularly important about this definition is its integration of the essential components of creating vision, inspiring others to follow, and the development of shared goals that benefit both leaders and followers. It should be noted that the influence between leaders and followers is not a one-way street. Followers also can have an impact on leaders. In fact, the most effective leaders are those who learn and benefit from their followers.

Essential Leadership Traits

An international leadership survey (Kouzes & Posner, 2008) found that people want leaders who are honest, forward thinking, confident, and inspiring. The central questions are: "How do we operationalize these essential characteristics?" and "How do we develop these traits in current and future leaders in psychiatric rehabilitation organizations?"

There are at least eight characteristics of all great leaders.

Leaders are good at their work. Leaders are competent both as human beings and within the context of their work. Confidence is important and can be contagious. It inspires others to follow and inspires confidence in their leadership. Generally speaking, good leaders know their work well and love it. They see its value, know that they can succeed with it, and are simply very good at what they do. Leaders need to "model the way" for their followers (Kouzes & Posner, 2008). Followers are most likely to join leaders in an effort to achieve great and difficult things when the leaders are competent.

Leaders understand their organizations intimately. It is hard to imagine a great leader who is not deeply knowledgeable about his or her organization and the external forces affecting it. Leaders know the core capacities of their organizations and their ability to contribute to others. Certainly, leaders have great command of facts and data and this knowledge supports their decision-making. However, decisions still need to be made when sufficient data is not available. A leader's intimate knowledge of the organization and its environment are critical to improving intuition and the odds that decisions will benefit the organization over time.

Leaders communicate a clear vision for the future. Leaders may not be able to predict the future, but they have a vision of what they want it to be. This vision may be quite specific or limited to a small group of strategic beliefs about the future. In either case, leaders know what they want and their chosen direction for getting there. They also understand that the team wants to know about the planned journey. Leaders take every opportunity to communicate the organization's vision, values, strategies, and tactics to followers and create a sense of common purpose. They use email, newsletters, staff meetings, events, informal conversation, and personal illustration to build a shared vision within the organization.

Leaders have strong emotional intelligence. Leadership is both an emotional and rational set of activities and experiences. In fact, as Goleman (2004) argues, the emotional components of leadership are at least as important as its rational aspects. Leaders need to inspire followers and this requires great emotional intelligence. Great leaders have the capacity to read other people and respond to their deepest wants and needs. Leaders are also deeply self-reflective and understand their own emotional strengths and potential blind spots. While this kind of insight is essential, leaders also are able to respond to the emotions of others and their own emotions in a way that mobilizes the energy of followers and helps them organize around shared goals to do their best work.

Leaders create positive forward movement. Leaders are key to providing clarity about the direction that the organization should take and in selecting the right strategies for moving in that direction. Leaders create movement in organizations that helps them make their mission and vision manifest, getting everyone to move forward together. Leaders organize their own energy and the energy of others to move ahead, while maintaining a focus on tangible outcomes. Leaders understand the importance of small steps within the context of the larger vision and strategic direction, organizing and mobilizing others to take the small steps that lead to the organization making big leaps.

Leaders act with courage. There is no simple cookbook for organizing and managing complex organizations in turbulent times. Every leader is faced with high-stakes decisions for which there are no clear right or wrong answers. For many of the most important decisions, it can take months or years to find out whether a decision was correct. Leaders need to live with ambiguity and act in spite of uncertainty about the best solution. In order to act courageously, leaders need three traits. First, leaders have true self-confidence. This is not bravado or empty bluster, but a clear sense of both competence and limitations that help a leader "see" correct choices. Second, leaders have genuine humility. LeRoy Spaniol, the founding director of research for the Center for Psychiatric Rehabilitation and one of the great teachers and mentors in the field of psychiatric rehabilitation, was fond of saying "humility is defined as the openness to being taught." Leaders understand this and learn every day from their experiences and from their organization's evolution in the larger environment. Finally, leaders have real optimism and resilience. This is not an irrational hope that things will be better someday. Instead, it is a well-founded belief in the ability of the leader and followers to change the organization's destiny for the better and to bounce back from adversity. This combination of true self-confidence, genuine humility, real optimism, and resilience enables leaders to act with courage even in the most uncertain high-stakes situations.

Leaders take good care of their followers. In the end, most people want to follow individuals who meet their needs, whether material (wages, benefits, and safety) or more often, emotional (the need to contribute to others, have a life that matters, or participate in a project with impact). Leaders recognize and understand the needs of their followers and go to great lengths to take good care of them. Leaders do their best for their followers while being honest about their limitations. They share the work, the stresses, and the difficulties of the work fully with followers and are willing to share the benefits, the credit, and the enjoyment of the work. In short, leaders watch out for their own interests and the interests of the organization by tending to the interests of their followers.

Leaders develop the next generation of leadership. Leaders need partners. They know that any leader has a limited lifespan, and they want their organizations to thrive even after they have moved on. Leaders need to develop other leaders. Any organization that fails to develop the next generation will soon find itself out of business. While leaders have characteristics that support their drive to organize others around a vision for the future, the best leaders know they are not a solo act. Developing additional leaders to share the responsibility extends the scope of a leader's effectiveness and supports the future success of an organization.

The central challenge is developing leadership, both in ourselves and in organizations. How do we find and retain true leaders? How do we develop young talent into seasoned leadership? How do we navigate relationships with other community, organization, and board leaders? And finally, how do we encourage our consumers to become leaders in their own right? The balance of this chapter offers some suggestions for developing great leaders in psychiatric rehabilitation organizations using examples or actual experiences from Thresholds, the oldest and largest organization delivering services to people with psychiatric disabilities in Illinois.

STRATEGIES FOR DEVELOPING ORGANIZATIONAL LEADERS

Psychiatric rehabilitation organizations must engage in leadership development to provide for their future and meet current challenges. In turn, leaders must accept responsibility for their own continuous development. Because leadership can be learned and nurtured, leaders must also identify and develop new organizational leaders. Organizations need leadership development strategies that allow them to define and hire for competency; identify, develop, and mentor high potential individuals; and engage in succession planning as a way to ensure the organization's future.

Hire for Leadership

When organizations recruit and hire leaders, they generally look for those who fit the normative definitions of leadership (i.e., candidates seen as visionary, motivating, and tenacious). However, we believe that leaders in psychiatric rehabilitation must do more in order to be credible. They must live a life that is compatible with their vision in order to persuade co-workers by their example. Their behavior establishes credibility and can turn detractors into believers and abstainers into supporters. Generally, employees watch leaders quite closely to see which actions they should imitate and which they should ignore. While staff may imitate their leader's behavior in the hope that their own behavior may be rewarded, many emulate their leaders as a means of learning how to lead.

Leaders affect and integrate an organization's success, encouraging its mission with their personal vision. Leaders who live the mission are more valuable to organizations because their behavior will make their values palpable to others and facilitate desired outcomes. Thresholds has a long history of hiring individuals with deep and often lifelong commitments to broad social justice issues. The dedication of staff to making the world a better place for the people they serve makes them stronger leaders and inspires others throughout the organization.

In addition to credibility, other leadership traits ensure that needs and challenges in psychiatric rehabilitation organizations are properly met. First among these is that leaders espouse empowerment. True leaders in the field are respectful and embrace self-determination and choice. They seek to empower their staff by listening to them, mentoring them, and removing obstacles to performance. Leaders also empower themselves by seeking opportunities for their own professional development as lifelong learners.

Organizations seeking to hire leaders define collaboration with the people they serve as a competency since collaboration is essential to recovery. In community-based psychiatric rehabilitation, individuals using services are encouraged to participate as partners in their recovery. Leaders who can mobilize resources to support recovery-based collaboration are essential.

Commitment to following recognized ethical principles is vital to the leader's credibility. Ethical behavior is all-encompassing, and standards help leaders actualize their capability to transform organizations, the people they serve, and the future of the mental health field.

When hiring entry level staff, we look less at experience than at an individual's personal values, enthusiasm, and ability to learn. We believe that if we find smart people who intuitively understand and believe in our mission, we can teach them the specifics of the job. In fact, past experience as a provider can be a hindrance if the experience did not teach the individual the basics of respect, good listening skills, and commitment to doing what it takes to support the recovery of the people we serve. For many of our very best staff, Thresholds was their first human service-related job, and they found that the job was a good match for their passion to help others.

When Thresholds hires for management positions, we strive to promote from within. Recognizing existing staff for their contributions is a positive message for the whole organization and provides leaders with proven track records and demonstrated fit within the organization. However, as jobs become bigger, they also require more proficiency in technical areas and more specific experience. Organizations need to hire for leadership traits and values, but also be certain that the leader develops the skills and experience needed to solve complex problems and implement sophisticated initiatives.

Insist on Diversity in Leadership

Having a diverse leadership team is integral to an organization's optimal functioning.

Diversity today encompasses many characteristics that shape attitudes, values, beliefs, and behaviors. A diverse leadership team can help ensure that the team reflects the population that the organization supports. If leadership is not diverse, individuals served can feel isolated or even that the organization cannot meet their needs, which may be influenced by different backgrounds. A cohesive recovery environment is not promoted if others perceive that leadership is not diverse, does not appreciate subcultures, or does not embrace cultural differences.

Thresholds has built a diverse team of leaders. We value and prioritize creating a rich mix of staff from different cultural, linguistic, ethnic, and racial backgrounds. Gender, sexual orientation, political views, personal experiences, psychiatric history, and many other factors also contribute to creating a vibrant leadership team. While it is essential that everyone share the organization's core values and mission, this diversity helps us to find innovative approaches to meeting our mission. Leaders who are interesting and unique help make Thresholds a unique and effective organization. We look both within and outside the organization to find leaders who are competent and add diversity to our team. Nurturing emerging leaders is one effective strategy. Many of the best leaders on our diverse team "grew up" at Thresholds.

Mentor Staff

Professional membership organizations provide a wealth of opportunities for networking and development, and friendships that arise often have mentorship aspects. Leaders can benefit from the experiences of other leaders, adapting knowledge to create positive outcomes for their own organizations. As an adjunct to a mentoring relationship, leaders also may seek coaching from someone outside the organization who understands their issues from a different perspective. Coaching is important for leaders because it can reinforce positive aspects of the relationship without the risk of punitive consequences if there is failure or disappointment.

Leaders are teachers, and mentorship is a natural role for them. By virtue of being at the top of an organization, leaders can identify, develop, and mentor staff in preparation for future leadership roles. Followers who aspire to leadership will often self-identify and find mentors through traditional paths, such as reporting relationships, or through informal methods, such as shared professional contacts. Thresholds creates opportunities for mentorship, both formal and informal. Everyone is expected to share support and advice with their peers. While a primary relationship exists between individuals and their supervisors, Thresholds is rich in people who have emerged as informal leaders and serve as hubs in deep, interdepartmental networks that link and support staff. Through regular meetings, training situations, and embedded consultation, staff members receive mentorship throughout their tenure.

In addition, we value interdisciplinary teams for working on projects. These teams create opportunities for leaders to emerge from all levels of the organization and contribute. A member of a team who distinguishes herself/himself is publicly acknowledged and asked to lead other teams. As we see leaders emerge, we strive to develop their skills and build on their willingness and abilities to mentor and lead.

Identify High Potential Employees to Become Leaders

A small group of employees seem to be born leaders, who readily assume formal leadership positions. However, most employees with promise are not born leaders, and it is up to management to identify and develop the organization's next generation of leaders. In a psychiatric rehabilitation center, unique challenges exist in identifying future leaders of the organization as a whole. Excellent clinicians may not have the skills to lead a team of program directors. Smart administrative employees may not be knowledgeable about evidence-based practices. Identifying and developing these key employees early in their careers is essential. Multi-functional work assignments can develop multiple skills, such as managing subject matter and external relationships, as well as nurture self-confidence. Some examples of development opportunities for potential leaders include formal mentoring and/or coaching programs with senior executives, job sharing and job shadowing to learn all aspects of the psychiatric rehabilitation process, formal training programs to expand research and evidence-based practices, and/or special projects or assignments to stretch and broaden their skill sets.

Thresholds uses all of these strategies in developing staff leaders at all levels and then gives them opportunities to lead and grow. For example, the Thresholds medical director was encouraged to apply for, and was chosen for, a national leadership fellowship, and he was encouraged to implement what he learned throughout the organization. Staff members at every level are empowered to make decisions and lead towards organizational goals. These decisions are validated and supported in weekly group meetings with peers and supervisors in a way that reinforces leadership skills.

Establish Career Ladders and Training

Developing career ladders in a psychiatric rehabilitation organization includes identifying meaningful career paths for key clinical employees whose professional preferences may lie outside traditional management roles. The challenge is that these staff may require significant coaching and development since their training and educational backgrounds lie in the clinical arena, not in management. Career ladders offer tangible opportunities to groom these staff as future leaders of the organization. Career ladder concepts imply upward movement by offering intellectual challenges, peer recognition, and increasing responsibility. This type of program may include job rotation, formal work assignments, or placing staff in a recognized consultative role with colleagues.

Career ladders are supported by apprenticeship programs within the organization or in an outside agency. An apprenticeship may be considered ideal for employees who are still in the development stages of their careers, but it is also useful to those with field experience. For example, employees shadow a current leader and participate in a variety of hands-on learning experiences to develop leadership skills. Thresholds recently worked with a graduate student from Northwestern University's Kellogg School of Business on a contingency plan for state budget cuts. The student worked directly with the chief executive officer, the chief financial officer, and several people in recovery who serve on the finance committee of the board of directors to produce detailed recommendations.

Apprenticeship programs often result in mentoring relationships and frequently include the promise of a promotion. Regardless of the result, the staff in the apprenticeship program should receive a tangible benefit from the program—namely, one that is designed to affect the progress of the individual and the organization. At Thresholds, we expect that working is always a fundamental learning opportunity, and learning usually translates to better leadership.

Support Formal Education

Because the mental health field is ever changing, supporting formal education is imperative for an organization. Emerging practices require that staff and leaders stretch to provide the most current and proven recovery services. Our leaders must have the benefit of formal post-graduate education. Organizations should have programs that support and encourage leaders to continue their education and disseminate what they learn. Grant-funded educational and/or research subsidies are one avenue that enables leaders to pursue their education. Organizations also should provide staff with incentives, such as tuition reimbursement, additional compensation for acquired certifications and licenses, and promotion opportunities for advanced degrees. Formal education and incentives are optimally tied directly to career ladder promotions. However, the success of any of these programs relies heavily on commitment and creative support from upper management.

At Thresholds, we strive to make education more achievable for our staff. Job sharing, flexible schedules, support for doing internships and school projects in the context of regular work, use of Thresholds' computers and copy machines for school papers, and support from supervisors are all available to eliminate barriers to staff completing school. We also have clear financial incentives associated with obtaining a new degree.

Encourage Self-expression

Leaders are often praised for genuineness and integrity, qualities describing the ability to show one's true self to others. Yet many employees fear they might be vulnerable if they show who they really are, deviate from some idealized fit with the organization, or fail to model their behavior after superiors. Effective managers help employees let down their guard and express their individual personalities. If a staff member has a sharp sense of humor, the ability to listen to and engage others, or a keen analytical way of looking at problems, then a manager should acknowledge those qualities and point out how they can be used positively. Similarly, managers should acknowledge and celebrate the differences among staff members.

Thresholds is intentionally informal and encourages personal expression on the job. Like many psychiatric rehabilitation organizations, we have long recognized the value of breaking down artificial barriers between service providers and service users. Thresholds also works hard to reduce barriers between departments, levels of the organization, and programs in different locations. Everyone is on a first-name basis, and doors are open across the organization. Informal opportunities for casual exchange are valued. Staff members have easy access to their supervisors and other leaders across the organization. Access and exposure are essential components of developing and identifying leaders.

Nurture Core Values

Leaders shape and guard the organization's values. Managers should make sure that employees understand what is valued within an organization and how those values are expressed on a daily basis. Newsletters, email, training sessions, formal orientation, and informal conversation are just a few of the ways that leaders share and reinforce core values with other staff, including emerging leaders. At Thresholds, we never miss an opportunity to talk about what is really important and why we are doing what we are doing.

Reward Risk-Taking

We define risk as a state of uncertainty where some of the possibilities involve loss, catastrophe, or another undesirable outcome. Organizations tend to be risk-averse because resources are scarce or they frequently operate in the public eye. Systems and processes may be entrenched. On the other hand, the willingness to take risks is the quality that most distinguishes leadership. Because taking risks can lead to solving entrenched problems, launching new programs, fostering innovation, and encouraging creativity, managers must motivate staff to put themselves in situations with potentially negative outcomes.

To accept this challenge, staff must feel they are operating within a safe environment. Without support, staff will not assume risk. Staff members who feel confident can put themselves in a position of risk despite a sense of vulnerability. Staff must understand that taking risks is a core value of the organization and that risk takers are highly regarded, often regardless of the outcomes. The knowledge that risk can result in failure should not justify avoidance of all risk. Failure can teach those who are willing to look at it honestly and learn from it. In reality, the path to success is paved with failure and trial-and-error learning. Staff must understand that the ultimate outcomes of risk-taking may not be known for a long time, and that short-term failure may lead to long-term success. The consequences of well-intentioned failure should never be job-threatening. Instead, the culture should be such that managers commend staff for risk-taking as an activity that is rewarded, regardless of outcomes.

An interesting example comes from the Thresholds development department. In 2009 staff suggested developing a monthly schedule of site visits to program facilities. The goal was to attract new donors and learn about the specific interests of current donors. In execution, however, these events were poorly attended, and guests were left with a less-than-complete understanding of the scope of the programs of Thresholds. By most measures, the project failed. What staff learned, however, was that they needed to set specific targets and goals for each event; they needed to tighten the program to make it more emotionally compelling, and they needed to encourage board members and younger volunteers to become involved in the programs and invite attendees. These lessons formed the basis for new and successful donor engagement initiatives.

Build Leadership Vision

To become a successful leader, one must develop a singular guiding vision as part of the overall initiative. The leader must create a picture of where he or she wants the organization to be in the future. Identifying components such as physical and public space, agency culture and communications, decision-making processes, and work-life issues are important steps in creating a leadership vision. Once identified, clarification of that vision through more compelling language and phrases will get to the heart of what a leader cares about.

Communicating that vision effectively is essential. Leaders talk about the vision as much as possible to describe the "big picture." A leader may alter, amend, or even radically change that vision after listening to feedback from others. Seeing people become animated and interested in the vision is a sign that a leader is on to something.

A leader also works with a group to develop and communicate the vision's details through strategic planning, so the big picture does not become meaningless. Mental health leaders must not only consider the group they are managing, but the people they wish to serve as well as the community partners with whom they collaborate, making detailed communication of the vision vital for successful implementation of systems. At this point, a leader will help others involved assume ownership of the vision. This requires building consensus, challenging ideas, and most importantly, creating compromise, so others feel vested in the vision of the leader. The leader is courageous, but is not afraid to modify his or her thoughts and uses the vision to act. Leaders don't underestimate the power of their ideas or words to inspire a significant systems change.

Build and Sustain Relationships

Relationships are the building blocks for all organizational activities, particularly in community psychiatric rehabilitation. Evidence-based practices are built on the concepts of integration of services and treatments, teamwork, and participation of multiple stakeholders, including people using the agency's services. This relationship building extends to collaborators, funding partners, community partners, other medical professionals, academic institutions, and civic agencies and organizations. Leaders build and maintain relationships rather than work in isolation. Relationships with colleagues, communities, people in recovery, and even adversaries are the means to achieving goals. Relationships are the foundation of an organized effort for systems change. The official leader in any movement will be most effective in the context of strong community relationships.

Relationship building occurs one-to-one. Some people become involved in organizations because they believe in the cause. The vast majority become involved because of a relationship with someone already involved. Relationships are crucial to win allies to the cause. Building relationships where knowledge and trust grow enables us to further reduce or eliminate prejudice and discrimination against people with mental health conditions in service communities and beyond. Finally, these relationships give meaning and richness to the work and to our lives. A leader does not create an "old boys network," but rather, leaders create a diverse consortium of those who share the common vision and goals for the initiatives at stake.

Ideally, relationships are built before a leader needs them or before a conflict arises. However, a good leader can establish a relationship even in a crisis. In fact, a crisis can be a good mechanism for bringing people together. In 2009, the state of Illinois was experiencing a significant social service budget crisis. Many organizations, leaders, advocates, and consumer groups united in a single voice to protest, and eventually, block draconian cuts to state-funded services for the most vulnerable populations. These relationships have carried over into meaningful partnerships, eliciting discussions and policy adjustments to prepare for further issues with public funding. Leadership at every level—executive, board, advocate, people in recovery, legislators, and community members—bonded successfully to communicate a single vision for the need for human services in Illinois.

Good leaders sustain relationships by paying attention to others, communicating openly, appreciating others, extending themselves, volunteering for other causes, challenging others, and backing each other when times get tough. Loyalty is essential to keeping relationships healthy, and while disagreements occur, a leader will stand by a peer when he or she is in a jam.

Finally, a leader knows how to maintain relationships with an adversary. Even during times of disagreement, whether due to political, philosophical, or other differences, it is important to build relationships with those working against your goals to understand how to better position your vision. A leader will listen to adversaries to learn their viewpoints on the issues. Knowing the opposition is just as critical for a leader as loving the ally. A leader who understands how to effectively work with constituents and potential allies will always be in a stronger position than someone who works in a vacuum.

Work with Community Leaders

Leaders in mental health advocacy come from every facet and level of society. While we pay particular attention to philanthropic leadership, it should be noted that community leaders can be clinicians looking to change or elevate best practices within a particular initiative, young volunteers seeking to raise awareness or effect change, advocates hoping to reduce stigma, other service providers hoping to create better collaborative environments, or other community leaders (politicians, clergy, activists) seeking to make a positive change in mental health and rehabilitation services.

Engaging energetic activists is a key factor in developing community leadership. By building relationships with key stakeholders—such as an organization's leader meeting regularly with local elected officials, senior clinical leaders providing training to local community groups, or people in recovery working with local police departments to discuss issues to help decriminalize mental illness—organizations will be better poised to identify, cultivate, and use local community leaders to promote mental health initiatives.

DEVELOPING PEER LEADERSHIP

Leadership among people using services and peer advocates is a crucial piece of the leadership puzzle as mental health recovery and the development of consumer leadership go hand-in-hand. The recovery perspective recognizes the fundamental need of the individual to develop his greater potential, express himself fully and freely, and live a self-directed and purposeful life. Voice, empowerment, and the process of becoming an integrated and independent human being also define leadership. This makes it impossible to have a complete discussion of leadership in a psychiatric rehabilitation organization without discussion of developing peer leaders.

Peer leaders model the vision, values, and concrete reality of recovery through self-management of their own health and lives despite the challenges of serious mental illnesses. They can then inspire, influence, and guide their peers in attaining these goals. Consumer leadership roles are rich and varied—from facilitator to philosophical visionary. The services peer leaders provide benefit themselves, their peers, their communities, and a mental health system that faces an increasing demand for services that cannot be met by credentialed professionals alone. As resources to meet the demand for mental health services shrink, consumer leaders can help fill this gap in many effective ways. Peer support specialists, peer crisis workers, warm line volunteers, crisis intervention trainers, and self-help and mutual support group leaders are just a few of the essential service roles that peer leaders can fill.

The importance of peer leaders goes far beyond their role as service providers. Peer leaders also serve as visionaries, guides, and teachers in the field of psychiatric rehabilitation. Their critical perspectives and innovative practices have helped define and shape the core principles and values of the rehabilitation field. The visionary works of Patricia Deegan (1988), Mary Ellen Copeland (1997), and other consumer leaders created a recovery community that supported, empowered, and gave a sense of belonging to people with a psychiatric disability.

Their advocacy efforts helped to shape a collective voice and will for this disenfranchised group. Their positive, strength-based approaches to life convey hope and respect and help their peers move beyond the stagnant and stultifying world of psychiatric labels, paternalistic caretaking, and institutional settings that had become their designated lot in life.

Peer leaders not only offered a vision of recovery, they also translated this vision into a set of values and practices by which the vision could be manifested. Their practical self-help strategies and recovery curricula did not employ confusing medical jargon. They used terms like wellness tools, person-first language, and shared decision-making that are easily understood and shared with their peers.

Thresholds offers people in recovery opportunities to actively participate in influential decision-making and service delivery roles. The Thresholds Peer Success Center, for example, is entirely staffed and run by people with lived experience. In addition, Thresholds pays about 30 people in recovery who have been selected to serve as consultants on the All Agency Consumers Council (AAMC), and who frequently evaluate policies, procedures, and services. People in recovery are also paid consultants on agency committees, including the recovery steering committee, which is directly responsible for planning and developing services.

The recovery perspective emerging from the work of both visionary and everyday peer leaders removes people from the devalued and demeaning role of "person with a mental illness" and puts them into active and valued roles as teachers, mentors, guides, and productive citizens. Peer leaders, as critics and guides, are serving the field of psychiatric rehabilitation well by questioning treatment strategies, encouraging a culture of recovery, and becoming advocates and owners of mental health services. They prove there is no real substitute for the experiential knowledge they have and are willing to share. The challenging nature of a mental health condition and the journey of recovery can serve as a call to leadership. Peer leaders are those who courageously answer this call.

Strategies for Developing Peer Leadership

The widespread growth of peer services requires skilled and experienced leadership. For professional service providers, the challenge is to offer people in recovery opportunities to develop the skills and access the resources needed to become successful leaders. Peer leadership develops when people using services (1) have opportunities to learn and practice necessary interpersonal, problem-solving, and decision-making skills and (2) have access to the knowledge and resources used by professionals. The learning environment that best promotes development of leadership skills encourages and supports the efforts of people in recovery to participate fully and purposefully at all levels of the service provision process.

At the organizational level, full consumer participation means having an active voice in the decision-making process and an influential role in the planning, development, and evaluation of services. A strengths-based philosophy may be taught through curricula such as the Wellness Recovery Action Plan® (WRAP; Copeland, 1997) and the *Pathways to Recovery* workbook (Ridgway, McDiarmid, Davidson, Bayes, & Ratzlaff, 2002), but it is only with opportunities to practice this philosophy that peers develop leadership competence.

For peer leadership to successfully develop, service providers must proactively address the enormous knowledge and communication divide that exists between service providers and service users. When people in recovery are engaged as full participants and partners in the service provision process, as well as given access to professional knowledge and resources, this knowledge and communication divide truly narrows.

Training is an essential component of peer leadership development and can be delivered in the classroom, on the job, or in a variety of other settings. Self-advocacy training, such as that offered by the National Mental Health Consumers' Self-Help Clearinghouse, can empower people to use their voices constructively to secure needed services and supports. The program In Our Own Voice, through the National Alliance for Mental Illness (www. nami.org), offers an excellent opportunity for a person in recovery to develop self-confidence and public speaking skills while educating the public about mental illnesses. The Depression and Bipolar Support Alliance (www.dbsalliance.org) training, Not a Pity Party, teaches how to run positive recovery-oriented peer support groups. The WRAP® Facilitator Certification Training (Copeland, 1997) is another excellent recovery skills curriculum that also sets forth a framework of values and ethics to assist people in recovery in becoming principled leaders. Peer specialist certification programs offer another avenue for competency development and help peer workers meet professional standards for the knowledge and skills needed in practice.

Hiring peer workers and integrating them into the workforce at all levels promotes the psychiatric rehabilitation goal of work and career development for persons in recovery. Hiring peers builds a culture of inclusion, trust, and acceptance. Working partnerships and the free flow of information between service providers and people who have experience using services (positive and negative) aligns the vision and mission of recovery with business practice. When peer service providers are an integral part of organizational activities, the "us vs. them" mentality is less the norm. At Thresholds, many years ago, it was common to attend a staff training and hear "those consumers this and those consumers that." With people in recovery now well integrated into all parts of the organization, including training and management roles, professional walls and attitudinal barriers have come down.

Establish Consumer Councils

A consumer council made up exclusively of people served by an organization is an excellent structure for fostering development of peer leadership and advocacy skills. Council members provide invaluable input for design and provision of services. They are also a ready source of feedback about current services, programs, and policies. Feedback is critical to improving services. Council members often voice unmet needs, thus spurring program innovation.

In addition to addressing their own issues and concerns, consumer councils foster open dialogue between the people using services and those providing them. At Thresholds, senior staff members are frequently invited to council meetings to present on topics of interest to council members and their peers. This access to administrative and clinical staff builds trust, understanding, and a collaborative relationship that benefits both service providers and people served. When council members' roles and responsibilities are clearly spelled out—a set of bylaws and a clear, compelling statement of purpose are useful here—and they are paid for their participation, there is a clear sense that their leadership role is valued by the organization. The Thresholds Consumers Council bylaws make it a responsibility of council members to share information and resources from monthly meetings with their peers. One significant barrier to recovery is the sharing of knowledge and resources and the free flow of information. Consumer councils offer a powerful way to address this need.

Consumer councils also have the added value of making it easier to mobilize large numbers of people in recovery around issues that impact the ability of organizations to provide behavioral healthcare services. Mobilized consumer activists can make a significant difference in decisions made at the community, state, and federal levels.

Engage Service Users in Strategic Participation

Committee work is another valuable opportunity for people in recovery to participate in an organization and develop valuable leadership skills. At Thresholds, people who use our services are participants on many committees traditionally reserved for staff, including housing, employment, and the staff executive committee. Other committees, such as the recovery steering committee and the trauma committee, pay a small stipend to consumer members who serve on them. Consumer involvement, much like active participation in the consumer council, gives service users greater access to professional knowledge and resources. Working alongside staff on organizational committees provides an opportunity to receive mentoring. People in recovery serving on one Thresholds committee were valued collaborators in producing a more person-centered new member handbook and in designing a care plan manual to make the care plan process more collaborative and person-centered.

Network with Other Peer Leaders

To develop leadership skills, a person needs opportunities to exchange ideas and information with established leaders who are dedicated to their own personal and professional development as well as to the interests of other peers. State and national consumer conferences, teleconferences, webinars, recovery workshops, and political advocacy events are all opportunities for people in recovery to build networks, develop skills, and access resources that can set them on a leadership path.

Fund Peer Services

Peer-delivered services are recovery services. Developing peer leadership is necessary, not only to meet the growing demand for quality recovery services, but also to meet the goals of a recovery-oriented system of mental health care. Providing people in recovery with opportunities to serve in productive and valued leadership roles is the very core of self and system transformation.

A commitment to peer leadership and peer-delivered services is an investment that has associated costs. Training a person to facilitate a WRAP® group or to participate in national conferences or agency councils costs an agency. However, compared to the monetary costs of developing peer leadership, not making any serious investment in developing peer leadership incurs the cost of low expectations and lost opportunities.

Peer leaders bring a new vision and set of values to the mental health system. They serve as its guide and its conscience. As we look to further transform the mental health system into one of fully integrated and holistic healthcare, peer leadership is critical to success.

SUMMARY

Thresholds has become the preeminent leader in psychiatric rehabilitation services and community behavioral healthcare in Chicago and strives to serve as a national and international model on building leadership qualities in every level of the organization. Whether developing leadership skills in a clinical or administrative staff member, an executive leader of the agency, board member, community leader, peer mentor, consumer advocate, family advocate, or volunteer, Thresholds dedicates considerable time and resources to the training, mentoring, and development of strong leaders throughout the rehabilitation world. Organizations with the history, breadth of knowledge, reach, and impact of Thresholds must fully realize the potential of organizational leaders, as well as community and consumer advocates, to ensure more effective public policy in community-based psychiatric rehabilitation services. Without strong advocates and leaders, the significant areas of treatment, policy, and research could be devoid of the voices necessary to effect the change necessary to reduce prejudice and discrimination and to encourage the use of evidence-based practices in all areas of recovery services. Highly trained, strong leaders can also emerge as mavens of cultural competence in developing and implementing better public policy. Furthermore, clinical and community leaders can give greater leadership and advocacy opportunities to peer and family leaders who better illustrate the power of evidence-based recovery services to the rest of the community and amplify, in their own words, the voices of researchers and clinicians who have been sounding the trumpet for the past 50 years.

Thresholds envisions a future where strong clinical, community, volunteer, consumer, and family leaders fight the serious battles against mental illnesses and psychiatric disabilities. Through continued belief in the power of leadership training, Thresholds can mentor other organizations, community groups, peer-to-peer advocacy organizations, and others in the power of strong, activist approaches in civic guidance and mentorship in psychiatric rehabilitation and community behavioral healthcare. With encouragement and formalized approaches to preparation and identification and cultivation of strong leaders, Thresholds hopes that the voice for recovery will carry far and wide to ensure that each and every individual with a psychiatric disability has the best possible outcomes.

BEST PRACTICES GUIDELINES FOR LEADERSHIP IN PSYCHIATRIC REHABILITATION

- Build competence and confidence; leaders are good at their work.
- Understand your organization intimately and develop a firm grasp of the environments that impact its operation.
- Communicate a clear vision for the future.
- Draw on your emotional intelligence—learn to read people and respond to their deepest wants and needs while recognizing your own strengths and potential blind spots.
- Create positive forward movement.
- Act with courage.
- Take good care of your followers.
- Develop the next generation of leaders: hire, train, and mentor service providers and service users in important leadership competencies.

ABOUT THE AUTHORS

Anthony M. Zipple is the president and CEO of Seven Counties Services in Louisville, Kentucky. Dr. Zipple holds a doctorate in rehabilitation counseling from Boston University and an MBA from the University of New Hampshire. He is a licensed psychologist and a Certified Psychiatric Rehabilitation Practitioner with 35 years of experience as a manager, consultant, researcher, and teacher. Dr. Zipple is the recipient of PRA's John Beard and the Irving Rutman Awards.

Daniel Billingsley is a public affairs and fundraising professional specializing in community improvement and coalition building. Currently, he serves as director of resource development and communications for the Oklahoma Center for Nonprofits where he leads fundraising efforts as well as strategic planning, sustainability and new initiatives. Billingsley has worked in public affairs, communications, and fundraising in psycho-social rehabilitation, fine arts, and child welfare. He holds master's degrees from the University of Kansas in journalism and music.

Ron Otto is the director of recovery at Thresholds in Chicago. Mr. Otto holds a bachelor of arts in philosophy from Ripon College and a bachelor of science in accounting from the University of Illinois at Chicago. He is a Certified Recovery Support Specialist and a Certified WRAP Facilitator. Mr. Otto is the recipient of the Illinois Rehabilitation Association's Personal Achievement Award for the state of Illinois and the National Rehabilitation Association's Belle Greve Memorial Award.

Gregory Salustro has spent his career in the nonprofit world. He has led development efforts at Columbia College, Howard Brown Health Center, Chicago Public Media, the San Francisco Museums of Fine Arts, and Thresholds. He has served on the boards of Adler School of Professional Psychology, Chicago Filmmakers, and Gerber Hart Library and Archives, and was an arts commissioner for the city of Evanston. Gregory has managed external affairs teams ranging from 4 to 28 individuals. He has presented on staff development issues at the Association of Fundraising Professionals and Professional Radio Development and Marketing conferences.

Catherine L. Batscha, DNP, RN, is an assistant professor at the University of Louisville School of Nursing. She has over thirty years of experience providing services to people with serious mental illnesses and holds a doctorate of nursing practice and is certified as a clinical nurse specialist in adult psychiatric mental health nursing.

The authors wish to acknowledge the contributions of Rhonda Rhodes to the preparation of this chapter.

REFERENCES

Anthony, W. A., & Huckshorn, K. A. (2008). *Principled leadership in mental health systems and programs.* Boston, MA: Boston University Center for Psychiatric Rehabilitation.

Copeland, M. E. (1997). *WRAP—Wellness recovery action plan.* Brattleboro, VT: Peach Press.

Deegan, P. E. (1988). Recovery: The lived experience of rehabilitation. *Psychiatric Rehabilitation Journal, 11*(4), 11-19.

Goleman, D., Boyatzis, R. E., & McKee, A. (2004). *Primal leadership: Learning to lead with emotional intelligence.* Boston, MA: Harvard Business Review Press.

Kouzes, J. M., & Posner, B. (2008). *The leadership challenge.* San Francisco, CA: Jossey-Bass.

Ridgway, P., McDiarmid, D., Davidson, L., Bayes, J., & Ratzlaff, S. (2002). *Pathways to recovery: A strengths recovery self-help workbook.* Lawrence, KS: University of Kansas School of Social Welfare.

Wills, G. (1994). *Certain trumpets.* New York: Simon & Schuster.

INDEX